Power Semiconductor Drives

Power Semiconductor Drives

S. B. DEWAN
Professor of Electrical Engineering

G. R. SLEMON
Professor of Electrical Engineering

A. STRAUGHEN
Emeritus Professor of Electrical Engineering

THE UNIVERSITY OF TORONTO

A Wiley-Interscience Publication
JOHN WILEY & SONS

New York • Chichester • Brisbane • Toronto • Singapore

Library of Congress Cataloging in Publication Data:
Dewan, S. B.
    Power semiconductor drives.

    "A Wiley-Interscience publication."
    Bibliography: p.
    Includes index.
    1. Electric driving.   2. Power semiconductors.
I. Slemon, Gordon R.   II. Straughen, A.   III. Title.

TK4058 D47   1984   621.31'7   84-7475

Printed in the United States of America

10 9 8 7 6 5 4 3

The operations of man participate in the character of their author; they are diminutive, but energetic during the short period of their existence: whilst those of nature, acting over vast spaces, and unlimited by time, are ever pursuing their silent and resistless career.

Charles Babbage Esq. A.M.

*Lucasian Professor of Mathematics in the
University of Cambridge and member of several Academies
On the Economy of Machinery and Manufactures*

Preface

This book is concerned with dc and ac electric motor drives and the speed and positional control systems that may be devised by using them. The power sources considered are also both dc and ac. Power semiconductor converters of various types are located between motor and source.

We hope that the book will be useful both to practicing engineers and to university students. At the University of Toronto this material is discussed in the final semester of the undergraduate course in electrical engineering. It is fully covered by graduate students in an advanced course.

The reader is assumed to have a sound basic knowledge of electric machines and of power semiconductor circuits. On this assumption, the text is designed to provide an analysis of the steady-state operation of drive systems that permits the specification of suitable converters and machines for the systems envisaged. Transient operation is glanced at but not discussed in detail because the full analysis of stability and response demands a text of its own.

After an introductory chapter that deals with the kind of mechanical systems that may need to be driven the chapters that follow are concerned with particular combinations of machines and power sources. In the worked examples in the text and the problems at the end of each chapter an effort has been made to illustrate the practical details that complicate system design. Problems in which these details are neglected for the sake of simplicity, or in which more are included in the interest of verisimilitude, can readily be prepared by the instructor, to whom solutions to the problems in the text will be supplied by the authors on request. All worked examples and the problems have been solved on a hand calculator. A programmable model is essential for some of them because numerical solution of some equations is necessary.

The semiconductor devices commonly used for converters in drive systems are the diode, the reverse-blocking triode thyristor (which, on the North American continent, at least, has arrogated to itself the generic title of "thyristor"), the triac, and power transistors. The last two types of device perform functions in the power circuit that may be performed equally well by one or more thyristors, and it is usually the power level of the circuit that determines which devices shall be used. In this text only converters with thyristors and diodes are illustrated. When gating signals are shown in a diagram they are appropriate for thyristors. It must be understood, however, that under some circumstances other types of device would be selected. Such change would not modify the operation of the power circuits, which are the subject matter of the book.

Superscripts 1 to 7 in the text refer to the Bibliography.

We must acknowledge our indebtedness to two persons who have helped us greatly. Professor Richard Bonert has used the draft for teaching and taken part in many helpful discussions. Dr. Timothy Miller, Manager of the Adjustable Speed Drives Program in the Research and Development Center of the General Electrical Company, has read and commented in detail on the draft of the text. The errors and inadequacies that remain in the book must be attributed only to the authors. We must also express our gratitude to Mrs. Amelia Ma for many hours of patient and accurate text entry and editing.

S. B. DEWAN
G. R. SLEMON
A. STRAUGHEN

Toronto, Ontario
July 1984

Contents

Symbols

In general, upper-case letters are used for direct or constant quantities or for rms values of alternating quantities. Lower-case letters are used for instantaneous values of variables.

A bar over a lower-case symbol ($\bar{a}$) means average value. A bar over an upper-case symbol ($\bar{A}$) means phasor or phasor operator value.

A "hat" over a lower-case symbol ($\hat{a}$) means peak value.

A "prime" added to a symbol (a') means "referred to the stator" (except for I_a' and I_M', for which see list).

A numerical subscript (a_2) indicates harmonic order.

Subscript *sh* (A_{sh}) indicates desired (should) value of a variable.

Subscript *is* (A_{is}) indicates actual value of a variable.

Subscript *R* (A_R) indicates rms or resistive value of a quantity.

Many other subscripts are defined in the following list.

B	viscous friction constant
C	capacitance
C_{eq}	per-phase equivalent capacitance
D	distance
e, E	electromotive force (emf)
e_a, E_a	armature or per-phase stator emf
e_L	inductive emf
E_{ma}	per-phase stator emf
E_{mA}	per-phase rotor emf
E_o	excitation emf
f	force, frequency
F	magnetomotive force
f_s	stator frequency
i_a, I_a	armature or stator current
I_a'	*rotor* current referred to stator
I_A	rotor current
I_{ah}	rms harmonic current
I_c	core-loss current, capacitor current
i_D	diode current

i_f, I_f	field current
i_G	gate current
i_l	line current
I_m	imaginary part
I_{ma}, I_M	magnetizing current
I_M'	field current referred to stator
I_{NL}	no-load current
i_O	converter output current
i_p, I_p	transformer primary current
i_Q	thyristor current
I_R	rms current
I_{REF}	reference current
i_s, I_s	source current
J	rotational inertia
k	dc machine constant
K_i	current ripple factor
k_T	tachometer transfer function
k_{TR}	transducer transfer function
L	inductance
L_a	armature inductance
L_f	field inductance
L_{ls}	per-phase stator leakage inductance
L_{lr}	per-phase rotor leakage inductance
L_L	per-phase leakage inductance
L_{ms}	per-phase magnetizing inductance
m	$E_a/\sqrt{2}$ V
n	motor speed, harmonic order
n', n''	effective turns ratio
N	number of turns
N_{re}	effective rotor turns
N_{se}	effective stator turns
p	number of poles
P	active power
P_a	armature power
P_{amech}	per-phase mechanical power
P_{FL}	full-load input power
P_{FW}	friction and windage power
P_I	inverter power rating
P_{in}	input power
P_{ma}	per-phase stator power
P_{mA}	per-phase rotor power
P_{mech}	mechanical power
P_R	resistive losses
P_{SL}	stray load loss
P_o	output power

P_w	work power
PF	power factor
PF_l	supply-system power factor
PF_1	fundamental power factor
R	resistance
R_a	armature resistance
R_c	per-phase core-loss resistance
R_d	external armature-circuit resistance
Re	real part
R_{ex}	per-phase external rotor-circuit resistance
R_f	field resistance
R_{in}	per-phase motor input resistance
R_r	per-phase rotor resistance
R_s	per-phase stator resistance
s	Laplace operator, slip
S	apparent power
t	time
T	torque, air-gap torque
T_B	viscous-friction torque
T_C	coulomb friction torque
t_d	dead time
T_F	friction torque
T_J	inertia torque
T_{loss}	loss torque
T_L	load torque
t_{off}	turn-off time
t_{ON}	conduction time
T_p	periodic time
t_q	time-available for turn-off
T_s	starting torque
T_S	static friction torque
T_W	work torque
t_α	delay time
v, V	potential difference (pd)
V_a	per-phase stator terminal pd
V_A	per-phase rotor terminal pd
v_{AK}	anode-to-cathode pd
v_f, V_f	field terminal pd
v_{LK}, V_{LK}	dc link pd
v_s, V_s	source pd
v_t, V_t	armature terminal pd
v_O	converter output pd
v_p, V_p	transformer primary pd
v_R	resistive pd
v_T	tachometer or transducer pd

X_d	per-phase direct-axis reactance
X_{in}	per-phase motor input reactance
X_{lr}	per-phase rotor leakage reactance
X_{ls}	per-phase stator leakage reactance
X_L	per-phase leakage reactance
X_q	per-phase quadrature-axis reactance
X_s	per-phase synchronous reactance
X_{ms}	per-phase magnetizing reactance
Z	impedance
Z_A	per-phase rotor impedance
Z_{ex}	per-phase external rotor-circuit impedance
Z_{in}	per-phase motor input impedance
Z_{ms}	per-phase magnetizing-branch impedance
Z_s	per-phase stator impedance
α	delay angle, phase angle
β	extinction angle, rotor position
γ	conduction angle
ζ	damping factor
η	$\sin^{-1}(E_a/\sqrt{2}\ V)$ efficiency
ϑ	angular displacement, phase angle
μ	angle of overlap
ν	translational speed
τ	time constant
τ_a	armature electrical time constant
τ_m	armature mechanical time constant
φ	flux per pole, impedance angle
Φ	flux per pole
ψ	phase angle
ω, Ω	angular speed, angular frequency
ω_b	base speed, base frequency
ω_f	filter resonance frequency
ω_m, Ω_m	motor angular speed
Ω_m	motor speed command
ω_n	natural frequency
ω_o	angular chopping frequency
ω_r	rotor angular frequency
Ω_r	rotor frequency command
ω_s	stator or source angular frequency
ω_{syn}	synchronous speed

Power Semiconductor Drives

Chapter 1

Variable Speed Drive Systems

1.1. ELEMENTS OF A DRIVE SYSTEM

The block diagram in Fig. 1.1 illustrates the main elements into which an electric drive system may conveniently be divided. Initially, the nature of elements 4 and 5 only will be known, whereas 1, 2, and 3 must be designed or chosen by an applications engineer. For this purpose, the mechanical system must be clearly specified. When a preliminary design of a desirable drive system has been carried out it may be discovered that the available electric power supply is, in some way, inadequate. It is logical therefore to start with a discussion of the kinds of mechanical system that may be encountered and the demands they will make on the power supply, regardless of the exact nature of the controller and motor.

1.2. THE MECHANICAL SYSTEM

The mechanical system is "seen" by the motor as a torque that must be applied to a shaft by the motor coupling. The relation between this load torque and the motor speed must be defined. For steady-state operation this definition may be made in terms of the four-quadrant, speed-torque diagram in Fig. 1.2 in which ω is the speed of the rotation of the motor, or the driven shaft, and T_L is the coupling torque developed by the motor or the load presented by the shaft of the mechanical system.

The first quadrant in Fig. 1.2 applies to normal forward driving. In the second quadrant the mechanical system demands a negative torque to provide braking. This braking torque may be produced in a variety of ways:

1. Friction braking, in which a mechanical brake is coupled to the motor shaft and the kinetic energy of the system is dissipated as heat due to friction.

1

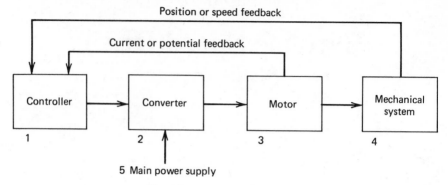

Fig. 1.1. Drive system elements.

2. Eddy-current braking, in which the kinetic energy of the system is dissipated largely as eddy-current losses, but partly as resistive losses, in a specially constructed electric machine.

3. Dynamic braking, in which the drive motor acts as a generator and the generated energy is dissipated as heat in resistors provided for the purpose.

4. Regenerative braking, in which the drive motor acts as a generator and pumps back energy into the electric supply system.

In the third quadrant the motor torque and direction of rotation are reversed. The operating conditions are similar to those in the first quadrant.

The fourth quadrant may represent one of two possible conditions. If the electrical conditions are the same as in first-quadrant driving, the mechanical

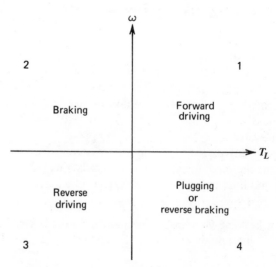

Fig. 1.2. Four-quadrant, speed-torque diagram.

system is driving the motor in a direction opposite to that which would result from its own developed torque. This is another type of braking, called "plugging." If the electrical conditions are changed to give reverse driving in the third quadrant, any of the types of braking described for the second quadrant are obtainable in the fourth quadrant.

The load torque may consist of components due to the following:

1. **Friction.** Torque used to drive the mechanical system without doing additional mechanical work.
2. **Windage.** Torque used to agitate or pump the air surrounding the moving parts of the mechanism.
3. **Acceleration** (which may be positive or negative). Torque developed under transient conditions and used to overcome the mechanical inertia of the mechanism.
4. **Mechanical work.**

If the mechanical system is devoted simply to *positioning* some piece of equipment, such as a subway train on a level track or an astronomical telescope, then 1 to 3 constitute the entire load torque.

The relation between torque due to friction in the mechanical system and speed of the driving motor is rarely simple, as shown typically in Fig. 1.3a. The friction torque, however, is usually small in relation to load torque and may be approximated to make analysis of the system practicable. A common approximation is shown in Fig. 1.3b, where

$$T_F = T_B + T_C + T_S \ \text{N} \cdot \text{m} \tag{1.1}$$

Component T_B, which is directly proportional to speed, is called *viscous friction* and is defined by

$$T_B = B\omega = \frac{B\,d\vartheta}{dt} \ \text{N} \cdot \text{m} \tag{1.2}$$

where B = constant for the system
ϑ = angular displacement in radians
ω = angular velocity in rad/s

The component T_C, which does not vary with speed, is called *coulomb friction*. It opposes motion at all speeds, thus constituting a load torque for forward *and* reverse driving. The small component T_S is due to static friction, or "stiction." It cannot be included in a linearized model of the system but frequently can be ignored.

Windage causes a component of load torque that, for rotating mechanisms, is approximately proportional to the square of the speed of rotation. Over the

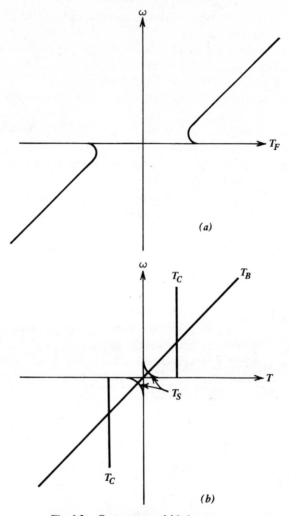

Fig. 1.3. Components of friction torque.

operating speed range the windage torque, combined with the viscous friction torque, may be represented to a good approximation by Eq. 1.2, in which the magnitude of constant B is appropriately chosen.

The torque required to accelerate the moving parts of the system may be expressed as

$$T_J = \frac{J\,d^2\vartheta}{dt^2} = \frac{J\,d\omega}{dt}\ \text{N}\cdot\text{m} \tag{1.3}$$

where J is the rotational inertia of the system in kg $\cdot$ m^2.

The torque used in mechanical work will be some function of ω peculiar to the load and may be defined by

$$T_W = T(\omega) = T\left(\frac{d\vartheta}{dt}\right) \text{ N} \cdot \text{m} \tag{1.4}$$

Thus the output torque of the motor may be expressed as

$$T_L = \frac{J\,d\omega}{dt} + B\omega + T_W \text{ N} \cdot \text{m} \tag{1.5}$$

A further complication may be the presence of elasticity in some part of the mechanical system; for example, if there is torsional elasticity in the shaft coupling the load to the motor, a further torque component will exist under transient conditions. This component is expressed as

$$T_K = K\vartheta_K \text{ N} \cdot \text{m} \tag{1.6}$$

where K is the rotational stiffness of the shaft in N $\cdot$ m/rad and $\dot{\vartheta}_K$ is the torsion angle of the coupling.

Whereas T_J stores kinetic energy in the system, T_K stores potential energy. The result of these two energy storages may be oscillation if T_B is small. When modeling a mechanism it is usually permissible to assume that shafts are perfectly stiff and that T_K may be neglected. Its presence, however, can cause mechanical noise or vibration and a shaft may break when the system is started.

The torque expressions developed in electric-machine analysis usually give the internal or air-gap torque T of the motor. Because the motor itself possesses inertia, friction, and windage, $T \neq T_L$, but if the factors J and B are modified to include the motor quantities then

$$T = \frac{J\,d\omega}{dt} + B\omega + T_W \text{ N} \cdot \text{m} \tag{1.7}$$

T may be calculated from the motor parameters and the nature of the power converter.

Hitherto a direct drive between motor coupling and mechanical load has been assumed. More often than not, however, gearing of some kind, possibly involving a transformation from rotation to translation or "linear" motion, as in a rotating motor driving a vehicle, will be introduced.

Inertia and friction may be referred through ideal gears, just as inductance and resistance are referred to one side or the other of an ideal transformer. Thus, if, in Fig. 1.4, N_1 and N_2 are the numbers of teeth on the gear wheels, then

$$\omega = \frac{N_2}{N_1}\omega_2 \text{ rad/s}; \qquad T_L = \frac{N_1}{N_2}T_2 \text{ N} \cdot \text{m} \tag{1.8}$$

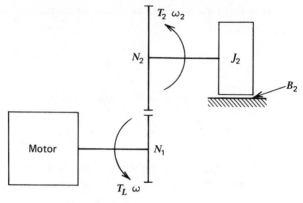

Fig. 1.4. Gear drive.

but

$$T_2 = J_2 \frac{d\omega_2}{dt} + B_2\omega_2 = J_2 \frac{N_1}{N_2} \frac{d\omega}{dt} + B_2 \frac{N_1}{N_2} \omega = \frac{N_2}{N_1} T_L \ \text{N} \cdot \text{m} \qquad (1.9)$$

and

$$T_L = J_2 \left(\frac{N_1}{N_2}\right)^2 \frac{d\omega}{dt} + B_2 \left(\frac{N_1}{N_2}\right)^2 \omega = \frac{J\,d\omega}{dt} + B\omega \ \text{N} \cdot \text{m} \qquad (1.10)$$

where J = the equivalent of J_2 referred to the motor shaft
$\quad\quad\;\; B$ = the equivalent of B_2 referred to the motor shaft

An alternative to gearing is the belt drive illustrated in Fig. 1.5, in which D_1 is the diameter of the driving pulley and D_2 is that of the driven pulley. If slippage is ignored or a toothed belt is used, Eqs. 1.8 to 1.10 apply to the pulley drive if D_1 and D_2 are substituted for N_1 and N_2. Among the disadvantages of belt, as opposed to gear drives are (a) slippage and (b) the possibility of oscillations due to elasticity of the belt.

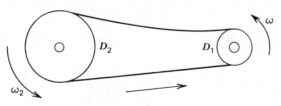

Fig. 1.5. Belt drive.

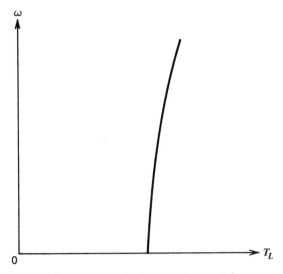

Fig. 1.6. Compressor load torque characteristic.

Usually the most important component of the load torque T_L on the motor is that used in mechanical work; that is, T_W, as described by Eq. 1.4. Each type of drive is a special case, and it is desirable therefore to discuss a few specific examples in relation to the speed-torque diagram in Fig. 1.2.

1.2.1. Compressor

The load torque presented by a compressor that supplies a constant pressure system may vary little with variation of speed, as illustrated in Fig. 1.6. This characteristic is linearized with little approximation.

A compressor drive is normally unidirectional, operating only in the first quadrant of Fig. 1.2. The possibility of oscillation at piston frequency in a reciprocating compressor due to system inertia and elasticity must be borne in mind when designing the drive.

1.2.2. Centrifugal Pump or Fan

This type of drive is normally not reversed and adequate braking is provided by the pumped fluid. Only the first quadrant in Fig. 1.2 is relevant. To a close approximation

$$T_W = k\omega^2 \text{ N} \cdot \text{m} \tag{1.11}$$

where k is a constant. The load characteristic is illustrated in Fig. 1.7. In the steady state the power developed at the motor coupling is expressed by

$$P_W = k\omega^3 \text{ W} \tag{1.12}$$

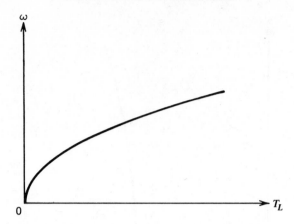

Fig. 1.7.   Centrifugal pump or fan load torque characteristic.

This drive will normally run for long periods at constant speed. It may be designed for several distinct speed settings or required to operate over a defined speed range.

1.2.3.   Constant-Power Drive

A fan drive operating at constant speed is, of course, developing constant power. There are, however, certain situations in which it is desirable to develop constant power over a range of speed. A typical application is the take-up roll in a steel strip, plastic, or paper mill illustrated in Fig. 1.8.

If a satisfactory roll is to be formed, the strip tension must be constant; it may be expressed by force f acting tangentially on the roll. Thus

$$T_W = fr \text{ N} \cdot \text{m} \tag{1.13}$$

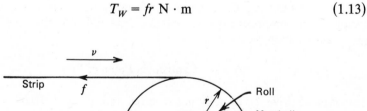

Fig. 1.8.   Take-up roll.

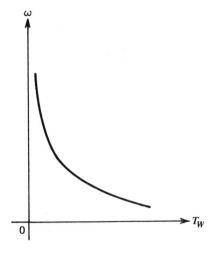

Fig. 1.9. Constant power curve.

where r is the radius of the roll. The strip will emerge from the mill rolls at constant speed v m/s. Thus one revolution of the roll takes $2\pi r/v$ s, and its speed of rotation is

$$\omega = \frac{v}{r} \ \text{rad/s} \qquad (1.14)$$

The power exerted by the drive is

$$P = fv = T_W \omega \ \text{W} \qquad (1.15)$$

This is constant because f and v are constant.

As r builds up, T_W increases and ω must fall. The curve of ω versus T_W is a hyperbola (Fig. 1.9). How a motor may provide this characteristic is discussed in some detail in later sections.

If the strip is elastic, the possibility of oscillation due to the inertia of the roll will exist.

1.2.4. Transportation Drive

A great variety of transportation drives exist, ranging from a freight train hauled by diesel-electric locomotives to small commercial road delivery vehicles. Some familiar examples within this range are

(a) subway trains
(b) streetcars
(c) trolley buses

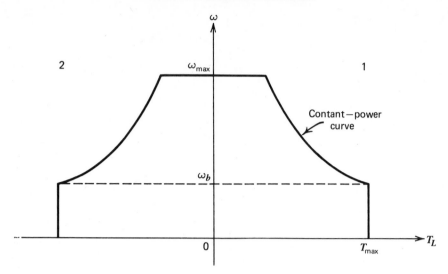

Fig. 1.10. Envelope of speed-torque characteristics.

In some cases the drive uses only one motor. In others several similar motors work in unison, sharing the load and operating under the same conditions of speed and shaft torque. The discussion that follows may apply to a single motor or to one of several motors in a multimotor drive system.

Because it is never necessary for a vehicle to reverse without a pause to permit switching, a transportation drive may be considered to operate in quadrants 1 and 2 of the speed-torque diagram in Fig. 1.2 but within the boundaries shown in Fig. 1.10. Reverse driving and braking differ in no way from forward operation. The particular feature of a transportation drive is the high inertia of the mechanical system. This inertia, when referred to the motor shaft, may be as much as 20 times that of the motor itself. (In an industrial drive the referred inertia of the mechanical system is frequently of the same order of magnitude as that of the motor.)

If station-to-station time is to be minimized, maximum positive and negative acceleration are required, with constant maximum speed in between. The permissible magnitude of acceleration may be dictated by passenger comfort, as also may the rate of change of acceleration, or *jerk*. Curves of motor speed, load torque, and output power are shown in Fig. 1.11 for an idealized transport drive in which it is assumed that regenerative braking is used and jerk is ignored.

The speed-torque envelope in Fig. 1.10 shows the limits of the system of source, converter, and motor. Because an important part of the duty cycle is that in which the vehicle is being accelerated, a motor will be chosen that can develop the required acceleration torque T_{max}. The *base speed* ω_b is determined by a limit on the maximum power which the source and converter can deliver

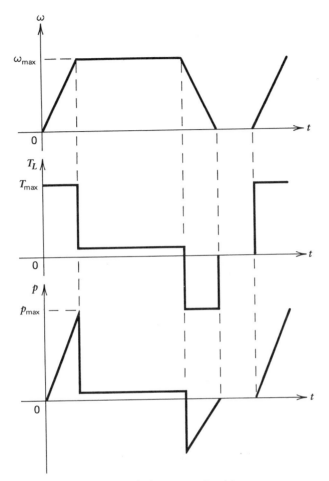

Fig. 1.11. Ideal transportation drive.

to the motor terminals. The constant-power curve is therefore dictated by this limitation. How the motor is constrained to follow this constant-power curve depends on the type of converter and motor and is discussed in some detail in the following. The maximum speed of the motor is directly related to the maximum speed of the vehicle.

The effect of the source-power limitation on the operation cycle is illustrated in Fig. 1.12. A comparison with Fig. 1.11 shows that, at the cost of a very small increase in station-to-station time, a much reduced maximum source power may be used.

Figure 1.13 shows a speed-time curve that may be considered typical for a modern rapid-transit system. In short station-to-station runs free running does not occur. The coasting period is useful for adjustment of station-to-station

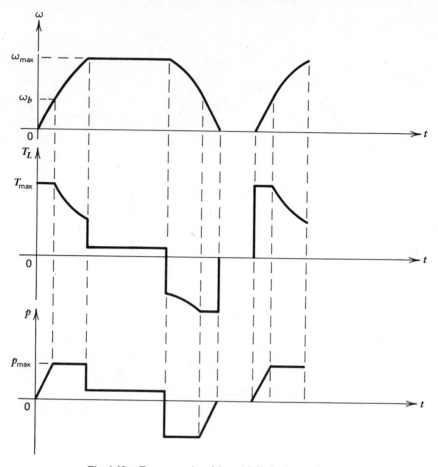

Fig. 1.12. Transportation drive with limited motor power.

time τ, but in very short runs this also may not occur because the drive switches from acceleration directly into regenerative braking.

The area beneath the speed-time curve gives the distance covered, but, at least for preliminary calculations, the speed-time curve may be replaced by a trapezoidal curve, shown by the broken line, of which the initial acceleration a_1 and braking deceleration a_2 are unchanged from the true curve. The free running speed, however, is somewhat reduced. The area beneath the speed-time curve is readily obtained and the average speed for a given distance D is

$$\bar{v} = \frac{D}{\tau} \text{ m/s} \qquad (1.16)$$

For the trapezoidal curve

$$D = \hat{v}_e\left(\tfrac{1}{2}t_1 + t_2 + \tfrac{1}{2}t_3\right) = \hat{v}_e\tau - \tfrac{1}{2}(\hat{v}_e)^2\left(\frac{1}{a_1} + \frac{1}{a_2}\right) \text{ m} \qquad (1.17)$$

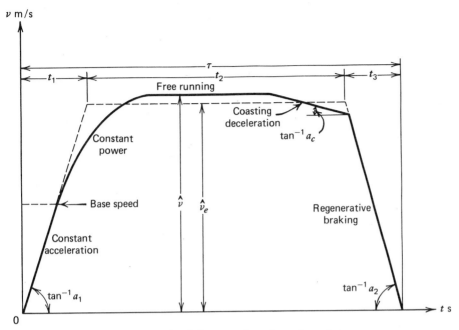

Fig. 1.13. Speed-time curve for urban subway train.

If a_1, a_2, and $\hat{v}_e$ are known, the station-to-station time τ may be calculated for any station spacing D.

Example 1.1

A train runs on a service in which there is one stop per kilometer. The schedule time per station is 120 s; stops are of 20-s duration. Determine the trapezoidal speed-time curve and the average speed for the run if the acceleration is 0.75 m/s² and the braking retardation is 1.25 m/s².

Solution

$$\text{Running time} \quad \tau = 120 - 20 = 100 \text{ s}$$

$$\text{Average speed} \quad \bar{v} = \frac{1000}{100} = 10 \text{ m/s}$$

$$D = 1000 = 100\hat{v}_e - \tfrac{1}{2}(\hat{v}_e)^2\left(\frac{1}{0.75} + \frac{1}{1.25}\right)$$

from which $\hat{v}_e = 11.38$ m/s.

$$t_1 = \frac{\hat{v}_e}{a_1} = \frac{11.38}{0.75} = 15.18 \text{ s}$$

$$t_3 = \frac{\hat{v}_e}{a_2} = \frac{11.38}{1.25} = 9.11 \text{ s}$$

$$t_2 = 100 - (15.18 + 9.11) = 75.71 \text{ s}$$

$$\text{Accelerating distance} = \tfrac{1}{2}\hat{v}_e t_1 = \frac{11.38}{2} \times 15.18 = 86.37 \text{ m}$$

$$\text{Free-running distance} = \hat{v}_e t_2 = 11.38 \times 75.71 = 861.6 \text{ m}$$

$$\text{Braking distance} = \tfrac{1}{2}\hat{v}_e t_3 = \frac{11.38}{2} \times 9.11 = 51.84 \text{ m}$$

$$D = 86.37 + 861.6 + 51.84 = 1000 \text{ m}$$

The maximum power required by a train may be as much as 10 MW. An accurate estimate of the energy required to operate it is essential in order that feeders, substations, and power-station equipment may be designed for economical working.

The total energy supplied to the train for propulsion may be expended in

(a) accelerating the train horizontally,
(b) accelerating the rotating parts,
(c) doing work against gravity on a gradient (possibly negative),
(d) doing work against the resistance to motion,
(e) supplying losses in the motors and power converters.

For short-distance runs on level track at high average speeds the energy required for acceleration forms a large proportion of the energy for propulsion. This accelerating energy is largely converted into kinetic energy and is therefore partly recoverable for propulsion during coasting and for return to the supply system during regenerative braking.

The torque at the motor coupling T_m required to accelerate the mass of the train horizontally at a m/s^2 is

$$T_m = \frac{rman}{n_1} \text{ N} \cdot \text{m} \tag{1.18}$$

where $r =$ radius of driving wheels
$m =$ mass of train in kg
$n_1 =$ number of driving motors
$n = N_1/N_2 =$ ratio of gearing
$N_1 =$ teeth on motor gear wheel
$N_2 =$ teeth on axle gear wheel

(n is analogous to the turns ratio of a transformer).

As the train is accelerated the wheels, axles, and gears must receive an angular acceleration. The torque at the motor coupling required to accelerate its share of the wheels is

$$T_w = \frac{2n_2 anJ_w}{n_1 r} \ \text{N} \cdot \text{m} \qquad (1.19)$$

where n_2 = the number of axles on the train
J_w = the moment of inertia of one wheel

The torque required to accelerate the gears and axles may be neglected in comparison with that for the wheels and train mass.

If the train is on a gradient, the grade force will produce another component of motor-coupling torque and may be positive or negative, according to whether the train is ascending or descending the gradient. The manner in which grade force is expressed is illustrated in Fig. 1.14. If the grade G is expressed by the ratio

$$G = \frac{Y}{S} \qquad (1.20)$$

the grade force is given by

$$f_G = Gmg \ \text{N} \qquad (1.21)$$

and the corresponding torque at each motor coupling is

$$T_G = \frac{Gmgrn}{n_1} \ \text{N} \cdot \text{m} \qquad (1.22)$$

Values of G may be as much as 0.01 for main-line railways and 0.06 for streetcars.

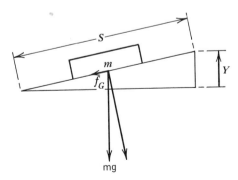

Fig. 1.14. Determination of grade force.

The term *train resistance* is applied to forces that resist the motion of a train when it is running at constant speed on a straight and level track. Part of the energy supplied to the motors is expended against internal friction of the rolling stock (including that of the motors) and part is expended against friction between the wheels and the rails. The remainder is expended against air resistance.

Train resistance is a complicated force and for the acceleration period is often assumed at an arbitrary value of about 20 N/tonne of train mass. This procedure is justified because the energy expended against train resistance during this period is small in comparison with that expended in accelerating the train.

The force of 20 N/tonne referred as a torque to the motor coupling is

$$T_R = \frac{20rmn}{10^3 n_1} \; N \cdot m \qquad (1.23)$$

The coupling torque of each motor required to accelerate the train is thus

$$T_L = T_m + T_w + T_R + T_G \; N \cdot m \qquad (1.24)$$

Example 1.2

A train unit is made up of three 4-wheel bogie coaches and has a mass of 96 tonnes unloaded. Each coach is equipped with four dc motors, each geared to a driving axle through single-reduction gearing for which the gear ratio $n = 0.356$. All wheels have a wheel tread of 1.08 m in diameter and each wheel has a mass of 455 kg.

Determine the coupling torque per motor required to accelerate the train at 1.25 m/s^2 and compare it with the torque required to accelerate the mass linearly on the horizontal track.

Solution

The torque required to accelerate the train horizontally is

$$T_m = \frac{0.356 \times 1.08 \times 96 \times 10^3 \times 1.25}{2 \times 4 \times 3} = 1922 \; N \cdot m$$

Assume that each wheel is a solid cylinder of diameter 1.08 cm. Then

$$J_w = \frac{1}{2} \times 455 \times \left(\frac{1.08}{2}\right)^2 = 66.34 \; kg \cdot m^2$$

This somewhat underestimates the wheel inertia because the thickness of the rim is greater than that of the web.

Each coach has two bogies, which gives a total of 12 axles. The torque required to accelerate the wheels is

$$T_w = \frac{2 \times 12 \times 0.356 \times 1.25 \times 66.34 \times 2}{3 \times 4 \times 1.08} = 109.3 \text{ N} \cdot \text{m}$$

By using the approximate train-resistance formula in Eq. 1.23

$$T_R = \frac{20 \times 1.08 \times 96 \times 0.356}{2 \times 4 \times 3} = 30.76 \text{ N} \cdot \text{m}$$

Thus

$$T_L = 1922 + 109.3 + 30.76 = 2062 \text{ N} \cdot \text{m}$$

To accelerate the mass linearly, disregarding the effect of the rotating masses, the torque would be

$$T_L = 1922 + 30.76 = 1953 \text{ N} \cdot \text{m}$$

Thus the apparent mass of the train is increased some 6% by the (underestimated) rotating masses.

A large number of empirical formulas that express the mechanical resistance to motion are available in the literature, and one must be used if calculations on the entire run are required. These formulas may be summarized as having the form

$$f_R = (a + bv)m + cv^2 \text{ N} \tag{1.25}$$

where a, b, and c are constants.

The first term on the right-side of Eq. 1.25 accounts for friction of all kinds, whereas the second expresses air resistance. The corresponding coupling torque per motor is

$$T_R = \frac{f_R rn}{n_1} \text{ N} \cdot \text{m} \tag{1.26}$$

The internal torque developed by the motor must accelerate not only the train, wheels and gears but also the motor armature. The torque required to accelerate an armature is

$$T_a = \frac{aJ_a}{nr} \text{ N} \cdot \text{m} \tag{1.27}$$

Thus for acceleration or deceleration the motor internal or air-gap torque is

$$T = T_L + T_a \text{ N} \cdot \text{m} \tag{1.28}$$

where it is assumed that the effect of the internal friction and windage of the motor is negligible in comparison with that of the train.

The kinetic energy stored in motor armatures is also available for driving the train during any coasting period.

For calculation of speed-time curves it is convenient to refer the effect of all rotating masses to the track. When these are combined with the actual train mass a fictitious quantity known as the *accelerating mass* is obtained. This mass may be expressed by

$$m_{acc} = m + \frac{2n_2}{r^2}J_w + \frac{n_1 J_a}{n^2 r^2} \text{ kg} \qquad (1.29)$$

Example 1.3

For the train in Example 1.2 the mass of each motor armature is 0.502 tonne and the diameter of the armature core is 0.450 m. The length L of each coach is 23 m and the transverse cross section area A of the coach body is 11.5 m². The ends of each coach are flat. Train resistance may be expressed by the formula

$$f_R = m(4.1 + 0.123v)10^{-3} + Av^2(151k + 2.16n_c L)10^{-3} \text{ N}$$

where n_c is the number of coaches and k is a factor that depends on the shape of the front end of the leading coach; in this case $k = 1$. The train is accelerated to a speed of 25 m/s and is then allowed to coast for 30 s on a level track. Estimate the distance covered during the coasting period.

Solution

An approximate distance may be obtained by breaking up the 30-s coasting period into a number of subperiods, calculating the distance covered on the assumption that f_R remains constant at the initial value, and then calculating the train speed at the end of the subperiod. In the solution that follows the 30-s period is broken into six 5-s subperiods.

Let $t = 0$ at the beginning of coasting. At that instant the decelerating force is

$$f_{R0} = 96(4.1 + 0.123v_0) + 11.5v_0^2(151 + 2.163 \times 3 \times 23)10^{-3}$$

$$= 393.6 + 11.81v_0 + 3.450v_0^2 = 393.6 + 295.2 + 2156$$

$$= 2845 \text{ N}$$

from which it is seen that the force due to air resistance predominates.

From Example 1.2

$$J_w = 66.43 \text{ kg} \cdot \text{m}^2$$

If it is assumed that each armature is a solid cylinder of mass 0.502 tonne and diameter 0.450 m, the moment of inertia of each armature is

$$J_a = \frac{502}{2}\left(\frac{0.450}{2}\right)^2 = 12.71 \text{ kg} \cdot \text{m}^2$$

This somewhat overestimates the armature inertia because the diameter of the commutator will be less than that of the core. From Eq. 1.29

$$m_{acc} = 96 \times 10^3 + 2 \times 12\left(\frac{2}{1.08}\right)^2 \times 66.34 + \frac{12}{0.356^2}\left(\frac{2}{1.08}\right)^2 \times 12.71$$

$$= 96 \times 10^3 + 5460 + 4128 = 105.6 \times 10^3 \text{ kg}$$

from which it is seen that the effect of the rotating mass of the armatures is comparable to that of the remaining rotating masses in the system. Deceleration during the first subperiod is

$$a_{c0} = \frac{f_{R0}}{m_{acc}} = \frac{-2845}{105.6 \times 10^3} = -26.94 \times 10^{-3} \text{ m/s}^2$$

Distance covered during the first subperiod is

$$s = v_0 t + \tfrac{1}{2}a_{c0}t^2 = 25 \times 5 - \tfrac{1}{2} \times 26.94 \times 10^{-3} \times 5^2 = 124.7 \text{ m}$$

Speed v_5 at the end of the first subperiod is

$$v_5 = v_0 - a_{c0}t = 25 - 26.94 \times 10^{-3} \times 5 = 24.87 \text{ m/s}$$

The new train resistance may now be calculated. Repetition of the foregoing procedure for the remaining five subperiods yields the quantities in Table 1.1. Had it been assumed that the deceleration remained constant at the initial value a total distance of 748.2 m would have been obtained. The error resulting

Table 1.1

t	v	f_R	a_c	s
0	25.00	2845	-26.95×10^{-3}	124.7
5	24.87	2821	-26.72×10^{-3}	124.0
10	24.74	2797	-26.49×10^{-3}	123.4
15	24.61	2774	-26.27×10^{-3}	122.7
20	24.48	2750	-26.04×10^{-3}	122.1
25	24.35	2727	-25.82×10^{-3}	121.7
30			Total distance =	738.6 m

from this assumption is negligible. Indeed, had it been assumed that there was no deceleration during coasting the distance covered would have been 750 m. This small error justifies the use of the trapezoidal speed-time curve in Fig. 1.13.

The total power output from all the motors at any instant is

$$P = n_1 T_L \omega_m \text{ W} \tag{1.30}$$

The energy output of the motors for a given period is obtained from the area beneath the power-time curve for the period.

For a run on level track made according to the approximate trapezoidal speed-time curve the total energy output of all the motors for the period of constant acceleration is

$$W_{a1} = n_1 \frac{T_{La1} \hat{\omega}_{me} t_1}{2} \text{ J} \tag{1.31}$$

where $\hat{\omega}_{me}$ is the motor speed corresponding to track speed $\hat{v}_e$ and

$$\hat{\omega}_{me} = \frac{\hat{v}_e}{nr} \text{ rad/s} \tag{1.32}$$

$\hat{v}_e$ is obtained from Eq. 1.17. Torque T_L is expressed to a good approximation by use of the constant train-resistance force of 20 N/tonne with which Eq. 1.23 was derived. Therefore

$$T_{La1} = T_m + \frac{2n_2}{n_1} T_w + \frac{20rmn}{n_1} \text{ N} \cdot \text{m} \tag{1.33}$$

The energy output for the constant-speed period is

$$W_R = f_R \hat{v}_e t_2 \text{ J} \tag{1.34}$$

The total regenerated energy input to all the motors for the period of constant deceleration is

$$W_{a2} = n_2 \frac{T_{La2} \hat{\omega}_{me} t_3}{2} \text{ J} \tag{1.35}$$

where

$$T_{La2} = T_m + \frac{2n_2}{n_1} T_w - \frac{20rmn}{n_1} \text{ N} \cdot \text{m} \tag{1.36}$$

For the entire run the net energy output of the drive system is

$$W_{RUN} = W_{a1} + W_R - W_{a2} \; J \qquad (1.37)$$

It is convenient to express the output in energy per tonne-kilometer to obtain the

$$\text{specific energy output} = \frac{W_{RUN}}{Dm} \; J/m \cdot kg \qquad (1.38)$$

This quantity forms a basis of comparison between the dynamical performances of trains operating on different schedules.

The net energy input to the motors is called the *energy consumption* of the train and must take into account the efficiency of the motors and the converters that supply them. If the rotational losses of the motor can be neglected in comparison with the train resistance, the energy expended in accelerating the armatures is recovered during the deceleration period and need not be introduced into energy calculations.

1.2.5. Winch Drive

A drive that operates in quadrants 1 and 4 of the speed-torque diagram in Fig. 1.2 is one that, among other applications, is used to warp a ship through a lock or hold it in some specific location.

This drive bears some resemblance to the constant-power drive discussed in Section 1.2.4. The principal difference is that, although constant tension is maintained in the cable between ship and shore, the motor spends much of its time stalled. The torque is unidirectional but the winch may be called on to take in or pay out cable and the direction of rotation may be reversed.

The motor in this system must be designed to exert its rated torque continuously at standstill.

1.2.6. Crane Hoist

This drive demands operation in all four quadrants of the speed-torque diagram (Fig. 1.15). In the first two quadrants the motor is connected for "forward" driving. The second quadrant thus implies regenerative braking. Because system decelerations are usually low and the braking due to the suspended load (or even the light hook) and winch is considerable, this quadrant is entered only during transient operation.

Prolonged steady-state operation may take place in quadrants 1, 3, and 4; "prolonged" indicates a period of a few minutes at most. For operation in the third quadrant the driving torque of the motor is reversed to give high-speed lowering. Under some circumstances this may result in movement of the system operating point to the fourth quadrant in which the load overhauls the

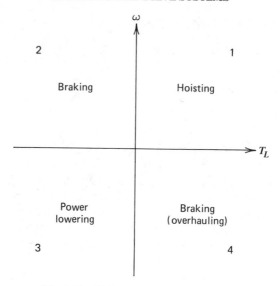

Fig. 1.15. Hoist speed-torque diagram.

motor and regenerative braking occurs at high speed. Eventually, however, the descending load must be decelerated and spotted at low speed, which may call for dynamic or mechanical braking. A mechanical brake is mandatory in a hoist system because a suspended load can be safely held stationary only by this means. It also protects against failure of the drive system.

A mechanical brake normally consists of a brake drum on which spring-loaded brake shoes bear with sufficient pressure to halt the descent of any load that the hoist is designed to handle. The brake is released by energizing an electromagnet that compresses the springs and lifts the brake shoes; it is a "fail-safe" device in the event of a power failure. Also for reasons of safety, a speed limit may be included in the control system, which, in the event of excessive speed, deenergizes the electromagnet and allows the brake to set.

The variation of ω versus T_W, due to the dead weight of the load, is shown in Fig. 1.16a. Because acceleration of the loaded hook is low, the torque required by system inertia is small. If, in addition, viscous friction is assumed, then, to a good approximation, the speed torque curves for loaded and light hook conditions are illustrated by the curves marked $T_B + T_W$ and T_B, respectively in Fig. 1.16b. This means that the torque at the motor coupling may be expressed as

$$T_L = B\omega + T_W \ \text{N} \cdot \text{m} \tag{1.39}$$

If coulomb friction is appreciable, the torque component T_C may be combined with the torque due to the dead weight of the suspended load. Coulomb friction would then assist in braking in the fourth quadrant.

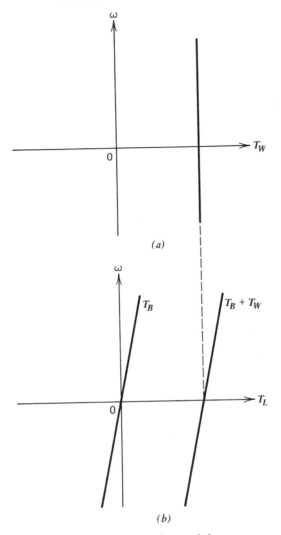

Fig. 1.16. Hoist torque characteristics.

To select a suitable driving motor a typical duty cycle must be specified. In the cycle illustrated in Fig. 1.17 the time interval between hoisting and lowering is taken up in slinging, moving the load horizontally, and unslinging. Motor power may be considered constant during each motion and is illustrated by the broken line in Fig. 1.17. While the motor torque is negative and the machine is regenerating it is still being heated by its internal losses. Thus to determine the size of motor needed the rating of the motor must be calculated from the whole operating cycle.

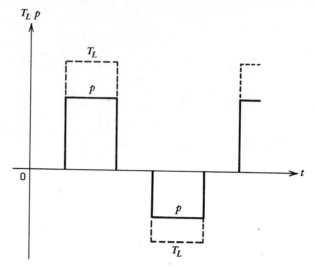

Fig. 1.17. Hoist duty cycle.

An elevator or a mine winder is a special type of hoist in that rapid acceleration of the conveyance is usually required; therefore the system inertia must be taken into consideration. Moreover, if the conveyance is intended for passengers, limitation of acceleration, elimination of jerk, and accurate decking control must be provided. For safety reasons braking of these systems is by friction brakes, assisted by the motor drive system.

1.3. REQUIRED DRIVE CHARACTERISTICS

Once the speed-torque characteristic demanded by the load has been determined it is possible to consider the most suitable motor-controller combination. This choice is also influenced by the nature of the available power source.

Any motor-converter combination can be represented in the steady state by a family of open-loop, speed-torque characteristics which corresponds to a series of control settings. Figure 1.18 shows two characteristics marked D_1 and D_2 which correspond to control settings 1 and 2. If the speed-torque characteristic presented by the load is the marked L, the system will operate in a steady-state condition at speed Ω_1 or Ω_2. However, the load characteristic may change; for example, the conveyance in a mine winder may be loaded or unloaded; a subway train may encounter a change in gradient or enter a tunnel. If the change results in a new load characteristic L', the possible operating speeds will change to Ω_1' or Ω_2'.

When the purpose of a drive system is speed control it is advantageous to allow the system speed for any given control setting to vary as little as possible.

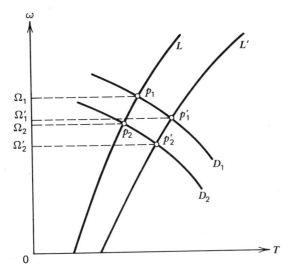

Fig. 1.18. Steady-state operating points.

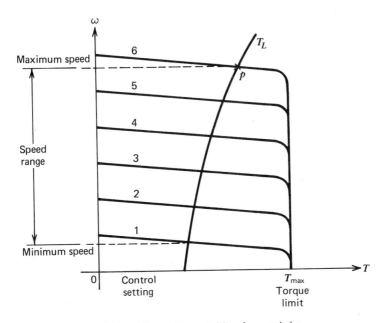

Fig. 1.19. Adjustable-speed drive characteristics.

As shown in Fig. 1.18, this requires that the motor-converter characteristics be as nearly horizontal as practicable.

The desirable characteristics of an adjustable-speed drive are shown in Fig. 1.19. The steady-state torque required by the load on any control setting is less than the torque limit set by the controller. This is necessary because some margin of motor torque must be available to accelerate the system and to stabilize it against transient overloads. If steady-state, full-load, full-speed operation occurs at point *p*, the *speed regulation* of the drive may be defined as

$$\text{speed regulation} = \frac{\text{speed on no load} - \text{speed on full load}}{\text{speed on full load}} \qquad (1.40)$$

This is usually a specified quantity, and the more closely the characteristics approach the horizontal, which may be regarded as ideal, the smaller the speed regulation. Maximum and minimum steady-state speed will also be specified. The ratio of maximum to minimum is commonly of the order of 6 to 1 and for special purposes ratios as high as 50 to 1 can be achieved. For a positional control and for many variable-speed drives, however, motor speed must be controllable right down to standstill.

1.3.1. Speed Changes

When a change in speed-control setting is made the operating point of the system moves from the intersection of the load characteristic with one drive characteristic to the intersection of the load characteristic with a new drive characteristic. The initial and final conditions can be represented in a steady-state, speed-torque diagram. What happens between these two steady states depends on the dynamic properties of the system. If it is assumed that the mechanical system is heavily damped and the operation of the control is fast, the process of transition from one operating point to another may be illustrated.

Consider a mechanical system in which static friction may be neglected and in which the load torque is composed of viscous and coulomb friction and the torque absorbed in doing useful work; that is,

$$T_L = T_B \pm T_C + T_W \; \text{N} \cdot \text{m} \qquad (1.41)$$

Let the load characteristic be that shown in Fig. 1.20*a*. The drive characteristics for four positive and four negative speed-control settings are shown in Fig. 1.20*b* as ideal horizontal lines between the limits imposed by the control.

Let the system operate on control setting +4 and give forward driving when a speed reduction is called for by a change to control setting +2. The speed

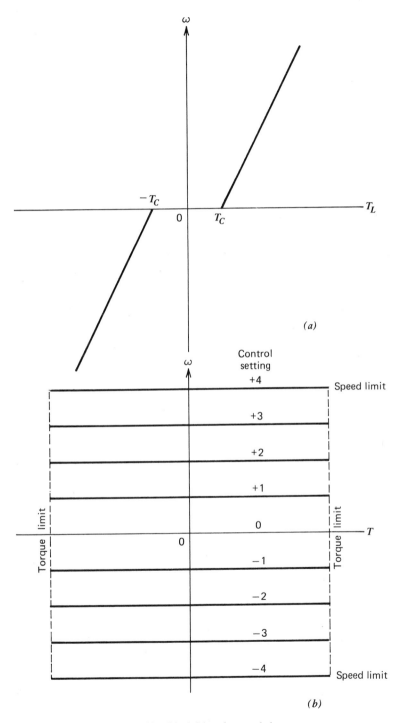

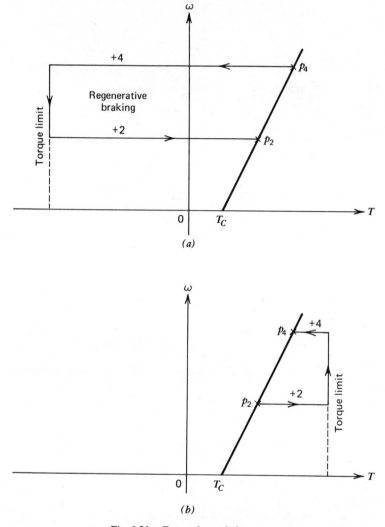

Fig. 1.21. Forward speed change.

cannot change instantaneously because of mechanical inertia; the torque may be considered to do so. The operating point therefore moves along drive characteristic +4 to the negative torque limit (Fig. 1.21a). The negative torque decelerates the system until it reaches the speed for control setting +2, at which time the operating point moves back to the first quadrant at point p_2, the new steady state. Regenerative braking takes place in the second quadrant. During the entire interval required for the speed change the operating point is moving vertically downward in the second quadrant. The horizontal movements of the operating point take place instantaneously. A return to control setting +4 is achieved entirely in the first quadrant (Fig. 1.21b).

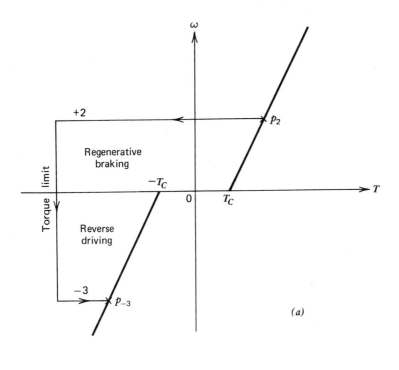

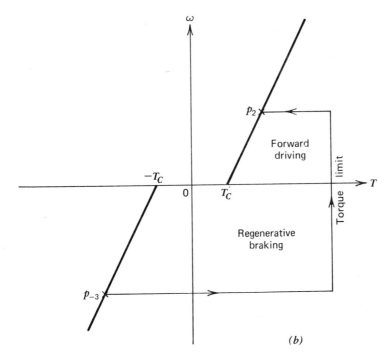

Fig. 1.22. System reversal.

29

If a transition from setting $+2$ to setting -3 is called for (Fig. 1.22a), regenerative braking again takes place; the system is brought to a standstill smoothly followed by reverse driving. A return to control setting $+2$ follows a similar sequence of events (Fig. 1.22b).

1.4. ELECTRIC POWER SUPPLY

The choice of the power converter or conditioner and motor cannot be arbitrarily made but depends on the nature of the power supply available. Once the drive elements have been chosen and a preliminary design of the system carried out it is possible to determine whether the available power source will satisfy the requirements of the drive system, particularly in regard to maximum power rating.

1.4.1. AC Sources

In general, for a system that can develop 2 kW of drive power a single-phase ac source is adequate. For higher powers a three-phase source is desirable and for more than about 5 kW of drive power it is usually essential. Source-potential difference can, if necessary, be transformed. The frequency and potential variation of the source should be specified, however, as should any limit to the acceptability of regenerated energy. If no statement on source potential is made, it should be assumed that it may fall to 15% below the rated value. There may also be restrictions on the harmonic content of currents drawn from the source and the power factor at which the drive system may operate.

An exception to the generalizations of the preceding paragraph must be made in the case of traction systems. Because power may be delivered to the train or vehicle by trolley/collector and overhead conductor, it is usually important that not more than two conductors be required; therefore single-phase power should be used. A traction system, however, normally has its own power system which is not shared by other users and high-power drive systems may be supplied from a single-phase source. The supply to the sections of track of a three-phase supply system may be transposed from one phase to another to keep the three phases in approximate balance.

1.4.2. DC Sources

It is unusual for a dc source to be available for general purposes in an industrial plant; therefore, if dc is particularly desirable, it must normally be provided by some form of conversion from the ac power system.

If rectification is employed the possibility of regeneration from the drive system must be considered because a simple diode rectifier cannot regenerate. This problem is discussed in more detail in the following. A motor-generator set that consists of an ac motor and a dc generator is capable of regeneration but is inefficient and expensive in comparison with a rectifier. If, however, the set is large and a synchronous motor is used, power-factor improvement for an entire industrial plant may be obtained.

In traction systems, large-scale conversion equipment capable of regeneration may be installed in substations. The advantage of dc for power distribution in a rail-guided traction system is great because the guiding rails and a third rail or overhead wire are conductors, whereas the high self-inductance of steel rails prohibits their use with ac of standard power frequency.

1.5. SELECTING THE DRIVE ELEMENTS

Once the characteristics of the source and the mechanical system are defined it is possible to select a suitable motor and converter. Frequently several combinations are possible; therefore the chapters that follow deal in some detail with the characteristics of motors and converters and with some of the mechanical systems with which they may be used.

The converter may be considered to consist of two parts: the power converter or modulator and the logic unit that receives the command and feedback signals and produces from them the signals that control the operation of the power converter.

Table 1.2 lists the main types of converter.

Important information required for each type of converter includes

(a)   converter transfer characteristic;

(b)   nature of output harmonics;

(c)   nature of current harmonics created in the power supply line;

(d)   ability to accept regenerated energy.

Table 1.2
Types of Converter

Converter	Conversion Function
Controlled rectifiers	Fixed or variable potential and frequency ac power to variable potential dc
dc-to-dc converters (choppers)	Fixed potential dc to higher or lower variable potential dc
AC power controller	Fixed potential ac to variable potential ac of same frequency
Inverters (voltage source or current source)	Fixed or variable potential dc to fixed or variable potential and frequency ac
Cycloconverters	Fixed potential and frequency ac to variable potential and frequency ac

As indicated in Fig. 1.1, the motor may be dc, ac induction, or ac synchronous of some type. Standard motors may be used but machines are also manufactured with special design features that enable them to be operated efficiently from the outputs provided by solid-state converters. In the interest of energy conservation the motor should be rated to prevent it from being needlessly underrun and the converter-motor combination must be such that if the power supply is ac the input power factor will be high.

PROBLEMS

1.1. In the mechanism shown in Fig. 1.23 the motor drives the winch drum through 1:10 reduction gears (i.e., $\omega/\omega_2 = 10$). Assuming that the shafts and cable are nonelastic, calculate the equivalent inertia of the motor and mechanism referred to the motor shaft.

1.2. A motor is required to drive the take-up roll on a plastic strip line. The mandrel on which the strip is wound is 10 cm in diameter and the strip builds up to a roll 30 cm in diameter. The strip emerges from the line at a speed of 20 m/s; the strip tension required is 10 kg. The motor is coupled to the mandrel by 1:2 reduction gearing. The gears may be considered to be 85% efficient at all speeds. Determine the speed and power rating of the motor needed for this service.

1.3. A 200-tonne train is accelerated at 1.2 m/s². Determine the force that must be exerted by the wheel rims on the track, assuming a train resistance of 20 N/tonne.

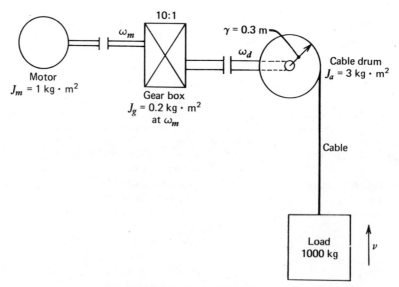

Fig. 1.23. Diagram for Problem 1.1.

1.4. A train is accelerated uniformly from rest until a speed of 15 m/s is reached 20 s after starting. Power is then cut off and the train coasts for 40 s. At the end of this period braking is applied and the train is brought to rest 70 s after starting. Retardation during coasting may be assumed constant at 0.045 m/s². Determine the distance run from start to stop and the average speed.

1.5. The train in Examples 1.2 and 1.3 operates between two stations 1.5 km apart, between which there is a uniform gradient of 1 in 80. The scheduled average speed, excluding stops, is 20 m/s up the gradient and 22.5 m/s down the gradient. On level track the control settings employed would give an acceleration of 1.25 m/s² and a deceleration of 1.5 m/s². Regenerative braking is used. With an approximate value for train resistance during acceleration and deceleration of 20 N/tonne and the formula for train resistance at constant speed of Example 1.3 calculate the specific energy output and the maximum speed for runs in both directions, assuming trapezoidal speed-time curves. Draw the trapezoidal curves of speed versus distance.

1.6. The train in Problem 1.5 makes the up and down runs repeatedly with a stopover time of 30 s at each station. Draw the diagrams of train-speed motor torque and motor power versus time (Fig. 1.11) for the complete return trip. Determine the rms motor power for the trip and the peak motor power required and suggest a practical power rating for the motor.

1.7. A crane hoist is required to raise 10 tonnes at a speed of 0.25 m/s. The hook is mounted on a block which carries a sheave that contains a single pulley. One end of the hoisting cable is anchored on the crane trolley and the other is wound up on a winch drum 25 cm in diameter. The drum is driven by worm reduction gearing of ratio 45 to 1. The whole mechanism may be considered to be 60% efficient. Determine the power and speed rating of the motor and the braking torque exerted by the motor when it lowers the load at 0.3 m/s.

1.8. Figure 1.24 shows the speed-torque characteristic L of a mechanical load mechanism and the drive characteristics D_1 and D_2 for two controller settings. The load characteristic is a straight line that passes through the origin and point [40, 2000]. The drive characteristics are also straight lines; D_1 passes through points [0, 1000] and [40, 800]; D_2 passes through points [0, 1600] and [40, 1400]. The rotational inertia of the motor and mechanical load referred to the motor shaft is 0.2 kg · m². The friction of the system may be neglected:

(a) Do the intersections of the load characteristic with the two drive characteristics represent two possible conditions of stable, steady-state operation? Explain.

(b) If the answer to (a) is affirmative determine the two operating speeds and torques.

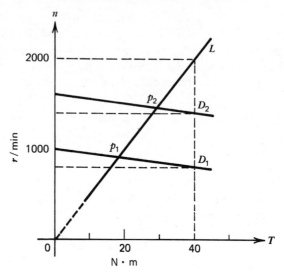

Fig. 1.24. Diagram for Problem 1.8.

(c) If the system is operating at point p_2 and the controller setting is abruptly changed to yield drive characteristic D_1 draw to scale curves of speed and torque as functions of time for the first half-second of the transition from p_2 to p_1.

Chapter 2

Separately Excited DC Motors

2.1. INTRODUCTION

In an industrial plant the normal power supply is 60 Hz (or 50 Hz) alternating current. Induction and synchronous motors operated from such a source with conventional control equipment provide essentially constant-speed drives. One way of obtaining a variable-speed drive in this situation is to convert the ac power to dc and exploit the ready controllability of the dc machine. If, however, a supply of dc power at appropriate potential difference is already available, it may be controlled by a dc-to-dc converter or chopper and provide a variable speed drive from a dc machine driven by this means. Because the use of dc is widespread in electric transportation systems, chopper drives find a ready application in that field.

The most flexible control is obtained by means of a separately excited dc motor in which the armature and field circuits are provided with separate sources. This arrangement produces speed-torque characteristics approximating closely to the ideal characteristics shown in Fig. 1.20. For the armature source a controlled rectifier or a chopper is required. If the field current is to be controlled, similar provision must be made for the field circuit.

Shunt or separately excited motors for drive systems that incorporate converters have special design features that should be mentioned. In systems that must respond rapidly to changes in command the rotor should have a large ratio of length to diameter to reduce mechanical inertia. If large peak torques are anticipated motors should have pole-face compensating windings.[1] These windings also reduce the armature-circuit inductance and thus lower the time constant of the armature circuit. This, however, has the adverse effect of reducing the smoothing of the armature current. For feed-drives in machine tools permanent-magnet motors are frequently used and are almost universal in servo drives of less than 1 kW of motor power.

Because the direct potential differences and currents provided by power-semiconductor converters may have a large harmonic content over much of their operating range, the motor must be designed to tolerate "mixed" current (i.e., a combination of dc and ac). Pulsating dc has a higher rms value than the smooth dc required to develop the same torque and conductor cross section must be increased to prevent excessive heating. To obtain good commutation the stator structure must be at least partly laminated (poles and interpoles) because of the damping effect of eddy currents in the iron on the fluctuating interpole flux. If rapid response to changes in field excitation is also required, lamination of the stator yoke is also needed. For prolonged operation at high torque and low speed motors may be forced-ventilated.

A short review of the operation of a separately excited motor is provided in the following sections.

2.2. SYSTEM MODEL

Figure 2.1 shows the equivalent circuit of a separately excited motor and the model of a general mechanical system that incorporates the mechanical parameters of the motor and the mechanism coupled to it.

For system analysis a linear model is desirable. However, there is one nonlinear relationship in the model of the dc machine that also affects the values of the inductances in the model. The relationship is that between field current i_f and flux per pole φ. It is convenient to express it by Eq. 2.1:

$$e_a = k\varphi\omega = F(i_f)|_{\omega=\Omega_{sc}} \text{ V} \qquad (2.1)$$

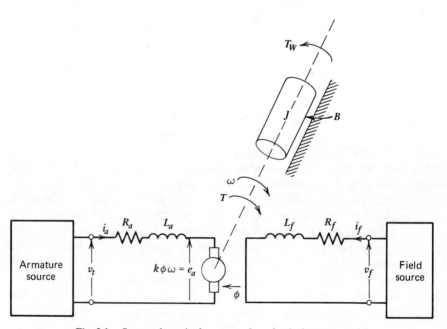

Fig. 2.1. Separately excited motor and mechanical system model.

where k is a constant for the machine and e_a is the emf induced in the armature winding. Equation 2.1 is usually presented by the motor manufacturer in the form of a saturation curve of the machine in which e_a is plotted versus i_f for some specified speed Ω_{sc}. In this curve, illustrated in Fig. 2.2, the effect of hysteresis is neglected. Its vertical axis may also be calibrated in values of φ: if this is done and field leakage flux is ignored, then, from the known number of turns on the field poles the field flux linkage per ampere of field current, that is, the field-circuit inductance L_f, may be obtained for any value of i_f. For the straight-line part of the saturation curve this inductance is constant. For a point not on the straightline part the incremental inductance is proportional to the slope of the curve. The armature-circuit inductance L_a also depends to some extent on the degree of saturation of the magnetic system; therefore to linearize the motor model both inductances must be determined for the particular value of field current to be used.

In the model of the mechanical system the parameters and working torque T_W are referred to the motor coupling. In Fig. 2.1 J and B account for the inertia and viscous friction of both motor and driven mechanism. The effect of coulomb friction is neglected or included in T_W.

For a chosen field current the equations that relate the terminal variables of the motor (where the shaft coupling is also a "terminal") are

$$v_f = R_f i_f + L_f \frac{di_f}{dt} \text{ V} \tag{2.2}$$

$$v_t = k\varphi\omega + L_a \frac{di_a}{dt} + R_a i_a \text{ V} \tag{2.3}$$

$$T = k\varphi i_a = J\frac{d\omega}{dt} + B\omega + T_W \text{ N} \cdot \text{m} \tag{2.4}$$

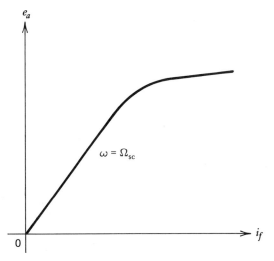

Fig. 2.2. Motor saturation curve.

where T is the air-gap or internal torque of the motor. For steady-state operation the time derivatives in these equations are zero and

$$v_f = R_f i_f \text{ V} \tag{2.5}$$

$$v_t = k\varphi\omega + R_a i_a \text{ V} \tag{2.6}$$

$$T = k\varphi i_a = B\omega + T_W \text{ N} \cdot \text{m} \tag{2.7}$$

2.2.1. Speed Control

From Eqs. 2.6 and 2.7, for steady-state operation,

$$\omega = \frac{v_t}{k\varphi} - \frac{R_a T}{(k\varphi)^2} = \frac{k\varphi v_t - R_a T_W}{(k\varphi)^2 + R_a B} \text{ rad/s} \tag{2.8}$$

Thus for $T_W = 0$ the no-load speed is determined by the values of the two variables φ and v_t. If these two are fixed and T_W increases from zero, then ω decreases. The system therefore has speed regulation. If the armature-circuit resistance R_a is small, however, the speed is essentially independent of the load torque.

From Eq. 2.8 it can be seen that the steady-state speed can be controlled directly by controlling the potential difference (pd) applied to the armature terminals. If the field current is adjusted to the maximum value for which the machine is designed so that φ is large, Eq. 2.8 shows that for a constant value of v_t the speed-torque relationship can be represented by a straight line of small negative slope with an intercept on the speed axis. This straight line is shown, marked v_{t1}, in Fig. 2.3.

Let the torque required to overcome the losses due to friction, windage, and core loss in the motor and mechanical system be designated T_{loss}. The internal torque of the motor is

$$T = T_{\text{loss}} + T_W \text{ N} \cdot \text{m} \tag{2.9}$$

The relation between torque T and speed can then be represented by the line marked $T_{\text{loss}} + T_W$ in Fig. 2.3. At armature terminal pd v_{t1} the system will therefore operate at point p_1. On the other hand, removal of the torque T_W will give the no-load operating point p_0.

If the armature is supplied from a source of controllable direct pd the speed may be controlled from zero up to a value for which v_t is equal to the maximum pd for which the motor has been designed. Any other fixed value of v_t, such as v_{t2}, will yield a characteristic parallel to that for v_{t1}.

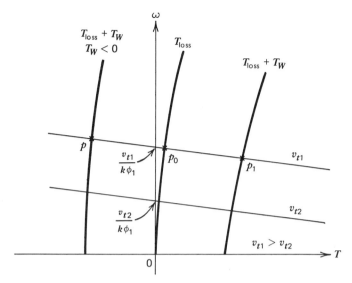

Fig. 2.3.   Speed control by variation of v_t.

Regeneration can also take place, for example, when a vehicle is descending a slope and tending to drive the motor at increased speed. Under these circumstances T_W in Eq. 2.8 becomes negative so that ω increases along the straight-line characteristic described. The motor operates at a point such as p_2 in Fig. 2.3. During this transition from motoring to regenerative braking the polarities of the field and armature pds are unchanged, as is also the direction of field current. The armature current reverses direction and so therefore does the flow of energy.

Reversal of the polarity of v_t would give a pattern of characteristics and operating points in the third and fourth quadrants similar to that in Fig. 2.3 but rotated through 180° about the origin. This would apply to the operation of the motor in the reverse direction.

When v_t and i_f are set at the rated or nameplate values and the motor is loaded and delivering rated power it should be running at rated speed ω_r. On the other hand, when v_t is set at the rated value and i_f is set at the maximum value that the field windings are designed to carry continuously the motor will be running at the somewhat lower *base speed* ω_b. Increase in speed above this value is obtained by *field weakening*; that is, by a reduction in v_f and consequent reduction in i_f and φ down to and beyond the rated values, as a result of which speeds above rated speed are reached. Equation 2.8 shows that the characteristic that results from weakened field will have an increased intercept on the axis of ω and an increased negative slope (Fig. 2.4). Maximum speed by field weakening is limited by the mechanical design of the motor and the tendency of the motor to become unstable at weak field due to the

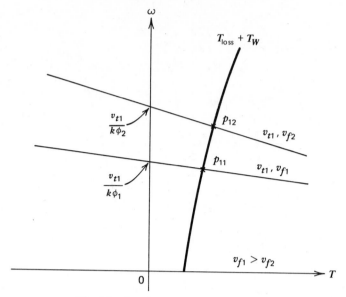

Fig. 2.4. Speed control by field weakening.

demagnetizing effect of armature reaction. In motors designed for speed control the maximum speed may be two to six times the base speed.

As a third possible method of speed control, effective only with a loaded motor, the resistance R_a of the armature circuit may be increased by including series resistance R_d. This alters the speed-torque relationship and gives the motor a large speed regulation. The effect of series resistance is shown in Fig. 2.5. This means of speed control is not normally used with separately excited motors and indeed is generally undesirable because it wastes energy. It is, however, the normal method of starting motors where speed control down to standstill is not required and may also be used for systems that need speed control only infrequently.

Consider now a system in which v_t may be controlled from zero up to the rated value. If i_f is set at the maximum permissible value and the effect of R_a is ignored control of motor speed is possible up to the base value ω_b. Over this speed range of $0 < \omega < \omega_b$ the armature current must normally be limited to the rated value; hence the developed torque will also be limited because

$$T = k\varphi i_a \ \text{N} \cdot \text{m} \tag{2.10}$$

Air-gap power is expressed by

$$P = T\omega \ \text{W} \tag{2.11}$$

At constant torque power is a linear function of ω with a maximum value for

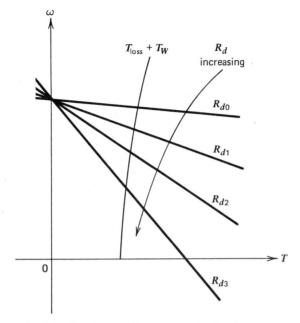

Fig. 2.5. Speed control by armature-circuit resistance.

$T = T_{max}$ and $\omega = \omega_b$. Any further speed increase requires field weakening. When the effect of R_a is ignored Eq. 2.8 shows that for constant v_t

$$\omega \propto \frac{1}{\varphi} \text{ rad/s} \qquad (2.12)$$

Because i_a must still be limited to its rated value, the developed torque for operation with weakened field is

$$T = k\varphi i_a \propto \frac{1}{\omega} \text{ N} \cdot \text{m} \qquad (2.13)$$

and

$$P = T\omega = \text{constant W} \qquad (2.14)$$

For four-quadrant operation of a separately excited motor the envelope of permissible speed-torque relations at rated current is illustrated in Fig. 2.6. It must be realized, however, that this envelope is ideal because motor losses have been ignored. The practical limits lie within those shown in the diagram.[1]

In the foregoing discussion it has been assumed that the energy source had no power limit. This is not true. In a diesel-electric locomotive a diesel engine drives a generator at constant speed and the generator supplies armature current to a separately excited dc motor. The power that can be developed by the diesel engine is limited, and this necessitates limiting the operation of the drive to a curve of constant power when base speed is exceeded. The rated output power of the electric motor must be matched to the rated output power of the diesel engine, allowing for generator and motor losses. The generator in this system may be a dc machine or an ac generator that supplies a diode rectifier. Either way, control of the generator field current provides speed control up to the base speed of the motor.

2.3.   MOTOR RATINGS

The motor can operate continuously at any operating point within the area enclosed in the four quadrants of Fig. 2.6. This is not to say, however, that for short periods of time it is impossible to operate beyond certain of these boundaries.

The boundary marked "maximum speed" is imposed by the mechanical design of the motor and/or the possibility of instability due to armature reaction. If this speed is exceeded there is danger of mechanical failure or runaway. This boundary, therefore, may not be crossed.

The torque boundary formed by the vertical line marked "maximum torque" and the constant-power curves is established by the permissible

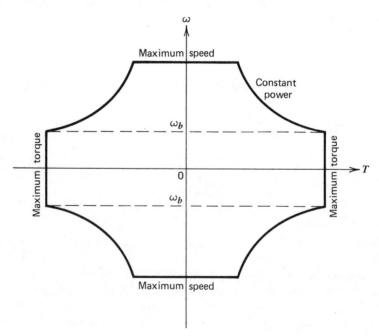

Fig. 2.6. Continuous torque and speed limits.

steady-state current of the motor. This boundary may be crossed for limited periods, but doing so will result in an armature current greater than the rated value. This may be dangerous on several counts.

High armature current results in high resistive losses and a consequent high rate of heating. If the high currents are prolonged the temperature of the conductors and their insulation will exceed that for which the insulation was designed; consequently the insulating materials deteriorate rapidly and eventually fail. Heavy armature current in machines without compensating pole-face windings[1] may also result in severe distortion of the flux-density distribution in the air gap, and the high flux densities at certain locations in the magnetic system will produce additional core losses that will contribute to the overheating of the motor.

Because of the thermal limitations, it is common practice to specify how long a motor may be operated at increased torque or to specify a short-time rating for the motor. A short-time rated motor can deliver a power that, if required continuously, would demand a much larger machine; for example, a half-hour rated machine may be run at rated conditions for half an hour, after which it must be run on no load or stopped for the same period. A short-time rated machine never reaches a steady operating temperature since this is still rising when the time limit is reached and a cooling-off period follows.

Current must also be limited in a dc machine because of the commutator. Commutation is a complicated matter, but the more serious effects of heavy current are due to high segment-to-segment pd on the commutator caused by (a) distortion of the flux-density distribution and (b) high rate of change of armature-coil current arising from the need to reverse a large current in the

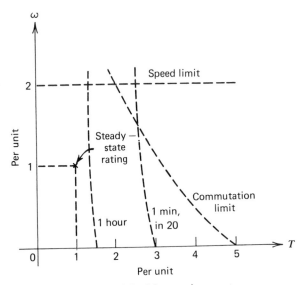

Fig. 2.7. Motor ratings.

time taken to commutate the coil. Both effects are dependent on speed, so that the machine can commutate large currents at lower speeds. The limitations on motor operation due to the factors described in the preceding paragraphs are illustrated in Fig. 2.7.

Example 2.1

A separately excited dc motor with constant field current has an armature source whose pd can be varied from 0 to 600 V. At maximum armature pd the speed of the motor is 1600 rpm. If all losses in the motor are neglected:

   (a) What is the armature current when the load torque is 420 N · m?

   (b) If the armature pd is held constant at 600 V and the field current is reduced until the motor runs at 4000 rpm, determine the torque that the motor may exert at this speed.

   (c) What is the required power rating of the source?

Solution

   (a) Armature power is

$$P_a = V_t I_a = T\omega \text{ W}$$

$$600 I_a = 420 \times 1600 \times \frac{2\pi}{60}$$

$$I_a = 117.3 \text{ A}$$

   (b) The motor is operating on the constant-power curve. At 4000 rpm

$$P_a = 600 \times 117.3 = T \times 4000 \times \frac{2\pi}{60}$$

$$T = 168 \text{ N} \cdot \text{m}$$

   (c) The power rating of the source is

$$P_a = 600 \times 117.3 = 70.37 \text{ kW}$$

2.4. MOTOR-MECHANISM DYNAMICS

If a separately excited motor is operated at constant field current the motor and the driven mechanism can be considered as a linear system. The system equations are then

$$I_f = \frac{V_f}{R_f} \text{ A} \tag{2.15}$$

$$\Phi = F(I_f) = \text{constant Wb} \tag{2.16}$$

$$v_t = k\Phi\omega + L_a \frac{di_a}{dt} + R_a i_a \text{ V} \tag{2.17}$$

$$T = k\Phi i_a = J \frac{d\omega}{dt} + B\omega + T_W \text{ N} \cdot \text{m} \tag{2.18}$$

Superposition may be used to combine the steady-state operation of the system with the transient operation that results from a small variation in one of the excitations v_t and T_W.

Transient behavior may be analyzed by transforming the system equations for zero initial conditions. Thus from Eqs. 2.17 and 2.18 the Laplace transforms of v_t and T are

$$V_t(s) = k\Phi\Omega(s) + sL_aI_a(s) + R_aI_a(s) \tag{2.19}$$

$$T(s) = k\Phi I_a(s) = sJ\Omega(s) + B\Omega(s) + T_W(s) \tag{2.20}$$

From Eq. 2.19

$$I_a(s) = \frac{V_t(s) - k\Phi\Omega(s)}{sL_a + R_a} = [V_t(s) - k\Phi\Omega(s)]\frac{1}{R_a(s\tau_a + 1)} \tag{2.21}$$

where the *armature-circuit time constant* is

$$\tau_a = \frac{L_a}{R_a} \text{ s} \tag{2.22}$$

From Eq. 2.20

$$\Omega(s) = \frac{T(s) - T_W(s)}{sJ + B} = [T(s) - T_W(s)]\frac{1}{B(s\tau_m + 1)} \tag{2.23}$$

where the *mechanical time constant* of the motor and coupled mechanism referred to the motor shaft is

$$\tau_m = \frac{J}{B} \text{ s} \tag{2.24}$$

The block diagram in Fig. 2.8 may be drawn from Eqs. 2.21 and 2.23. The system it illustrates has two excitations, $V_t(s)$ and $T_W(s)$. The separate responses to these two excitations may be determined and combined with a given steady-state condition of operation by superposition.

The response to a change in torque T_W is obtained by setting V_t to zero. The block diagram in Fig. 2.9 is then obtained from Fig. 2.8. From Fig. 2.9

$$\frac{\Omega(s)}{-T_W(s)} = \frac{(1/B)(s\tau_a + 1)}{(s\tau_a + 1)(s\tau_m + 1) + (k\Phi)^2/R_aB} = \frac{K(s\tau_a + 1)}{(s\tau_1 + 1)(s\tau_2 + 1)} \tag{2.25}$$

In Eq. 2.25 K is the dc gain and τ_1 and τ_2 may be real or conjugate complex

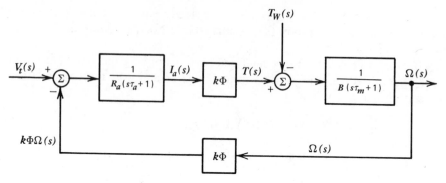

Fig. 2.8. Motor-mechanism block diagram.

quantities. If the latter is the case the response to a change in T_W will be oscillatory.

The response to a change in V_t is obtained by setting T_W to zero. From Fig. 2.8

$$\frac{\Omega(s)}{V_t(s)} = \frac{k\Phi/R_a B}{s^2(\tau_a \tau_m) + s(\tau_a + \tau_m) + 1 + (k\Phi)^2/R_a B} \qquad (2.26)$$

Usually

$$\frac{(k\Phi)^2}{R_a B} \gg 1 \qquad (2.27)$$

and

$$\frac{\Omega(s)}{V_t(s)} = \frac{1}{k\Phi(s\tau_1 + 1)(s\tau_2 + 1)} \qquad (2.28)$$

where again τ_1 and τ_2 may be conjugate complex, in which case Eq. 2.28 may be written in the form

$$\frac{\Omega(s)}{V_t(s)} = \frac{1/k\Phi}{s^2/\omega_n^2 + 2\zeta s/\omega_n + 1} \qquad (2.29)$$

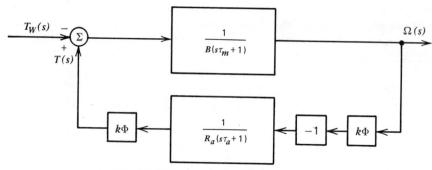

Fig. 2.9. Response to variation of $T_w(s)$.

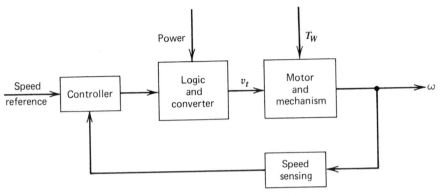

Fig. 2.10. Block diagram for complete drive system.

In Eq. 2.29, assuming that inequality 2.27 is valid,

$$\omega_n^2 = \frac{(k\Phi)^2}{\tau_a \tau_m R_a B} = \frac{(k\Phi)^2}{L_a J} \tag{2.30}$$

$$\zeta = \frac{(\tau_a + \tau_m) R_a B \omega_n}{2(k\Phi)^2} = \frac{L_a B + J R_a}{2k\Phi\sqrt{L_a J}} \tag{2.31}$$

For many motors $\tau_a \ll \tau_m$; the foregoing analysis may then be carried out on the assumption that $L_a = 0$ and

$$v_t = k\Phi\omega + R_a i_a \quad \text{V} \tag{2.32}$$

This approximation yields a transfer function

$$\frac{\Omega(s)}{V_t(s)} = \frac{1}{k\Phi(s\tau + 1)} \tag{2.33}$$

where

$$\tau = \frac{R_a J}{(k\Phi)^2} \quad \text{s} \tag{2.34}$$

The transfer function of the motor and mechanism may be introduced into the block diagram for a complete speed-control system (Fig. 2.10).

This analysis has not dealt with the consequences of a variation of field current. Since the relationship between φ and i_f is nonlinear, this would yield a nonlinear system possibly needing an adaptive controller to stabilize it.[2]

2.5. CLOSED-LOOP SPEED CONTROL

Although the transfer functions of the controller or regulator and converter are not yet known, the steady-state operation of the system in Fig. 2.10 may be described if these two elements are merely given a gain factor for the operating

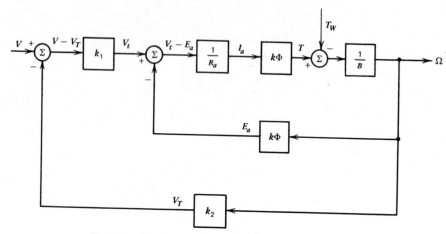

Fig. 2.11. Steady-state operation of a speed control system.

condition envisaged. The steady-state operation of the motor and mechanism can then be described by setting the derivatives in Eqs. 2.17 and 2.18 to zero. The effect on the transfer functions of the system elements is to set all terms containing s^n to zero. The block diagram of the speed control system then becomes that shown in Fig. 2.11, where the transfer function of the controlling system, which is comprised of the controller converter and logic, is

$$k_1 = \frac{V_t}{V - V_T} \tag{2.35}$$

In Eq. 2.35 V is the reference input pd that results from the speed command and V_T is the output pd of the speed-sensing transducer (possibly a tachometer) for which

$$k_2 = \frac{V_T}{\Omega} \tag{2.36}$$

By setting T_W to zero the transfer function of the internal closed loop is

$$\frac{\Omega}{V_t} = \frac{k\Phi/R_a B}{1 + (k\Phi)^2/R_a B} \tag{2.37}$$

If inequality 2.27 is applicable Eq. 2.37 becomes

$$\frac{\Omega}{V_t} \simeq \frac{1}{k\Phi} \tag{2.38}$$

The closed-loop, steady-state transfer function for the entire system in Fig. 2.11 is then

$$\frac{\Omega}{V} = \frac{k_1}{k\Phi + k_1 k_2} \tag{2.39}$$

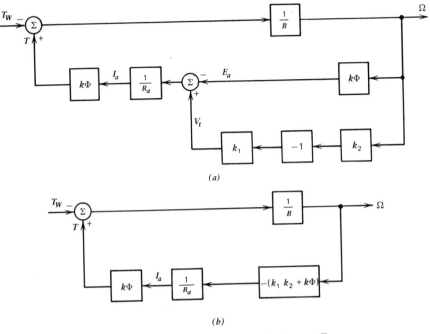

Fig. 2.12. Steady-state response to load torque T_w.

The steady-state response to a change of load torque can be obtained by setting V to zero and rearranging the block diagram in Fig. 2.11 in the form shown in Fig. 2.12a, where for the two parallel branches

$$(V_t - E_a) = -k_1 k_2 \Omega - k\Phi\Omega = -(k_1 k_2 + k\Phi)\Omega \qquad (2.40)$$

Equation 2.40 gives the block diagram in Fig. 2.12b. For this feedback loop

$$\frac{\Omega}{-T_W} = \frac{R_a}{R_a B + k\Phi(k_1 k_2 + k\Phi)} \qquad (2.41)$$

Therefore a positive load torque for zero speed command results in negative speed.

When the system is running at speed on load the responses to the two separate inputs V and T_W may be determined separately and combined by superposition to give the resultant response.

Example 2.2

A 40-kW, 240-V, 1150-rpm separately excited dc motor is to be used in a speed control system, which may be represented by the block diagram in Fig. 2.11. The field current is held constant at a value for which $k\Phi = 1.95$ V · s/rad. Resistance $R_a = 0.089$ Ω, and viscous friction factor $B = 0.275$ N · m · s/rad. The tachometer delivers 10 V/1000 rpm and the amplification of the controller, etc., is $k_1 = 200$.

(a) Determine the value of the reference input signal V required to drive the motor at rated speed on no load.

(b) If the reference signal is unchanged determine the speed at which the motor would run when supplying rated torque.

(c) If the motor were driven with a constant armature pd of 240 V (i.e., no feedback system) determine the no-load and full-load speed.

Solution

$$\text{Rated speed} = 1150 \times \frac{2\pi}{60} = 120.4 \text{ rad/s}$$

$$k_2 = \frac{10}{1000 \times 2\pi/60} = 95.49 \times 10^{-3} \text{ V} \cdot \text{s/rad}$$

$$\text{Rated torque} = \frac{40 \times 10^3}{120.4} = 332.2 \text{ N} \cdot \text{m}$$

(a) From Eq. 2.37

$$\frac{\Omega}{V_t} = \frac{1.95/(0.089 \times 0.275)}{1 + 1.95^2/(0.089 \times 0.275)} = \frac{79.67}{1 + 155.4} = 0.5095$$

and these figures justify the approximation of inequality 2.27.

At rated speed $V_t = \dfrac{120.4}{0.5095} = 236.3 \text{ V}$

$$V_T = 95.49 \times 10^{-3} \times 120.4 = 11.50 \text{ V}$$

$$\frac{V_t}{V - V_T} = \frac{236.3}{V - 11.50} = 200$$

$$V = 12.68 \text{ V}$$

(b) From Eq. 2.41 at full load torque

$$\Omega = \frac{-332.2 \times 0.089}{0.089 \times 0.275 + 1.95(200 \times 95.49 \times 10^{-3} + 1.95)}$$

$$= -0.7200 \text{ rad/s}$$

$$= -6.875 \text{ rpm}$$

By superposition full load speed is

$$1150 - 6.875 = 1143 \text{ rpm}$$

(c) From Eq. 2.8, for $T_W = 0$

$$\omega = \frac{1.95 \times 240}{1.95^2 + 0.089 \times 0.275} = 122.3 \text{ rad/s}$$

$$= 1168 \text{ rpm}$$

For $T_W = 332.2$ N · m

$$\omega = \frac{1.95 \times 240 - 0.089 \times 332.2}{1.95^2 + 0.089 \times 0.275} = 114.6 \text{ rad/s}$$

$$= 1094 \text{ rpm}$$

By feedback the speed regulation of the motor is reduced by a factor of 10.

PROBLEMS

2.1. The circuit in Fig. 2.13 shows part of the test arrangement for loading the motor of a low-power drive system, positively or negatively; that is, with the drive machine motoring or regenerating. Two similar machines M_1 and M_2 are mechanically coupled; M_1 is the drive motor, M_2, the loading machine. The armature-circuit resistance of each machine is 0.65 Ω and the rated current is 9 A. The field current of each machine is adjusted to give $k\Phi = 0.525$ V · s/rad. The direction is such that both machines motor with the same direction of rotation. The resistance of the voltage divider in the armature supply circuit of the loading machine is 30 Ω. If friction, windage, and core losses are neglected, the drive motor armature current is maintained at the rated magnitude, and the armature terminal pd of that machine is held constant at 50 V, determine the speed of rotation and the setting of the slider of the voltage divider (i.e., the value of R_2) for motoring and regenerating operation of M_1.

2.2. In the test system in Problem 2.1 determine the maximum and minimum speeds for M_1, both motoring and generating, the corresponding values of V_{t1}, and the slider settings of the voltage divider (i.e., the values of R_2). Again the armature current is to be maintained at the rated value.

2.3. A 40-kW, 230-V, 1750 rpm, permanent-magnet, dc motor has a full-load current of 205 A and an armature-circuit resistance of 0.097 Ω. The rotational (friction, windage, and core) loss torque may be assumed to be directly proportional to speed.

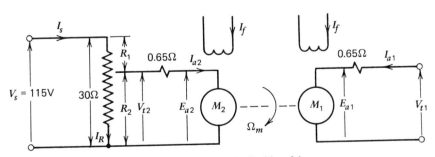

Fig. 2.13. Diagram for Problem 2.1.

(a) Determine the speed when the load torque is 150 N · m and 230 V is applied to the armature circuit terminals.

(b) Determine the armature terminal pd required to drive the motor at half-rated speed with the same load torque.

2.4. The motor in Problem 2.3 is to drive a load that requires a shaft torque expressed by the relationship

$$T_W = 1.25\omega$$

where ω is in rad/s. Determine at what speed the drive will run with (a) $v_t = 230$ V, (b) $v_t = 200$ V.

2.5. A 230-V, 20-kW, variable-speed, dc motor may be controlled by field weakening over the speed range of $1200 < n < 3600$ rpm. Its full-load current is 101 A, the armature-circuit resistance is 0.175 Ω, and it may be assumed that the rotational loss torque is directly proportional to speed. The motor is ventilated by a separate motor-driven blower and the armature-terminal pd is held constant at 230 V for all conditions of operation.

(a) Neglecting all losses, draw a theoretical speed-torque diagram that corresponds to the first and second quadrant of Fig. 2.6.

(b) Superimpose on the diagram obtained in (a) the actual curves obtained when losses are taken into consideration. (On the constant-power curves determine only the points for $\omega_m = 2\omega_b$.)

2.6. Figure 2.14 illustrates an arrangement for charging a blast furnace. The mass of the empty conveyance is 400 kg and that of a full load of material is 1600 kg. The conveyance is to travel up the slope at a maximum speed of 5 m/s and down at a maximum speed of 10 m/s. The stop for loading is 10 s and that for unloading is 5 s. The winch drum is 2 m in diameter and is coupled to the driving motor by reduction gearing. The arrangement of the cable is such that the motor is able to drive the conveyance down as well as up. The cycle is to be repeated continuously.

A separately excited 230-V, dc motor with speed control and regenerative braking is to be used and it may be assumed that the downward speed is achieved by field weakening; the reduced field is to be applied during the entire downward trip. The maximum allowable armature current is twice the rated value. The rotational inertia of the drum and gears referred to the motor shaft may be assumed to be equal to that of the motor. Motor and mechanism losses may be neglected.

Choose a suitable motor from Appendix B and the corresponding gear ratio. This ratio should be an integer suitable for two-stage gearing. Draw a speed-time diagram for one complete cycle of operation and a corresponding diagram of equivalent horsepower in terms of heating effect on the motor.

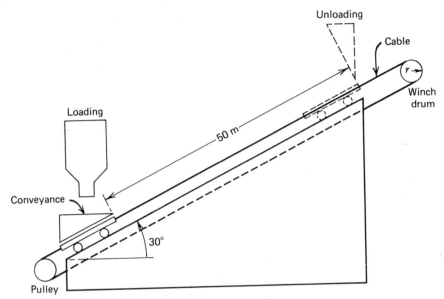

Fig. 2.14. Diagram for Problem 2.6.

2.7. For the 20-hp (14.9-kW), 1750-rpm frame size 288 motor in Appendix B

(a) obtain the transfer functions $\Omega(s)/V_t(s)$ and $\Omega(s)/- T_W(s)$ for the motor;

(b) calculate the motor speed when the field excitation is that required for rated operation at 230 V but the terminal pd is 210 V and the load torque is 0.75 of the rated value.

Assume that the rotational-loss torque is directly proportional to speed.

2.8. The motor in problem 2.7 is to be used in the speed-control system illustrated in Fig. 2.10. The converger is a dc-to-dc converter (chopper), the speed sensing device is a tachometer generator, and the speed reference signal is obtained from a regulated 50-V, dc source. The normal full-load setting of V is 40 V. For steady-state behavior the controller may be considered to be simply a summer. If the speed is not to vary more than 1% of rated value when full load is applied or removed choose a suitable tachometer gain and calculate the required gain of the logic and converter.

Chapter 3

Single-Phase Rectifiers with Motor Load

3.1. INTRODUCTION

Rectifiers may be classified by the number of phases of the ac source that supplies them or by the number of pulses of current that they supply to the load circuit during one cycle of the ac source. Both methods of classification are useful.

The discussion that follows in this and the succeeding chapter is limited to systems that draw from the ac source an alternating current with a symmetrical waveform; that is, a current that contains no direct component or even harmonics, both of which cause asymmetrical saturation of transformer cores with consequent distortion of the waveforms of potential difference.

3.2. FULLY CONTROLLED RECTIFIER DRIVES

There are two commonly used converter configurations, the main power-circuit elements of which are shown in Fig. 3.1a and b. The method of controlling the field current is not shown in either case. If a diode rectifier were used as the field source a field rheostat would be required for control. Provided that the rated motor armature pd and that of the ac source are compatible, the transformer in Fig. 3.1a is not essential; it may, however, be desirable for isolation. In this configuration thyristors Q_1 and Q_2 are turned on simultaneously at the chosen delay angle $\omega t = \alpha$, where $\omega t = 0$ at the beginning of the sinusoidal variation of source pd. Thyristors Q_3 and Q_4 are turned on one-half cycle later when the gating signals are already removed from Q_1 and Q_2. In the converter of Fig. 3.1b the two thyristors are turned on alternately.

For low-potential motors operating down to low speeds the system in Fig. 3.1b is preferable because only one thyristor is in series with the armature circuit; therefore there is only one thyristor terminal pd to reduce the armature pd. Equally important is the fact that losses occur in only one thyristor instead of in two in series, as in the converter of Fig. 3.1a. The transformer of the

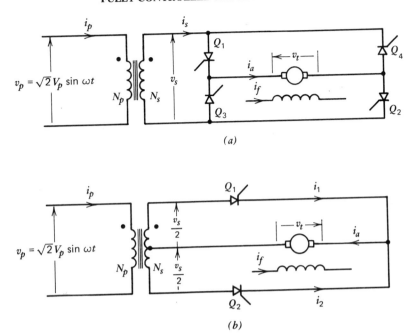

(a)

(b)

Fig. 3.1. Single-phase controlled rectifiers.

converter in Fig. 3.1b, however, is somewhat larger than that in Fig. 3.1a because only one-half of the secondary winding is carrying current at any instant.

Each of the systems in Fig. 3.1 may be represented for purposes of analysis by the equivalent circuit in Fig. 3.2. In this circuit equivalent thyristor Q_A represents Q_1 and Q_2 in Fig. 3.1a in series or simply Q_1 in Fig. 3.1b. The pd

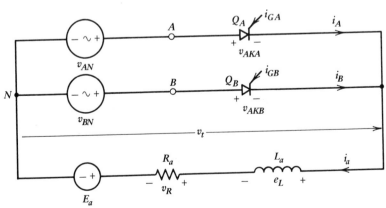

Fig. 3.2. Equivalent circuit of the systems in Fig. 3.1.

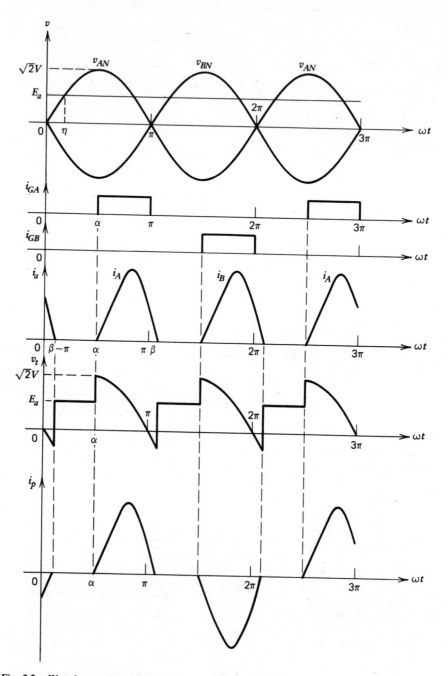

Fig. 3.3. Waveforms of variables in Figs. 3.1 and 3.2. Discontinuous-current operation with $\alpha > \eta$.

56

v_{AKA} in Fig. 3.2 may therefore represent the pd across the terminals of two thyristors or of one only. Discussion of the converter operation may now be conducted in terms of the equivalent circuit.

Figure 3.3 shows the steady-state waveforms of the principal equivalent-circuit variables for operation of the loaded motor at a delay angle α and field current I_f to produce flux per pole Φ. This results in effectively constant motor speed Ω_m and induced armature emf E_a, where

$$E_a = k\Phi\Omega_m \text{ V} \tag{3.1}$$

The waveform of the primary current i_p in both transformers in Fig. 3.1 is also shown in Fig. 3.3. It will be noted that i_a is discontinuous. This is the

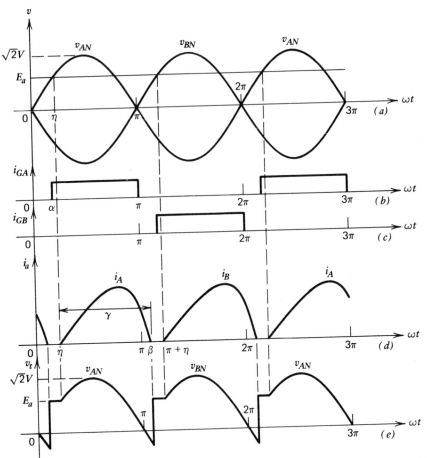

Fig. 3.4. Waveforms of variables in Figs. 3.1 and 3.2. Discontinuous-current operation with $\eta > \alpha > (\beta - \pi)$.

normal condition of operation for the low-power drives that incorporate a single-phase full-wave controlled rectifier. The waveform of i_a shows that the converters in Fig. 3.1 may be classified as two-pulse rectifiers.

Figure 3.4 shows a set of possible waveforms for discontinuous-current operation where L_a is low. Here α has been reduced until $\alpha < \eta$, where

$$\eta = \sin^{-1}\frac{E_a}{\sqrt{2}\,V} = \sin^{-1}m \text{ rad} \tag{3.2}$$

It will be noted that the current i_A begins to flow only at $\omega t = \eta$ because current i_a falls to zero before thyristor Q_A is turned on. A further reduction in α may bring about the condition shown in Fig. 3.5, where, because Q_A is turned on before i_a falls to zero, Q_B is commutated and Q_A begins to conduct at $\omega t = \alpha$; L_a, however, is not great enough to prolong i_A until $v_{AN} > E_a$.

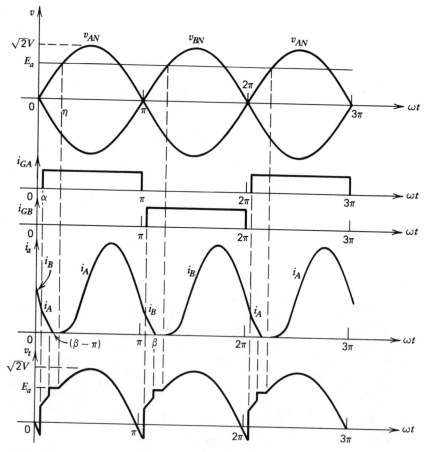

Fig. 3.5. Waveforms of variables in Figs. 3.1 and 3.2. Discontinuous-current operation with $\eta > \alpha$; $(\beta - \pi) > \alpha$.

Thus in the first half-cycle shown in Fig. 3.5 i_A ceases at $\omega t = \beta - \pi$ and recommences at $\omega t = \eta$.

It is also possible that a reduction in α below the value that produces the conditions shown in Fig. 3.4 or 3.5 will result in continuous-current operation. The corresponding steady-state waveforms are shown in Fig. 3.6. For normal power frequencies and motor inductances, however, these conditions would result only from a value of α less than that of the lower limit normally anticipated, in gross overloading of the motor, or in a combination of these two.

Returning to the normal conditions of operation shown in Fig. 3.3, when no armature current is flowing,

$$v_t = E_a \text{ V} \qquad \beta - \pi < \omega t < \alpha \text{ rad} \qquad (3.3)$$

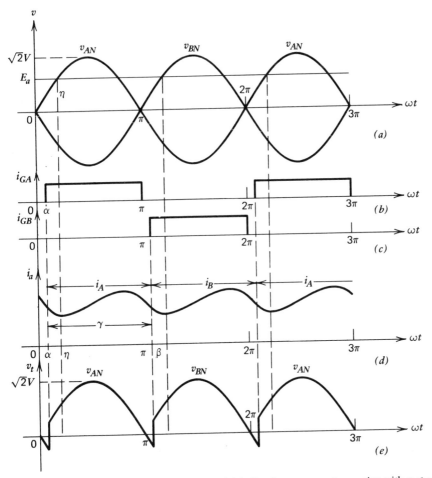

Fig. 3.6. Waveforms of variables in Figs. 3.1 and 3.2. Continuous-current operation with $\alpha < \eta$.

where β is the extinction angle or point in the cycle at which thyristor Q_A ceases to conduct.

When armature current is flowing

$$v_t = v_{AN} \text{ V} \qquad \alpha < \omega t < \beta \text{ rad}$$

$$v_t = v_{BN} \text{ V} \qquad \pi + \alpha < \omega t < \pi + \beta \text{ rad} \tag{3.4}$$

From an analysis of the circuit in Fig. 3.2 and substitution from Eq. 3.1 it can be shown that[5]

$$i_A = i_a = \frac{\sqrt{2} V}{Z} \sin(\omega t - \varphi) - \frac{k\Phi\Omega_m}{R_a}$$

$$+ \left[\frac{k\Phi\Omega_m}{R_a} - \frac{\sqrt{2} V}{Z} \sin(\alpha - \varphi) \right] \varepsilon^{(\alpha - \omega t)/\tan\varphi} \text{ A} \tag{3.5}$$

where

$$Z = \left[(\omega L_a)^2 + R_a^2 \right]^{1/2} \Omega \tag{3.6}$$

and

$$\varphi = \tan^{-1} \frac{\omega L_a}{R_a} \text{ rad} \tag{3.7}$$

Equation 3.5 applies during the interval $\alpha < \omega t < \beta$ and at

$$\omega t = \beta \text{ rad} \qquad i_a = 0 \tag{3.8}$$

Substitution from Eq. 3.8 in Eq. 3.5 yields

$$0 = \frac{\sqrt{2} V}{Z} \sin(\beta - \varphi) - \frac{k\Phi\Omega_m}{R_a} + \left[\frac{k\Phi\Omega_m}{R_a} - \frac{\sqrt{2} V}{Z} \sin(\alpha - \varphi) \right] \varepsilon^{(\alpha - \beta)/\tan\varphi}$$

$$\tag{3.9}$$

If all the system parameters, including $k\Phi$, are known, this is a relationship between β and Ω_m for any chosen value of α. If α and a series of values of Ω_m are specified the corresponding values of β can be determined numerically. The limiting value is $\beta = \pi + \alpha$, when current becomes continuous.

For any set of values of Ω_m, β, and α the average armature current $\bar{i}_a$ may be obtained by substitution from Eq. 3.5 in

$$\bar{i}_a = \frac{1}{\pi} \int_\alpha^\beta i_a \, d(\omega t)$$

$$= \frac{1}{\pi} \left\{ \frac{\sqrt{2}\,V}{Z} [\cos(\alpha - \varphi) - \cos(\beta - \varphi)] - \frac{k\Phi\Omega_m}{R_a}(\beta - \alpha) \right\}$$

$$- \frac{1}{\pi} \left\{ \tan\varphi \left[\frac{k\Phi\Omega_m}{R_a} - \frac{\sqrt{2}\,V}{Z}\sin(\alpha - \varphi) \right] [\varepsilon^{(\alpha - \beta)/\tan\varphi} - 1] \right\} \text{ A} \quad (3.10)$$

It may also be possible to obtain $\bar{i}_a$ from

$$\bar{i}_a = \frac{\bar{v}_t - k\Phi\Omega_m}{R_a} \text{ A} \quad (3.11)$$

where $\bar{v}_t$, the average terminal pd of the armature, may be obtained from the waveform in Fig. 3.3; that is,

$$\bar{v}_t = \frac{1}{\pi} \left[k\Phi\Omega_m(\pi + \alpha - \beta) - \sqrt{2}\,V(\cos\beta - \cos\alpha) \right] \text{ V} \quad (3.12)$$

The average *internal* torque is given by

$$\bar{T} = k\Phi\bar{i}_a \text{ N} \cdot \text{m} \quad (3.13)$$

so that the torque at each value of Ω_m may be determined and the speed-torque curve for discontinuous-current operation at a given value of α is known.

The physical sequence of events that results in movement of the operating point along this speed-torque curve may be summarized. If the motor is running at constant speed and is partly loaded an increase of load results in a reduction of speed. Thus E_a falls, allowing i_a to rise, so that the motor develops the required increased average torque; that is to say, while α remains at its set value β increases. As may be seen from the waveform of v_t, the average pd $\bar{v}_t$ is reduced, causing a further reduction in speed and in E_a, until a new equilibrium condition is reached. The rectifier thus has considerable regulation and this increases the speed regulation of the drive.

Steady-state waveforms for continuous-current operation brought about by excessive load torque and a low value of α are shown in Fig. 3.7. The conduction angle γ is now π rad, and

$$\bar{v}_t = \frac{2\sqrt{2}\,V}{\pi}\cos\alpha \text{ V} \quad (3.14)$$

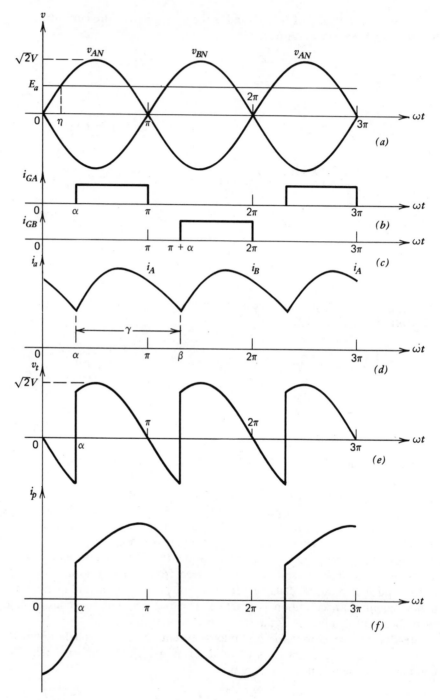

Fig. 3.7. Waveforms of variables in Figs. 3.1 and 3.2. Continuous-current operation with $\alpha > \eta$.

If the load torque is further increased $\bar{v}_t$ will not change if α is held constant. The drive will still have a small speed regulation, however, because

$$E_a = k\Phi\Omega_m = \bar{v}_t - R_a\bar{i}_a \text{ V} \qquad (3.15)$$

Thus, as torque, and consequently $\bar{i}_a$, increases, E_a is reduced and speed falls correspondingly. From Eqs. 3.13 and 3.15

$$\Omega_m = \frac{2\sqrt{2}\,V}{\pi k\Phi}\cos\alpha - \frac{R_a\bar{T}}{(k\Phi)^2} \text{ rad/s} \qquad (3.16)$$

The first term on the right side of this equation gives an intercept on the vertical axis of the speed torque diagram of a straight line whose negative slope is determined by the coefficient of $\bar{T}$ in the second term.

It would appear from Eqs. 3.9 to 3.13 and the accompanying discussion that a speed-torque curve for discontinuous-current operation can be calculated for any value of α with its limiting point for $\beta = \pi + \alpha$ lying on the line for the same value of α given by Eq. 3.16. This, however, would ignore the occurrence of the conditions shown in Figs. 3.4 and 3.5. Apart from the point of intersection with the straight line of Eq. 3.16, the only other point on the curve for discontinuous current that can be fixed without a great deal of calculation is for $\bar{T} = 0$, at which E_a reaches the peak value of v_t and pulses of current cease. For this condition, from Eq. 3.1,

$$\Omega_m = \frac{\hat{v}_t}{k\Phi} \text{ rad/s} \qquad (3.17)$$

From Fig. 3.3

$$\hat{v}_t = \sqrt{2}\,V \text{ V} \qquad 0 < \alpha < \pi/2 \text{ rad}$$

$$\hat{v}_t = \sqrt{2}\,V\sin\alpha \text{ V} \qquad \pi/2 < \alpha < \pi \text{ rad} \qquad (3.18)$$

In Fig. 3.8 a family of characteristics of speed versus internal torque is shown for a motor driven by a single-phase, full-wave rectifier. Each curve is for a constant value of α. The rectifier was supplied with 270 V at 60 Hz. The motor considered was the 500-rpm, frame-size 283 machine in Appendix B, with the field current set for operation under rated conditions.

The points at which transition from the operating conditions in Figs. 3.3 to those in Fig. 3.7 took place were determined by choosing a value of α and setting $\beta = \alpha + \pi$ in Eq. 3.9 to obtain a value of Ω_m. Equations 3.14, 3.11, and 3.13 were then used in that sequence to give the corresponding value of $\bar{T}$. This point was found to lie on the straight line obtained from Eq. 3.16. The curved parts of the characteristics were calculated by using Eqs. 3.9 and 3.11 to 3.14. The break points in Fig. 3.8 show that, except for operation at extreme values of α, current is discontinuous for torques up to rated value.

The curves in Fig. 3.8 also show that no reasonable amount of approximation can produce a linear transfer function for the converter-motor combina-

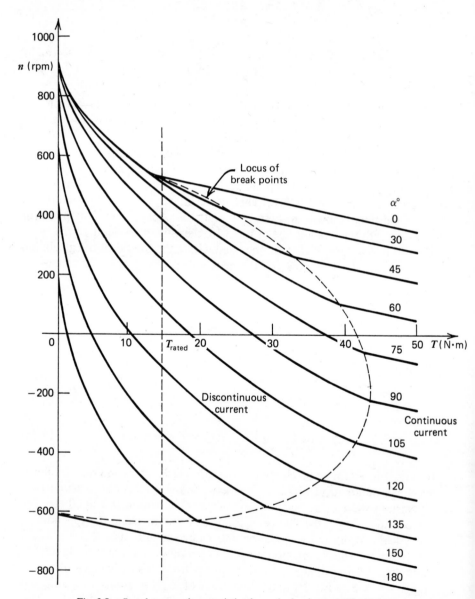

Fig. 3.8. Speed-torque characteristics for a single-phase rectifier drive.

tion. If a stability analysis is required it is best done by simulation on an analog computer. When a simulation is carried out it is found that the dynamic behavior of the system for discontinuous current differs markedly from that for continuous current and that it is very difficult to design a control system that will operate satisfactorily on both continuous and discontinuous current.[2]

Continuous-current operation can be obtained by including additional inductance in the motor armature circuit, but even a large inductor cannot ensure continuous-current operation under all conditions of load and speed. Other converter configurations can be used to reduce the size of the necessary inductor considerably, even if they do not eliminate it completely.

3.2.1. Inverter Operation

The converters in Fig. 3.1 can operate as fixed-frequency inverters, with the motor acting as a generator and delivering energy to the ac source. Because current i_a cannot reverse, the only way in which the motor in Fig. 3.1 can invert without change of armature connections is by reversal of the field current or direction of rotation. Either of these changes would make E_a negative and, in effect, operation would take place in the fourth quadrant of Fig. 3.8.

Figure 3.9 shows waveforms for inverter operation with discontinuous current and Fig. 3.10 illustrates the increased inverter power obtained when the gating signals are extended. Extension of the gating signals is, in fact, desirable for all conditions of inverter operation, for, if they are not extended, an abrupt change in $\bar{v}_t$ takes place on transition from discontinuous to continuous current or conversely.[3] Figure 3.11 shows waveforms for inverter operation with continuous current in which the interval ωt_q is marked on the waveform of v_{AKA}. Time t_q is the time available for turn-off of the thyristors. Because it is essential that $\omega t_q \geq \omega t_{off} + \mu$, where t_{off} is the turn-off time for the thyristors of the converter and μ is the overlap angle, it is not possible to invert with continuous current when $\alpha > \pi - \omega t_{off} - \mu$. This means that the characteristic marked $\alpha = 180°$ in Fig. 3.8 is a theoretical boundary to the operation of the drive and should be replaced by one for the angle $\alpha = 180° - \omega t_{off} - \mu$.

Example 3.1

The 230-V, 850-rpm, frame-size 283 motor listed in Appendix B is used to drive an antenna. The loss torques of motor and drive mechanism are directly proportional to speed; that of the mechanism is twice that of the motor. The motor armature is supplied from a converter of the type shown in Fig. 3.1a and the ac supply of the rectifier is 260 V, 60 Hz. The field current is fixed at the value that gives rated speed at rated load when $\bar{v}_t = 230$ V.

Determine $\bar{i}_a$, $\bar{v}_t$, and α when the motor is driving the antenna at constant rated speed.

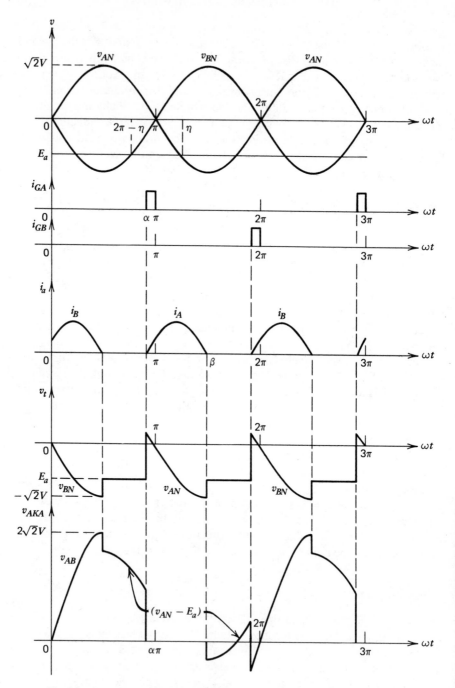

Fig. 3.9. Inverter operation with discontinuous current. Waveforms for Fig. 3.2.

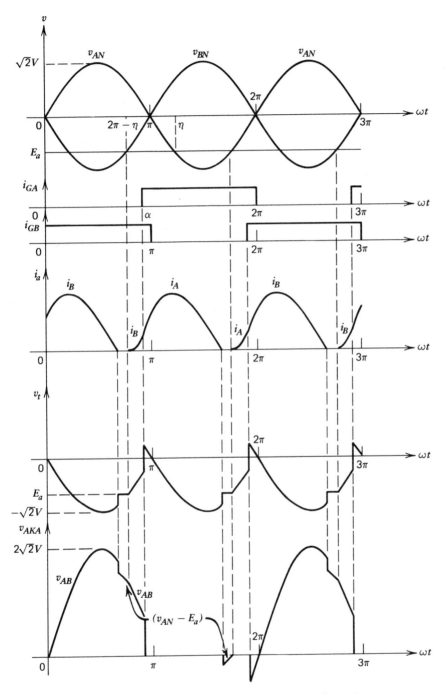

Fig. 3.10. Effect of extended gating signal when $\alpha > (2\pi - \eta)$.

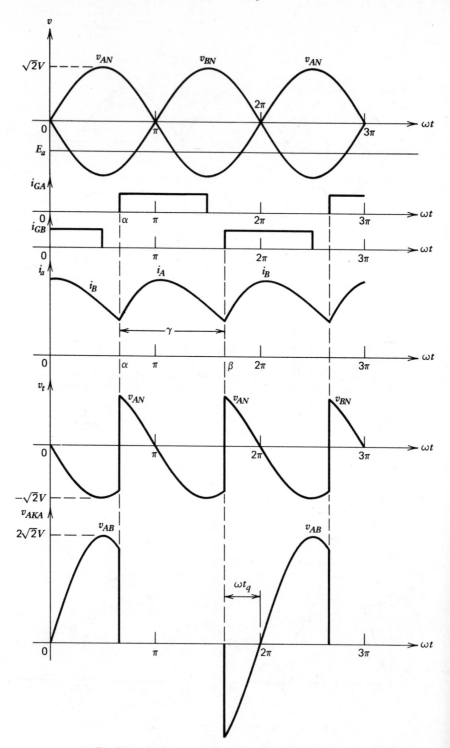

Fig. 3.11. Inverter operation with continuous current.

Solution

For the 2-hp (1.49-kW) motor the rated current is $I_{\text{rated}} = 7.8$ A; $R_a = 2.61\ \Omega$
and $L_a = 19.2$ mH. Under rated operating conditions

$$\text{motor speed} = 850 \text{ rpm} = 85.01 \text{ rad/s}$$

$$\text{motor input} = 230 \times 7.8 = 1794 \text{ W}$$

$$\text{motor output} = 2 \times 746 = 1492 \text{ W}$$

$$\text{armature copper loss} = 2.61 \times 7.8^2 = 159 \text{ W}$$

$$\text{rotational losses} = (1794 - 1492 - 159) = 143 \text{ W}$$

Motor loss torque at rated speed is

$$\frac{143}{89.01} = 1.607 \text{ N} \cdot \text{m}$$

$$E_a = 230 - 2.61 \times 7.8 = 209.6 \text{ V}$$

$$k\Phi = \frac{209.6}{89.01} = 2.355$$

$$Z = \left[(120\pi \times 19.2 \times 10^{-3})^2 + 2.61^2\right]^{1/2} = 7.694\ \Omega$$

$$\tan\varphi = \frac{120\pi \times 19.2 \times 10^{-3}}{2.61} = 2.773$$

$$\varphi = 70.17°$$

At constant rated speed when driving the antenna average internal torque to be developed by the motor is

$$\overline{T} = 3 \times 1.607 \text{ N} \cdot \text{m}$$

$$\bar{i}_a = \frac{3 \times 1.607}{2.355} = 2.047 \text{ A}$$

$$\bar{v}_t = k\Phi\Omega_m + R_a\bar{i}_a = 209.6 + 2.61 \times 2.047 = 214.9 \text{ V}$$

The system will be operating under the conditions illustrated in Fig. 3.3; therefore Eqs. 3.10 and 3.12 apply. Substitution of the known numerical values in Eq. 3.12 yields

$$1.164(180 + \alpha - \beta) - 117.0(\cos\alpha - \cos\beta) - 214.9 = 0 \qquad \text{(A)}$$

where α and β are expressed in degrees. Substitution in Eq. 3.10 yields

$$15.21\left[\cos(\alpha - 70.17) - \cos(\beta - 70.17)\right] - 0.4461(\alpha - \beta)$$

$$-\left[70.88 - 42.18\sin(\alpha - 70.17)\right]\left[\varepsilon^{(\alpha-\beta)/158.9} - 1\right] - 2.047 = 0 \quad \text{(B)}$$

where again α and β are expressed in degrees. Numerical solution of Eqs. (A) and (B) yields

$$\alpha = 103.0 \qquad \beta = 176.0$$

3.2.2. The Dual Converter

As explained in the preceding section, the rectifier-motor systems in Fig. 3.1 are capable of operating in the two quadrants of Fig. 3.8 but four-quadrant operation may be required in motor drives. Although it is a simple matter to obtain operation in the second and third quadrants by switching connections, this is not satisfactory if smooth uninterrupted transitions from one quadrant to another are required. Smooth transitions may be achieved by using two rectifiers in the connection illustrated in Fig. 3.12.

The gating signals to the thyristors are arranged so that at all settings $\bar{v}_{op} = -\bar{v}_{on}$. These two pd's, therefore, oppose one another. If no steps were taken to prevent them, however, large harmonic currents would flow round the

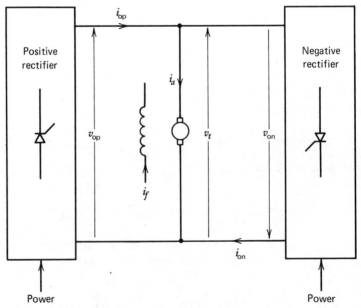

Fig. 3.12. Dual converter.

mesh formed by the lines that connect the output terminals of the two converters. The introduction of an inductor into this mesh would limit the harmonic currents, but for two-pulse rectifiers the inductor required would be large. As an alternative circulating harmonic currents may be prevented by blanking out the gating signals in the converter that does not operate in the desired quadrant. This presents a virtual open circuit to the other rectifier, all of whose output current then flows in the motor armature.

A transition between quadrants 1 and 2 in Fig. 2.6 thus entails the following sequence of events: the delay angle α_p of the positive rectifier is increased until $i_a = 0$. The gating signals to this rectifier are then blanked out and those to the negative rectifier are applied, thus presenting the same value of $\bar{v}_t$ to the armature circuit as before. Delay angle α_n is then reduced to permit negative current i_a to flow in the armature circuit at positive pd $\bar{v}_t$.

3.3. HALF-CONTROLLED RECTIFIER DRIVES

If thyristors Q_2 and Q_3 in Fig. 3.1a are replaced by diodes the circuit obtained is shown by Fig. 3.13a. This provides a path for i_a when that current is prolonged by the armature-circuit inductance, a path through which it can flow unopposed by the negative secondary terminal pd v_s. The equivalent circuit of this arrangement is shown in Fig. 3.14 and the waveforms of the circuit variables are shown in Fig. 3.15. From these waveforms it can be seen that during interval $\pi < \omega t < \beta$ current i_a decreases exponentially until thyristor Q_4 (or equivalent thyristor Q_B) is turned on and i_a again begins to rise. This substitution of diodes for thyristors may have the effect of producing continuous-current operation under conditions that would result in discontinuous current in the fully controlled rectifier. The circuit in Fig. 3.13a can also deliver discontinuous current, but for similar load conditions the current pulse is longer than in the fully controlled converter. Waveforms for discontinuous-current operation are shown in Fig. 3.16.

The effect of replacing the two thyristors in Fig. 3.1a with diodes may also be obtained if a diode is connected across the load branch in either of the circuits in Fig. 3.1, thus giving the circuits shown in Fig. 3.13b and c. This added diode is called a *freewheeling diode* because it permits the load current to continue while the source is supplying no energy. During the interval $\pi < \omega t < \beta$ the energy stored in the armature-circuit inductance is converted to mechanical form or dissipated in the circuit resistance. The equivalent circuit in Fig. 3.14 is valid for all three circuits in Fig. 3.13.

Necessarily, in the circuits in Fig. 3.13 $v_D = -v_t$. It may also be seen that v_t cannot at any instant be negative because diode D cannot have a positive pd between its terminals. This means that the system cannot regenerate. Its operation is therefore confined to the first quadrant in Fig. 2.6.

Because dc motors operate better with a continuous armature current that varies between narrow limits than with a discontinuous current that varies

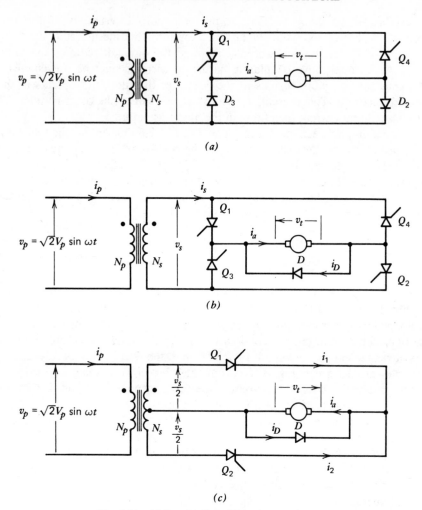

Fig. 3.13. Half-controlled, single-phase rectifiers.

between wide limits, it is of practical interest to determine under what conditions continuous current is achieved by fitting a freewheeling diode. It may be anticipated, when a drive is to be designed, that it will be possible to specify the minimum torque and maximum speed at which it will be required to operate. These two conditions occurring simultaneously will provide the worst case in which discontinuous current is most probable.

If discontinuous current is to be avoided the worst case must give rise to the boundary conditions illustrated in Fig. 3.17, at which the current is on the point of becoming discontinuous. The pulse of i_A lasts for the interval

$$\alpha < \omega t < \pi \text{ rad} \qquad i_A \neq 0 \tag{3.19}$$

Diode current i_D will flow for part of the interval $\pi < \omega t < \pi + \alpha$ and it must

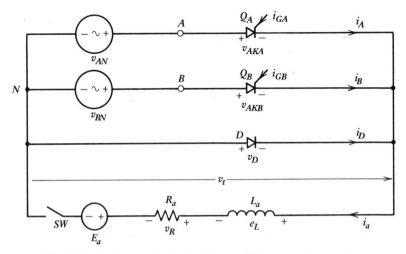

Fig. 3.14. Equivalent circuit of a half-controlled, single-phase rectifier.

be determined whether i_D will fall to zero before Q_B is turned on at $\omega t = \pi + \alpha$.

At $\omega t = \pi$ let $i_a = I_{a\pi}$, as indicated in Figs. 3.15 and 3.16. Substitution of these end conditions in Eq. 3.5 yields

$$I_{a\pi} = \frac{\sqrt{2} V}{Z} \sin\varphi - \frac{k\Phi\Omega_m}{R_a} + \left[\frac{k\Phi\Omega_m}{R_a} - \frac{\sqrt{2} V}{Z}\sin(\alpha - \varphi)\right]\varepsilon^{(\alpha - \pi)/\tan\varphi} \text{ A}$$

(3.20)

If α and $E_a = k\Phi\Omega_m$ are known $I_{a\pi}$ may be calculated. When i_D flows

$$L_a\frac{di_a}{dt'} + R_a i_a + E_a = 0 \text{ V}$$

(3.21)

where

$$\omega t' = \omega t - \pi \text{ rad}$$

(3.22)

The solution of Eq. 3.21 for the initial conditions $i_a = I_{a\pi}$ at $\omega t' = 0$ is

$$i_a = i_D = \left(I_{a\pi} + \frac{E_a}{R_a}\right)\varepsilon^{-\omega t'/\tan\varphi} - \frac{E_a}{R_a} \text{ A}$$

(3.23)

In Fig. 3.17 the boundary between continuous and discontinuous current occurs when i_D falls to zero at $\omega t' = \alpha$. For this to occur let $I_{a\pi} = I_{a\pi b}$ (Fig. 3.17). Substitution of these end conditions in Eq. 3.23 yields

$$I_{a\pi b} = \frac{k\Phi\Omega_m}{R_a}\left(\varepsilon^{\alpha/\tan\varphi} - 1\right) \text{ A}$$

(3.24)

If $I_{a\pi} \geq I_{a\pi b}$ current is continuous.

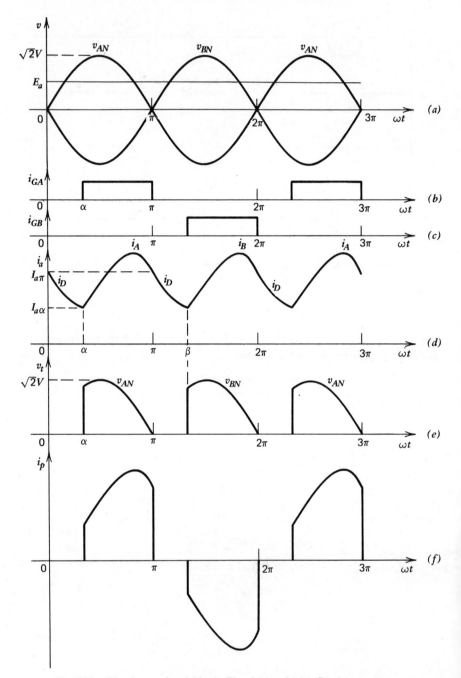

Fig. 3.15. Waveforms of variables in Figs. 3.13 and 3.14. Continuous current.

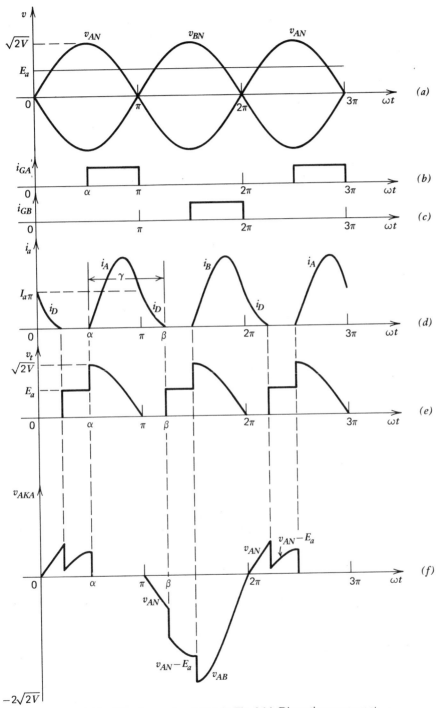

Fig. 3.16. Waveforms of variables in Fig. 3.14. Discontinuous current.

75

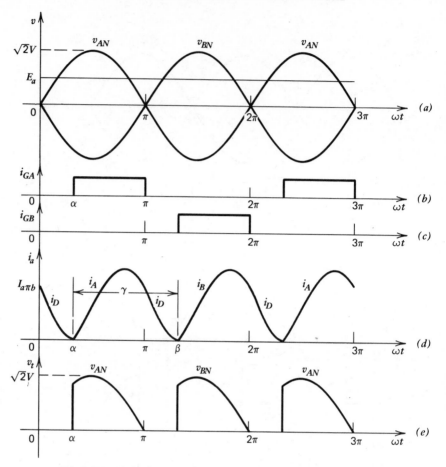

Fig. 3.17. Single-phase rectifier with freewheeling. Boundary condition.

From Eqs. 3.20 and 3.24 $I_{a\pi} - I_{a\pi b} = 0$ gives

$$\frac{\sqrt{2}\,V}{Z}\sin\varphi - \frac{k\Phi\Omega_m}{R_a}\varepsilon^{\alpha/\tan\varphi} + \left[\frac{k\Phi\Omega_m}{R_a} - \frac{\sqrt{2}\,V}{Z}\sin(\alpha - \varphi)\right]\varepsilon^{(\alpha-\pi)/\tan\varphi} = 0$$

$$(3.25)$$

For a given set of system parameters, as well as load, speed, and field excitation, this equation can be satisfied by determining the required value of α. If, however, $\alpha = 0$ substituted in the left side gives a negative result continuous current operation is impossible at any load.

When current in the armature reaches the boundary condition in Fig. 3.17

$$\bar{v}_t = \frac{\sqrt{2}\,V}{\pi}(1 + \cos\alpha)\ \text{V}$$

$$(3.26)$$

and this equation applies to all conditions of continuous current. Because $\bar{v}_t$

can be calculated from the known speed and load torque, α may be obtained from Eq. 3.26 and substituted in Eq. 3.25 to verify that it determines a possible condition of continuous-current operation.

If Eq. 3.26 is combined with Eqs. 3.13 and 3.15 the following relationship between average torque and speed is obtained:

$$\Omega_m = \frac{\sqrt{2}\,V}{\pi k \Phi}(1 + \cos \alpha) - \frac{R_a \bar{T}}{(k\Phi)^2} \text{ rad/s} \qquad (3.27)$$

This is a linear relationship similar to that for the rectifier without freewheeling given in Eq. 3.16.

Example 3.2

The 500-rpm, frame-size 288 motor in Appendix B is to be operated in a one-quadrant drive with its armature circuit supplied by a half-controlled rectifier. The rectifier is supplied from the 230-V, 60-Hz system by a 230:300-V, step-up transformer. Rated speed must not be exceeded and the field current must be held at the value required to provide rated operation on a 230-V, dc source. The rotational loss torque is to be modeled by components T_B and T_C, illustrated in Fig. 1.3b, and the two components are of equal magnitude at rated speed. However, when the motor is driven from the rectifier T_B increases by 50%, due to additional core losses induced by armature-current harmonics. Draw curves of motor speed and rectifier angle α versus coupling torque T_L for the boundary condition of operation illustrated in Fig. 3.17.

Solution

From Appendix B, for this 5-hp (3.73-kW) motor the rated current is 22 A, $R_a = 1.33$ Ω, and $L_a = 36$ mH. Under rated operating conditions on the dc source

$$\text{speed} = 500 \times \frac{2\pi}{60} = 52.36 \text{ rad/s}$$

$$\text{rated torque} = \frac{5 \times 746}{52.36} = 71.24 \text{ N} \cdot \text{m}$$

$$E_a = 230 - 1.33 \times 22 = 200.7 \text{ V}$$

$$k\Phi = \frac{200.7}{52.36} = 3.833 \text{ V} \cdot \text{s/rad}$$

$$\text{input power} = 230 \times 22 = 5060 \text{ W}$$

$$\text{output power} = 5 \times 746 = 3730 \text{ W}$$

$$R_a I_a^2 \text{ loss} = 1.33 \times 22^2 = 644 \text{ W}$$

$$\text{rotational losses} = 5060 - 3730 - 644 = 686 \text{ W}$$

$$T_{\text{loss}} = \frac{686}{52.36} = 13.10 \text{ N} \cdot \text{m}$$

At rated speed $T_B = T_C = 13.10/2 = 6.55$ N $\cdot$ m

$$T_B = B\Omega_m$$

$$B = \frac{6.55}{52.36}$$

When operating from the rectifier

$$T_{\text{loss}} = 6.55\left(\frac{1.5\Omega_m}{52.36} + 1\right) = 6.55\left(\frac{\Omega_m}{34.91} + 1\right) \text{ N} \cdot \text{m}$$

$$Z = \left[(120\pi \times 0.036)^2 + 1.33^2\right]^{1/2} = 13.64 \ \Omega$$

$$\tan\varphi = \frac{120\pi \times 0.036}{1.33} = 10.20$$

$$\varphi = 84.40°$$

Substitution of the known numerical values in Eq. 3.25 yields

$$10.74 - \Omega_m \varepsilon^{\alpha/10.20} + \left[\Omega_m - 10.79\sin(\alpha - 84.40)\right]\varepsilon^{(\alpha - \pi)/10.20} = 0$$

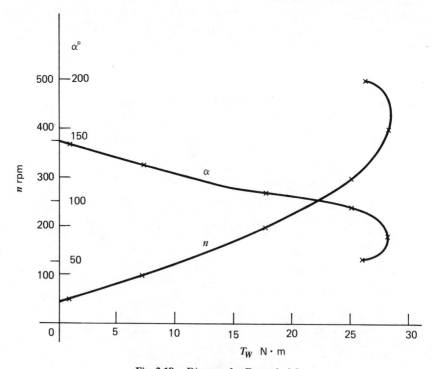

Fig. 3.18. Diagram for Example 3.2.

where α is expressed in radians or degrees, as necessary. Solution of this equation for α at a specified value of Ω_m and subsequent calculation of T_L yielded the following results:

n rpm	500	400	300	200	100	50	25
α deg	53.5	72.6	90.7	109.4	131.4	146.0	156.1
T_L N·m	26.0	28.1	24.9	17.8	7.4	1.0	−2.6

The required curves are shown in Fig. 3.18, from which it may be seen that the worst case occurs at somewhat less than rated speed. The proportion of coupling torque required to produce continuous armature current approaches 40% of rated torque, even with this relatively large and low-speed motor.

3.3.1. Freewheeling with Regeneration

The disadvantage of the converters described in Section 3.3 is that they will not permit regeneration in the fourth quadrant in Fig. 2.6. If the advantage of continuous-current operation, which can be produced by freewheeling, can be combined with that of regeneration, the best possible drive from a single-phase rectifier (or two such rectifiers in a dual converter) will be achieved. By controlling the four thyristors of a bridge rectifier individually instead of in pairs this drive can be obtained.

It is convenient, in discussing this converter, to renumber the thyristors (Fig. 3.19) and to show the individual circuit elements modeling the motor armature circuit. The waveforms of the circuit variables for operation in the first quadrant in Fig. 2.6 are shown in Fig. 3.20. All the gating signals consist of 180° trains of pulses. Those for thyristors Q_2 and Q_4 remain fixed in the positions shown in Fig. 3.20. Those for thyristors Q_1 and Q_3 may be moved simultaneously along the ωt axis by the logic circuits that control the operation of the converter. Thyristor Q_1 is taken as the reference device that is turned on at delay angle $\omega t = \alpha$; Q_3 is therefore turned on at $\omega t = \pi + \alpha$. Operation is

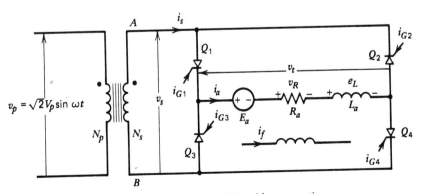

Fig. 3.19. Circuit for freewheeling with regeneration.

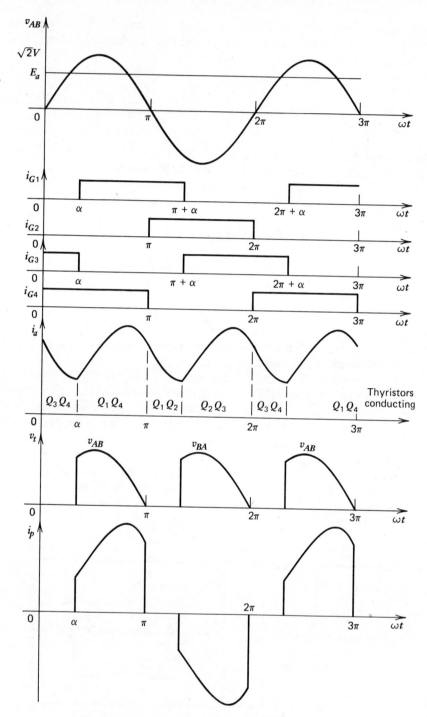

Fig. 3.20. Waveforms of variables in Fig. 3.19—$\bar{v}_t > 0$.

80

most easily explained by a tabulation of the sequence of events occurring during one cycle of the supply pd.

At $\omega t = 0$ Q_3 and Q_4 are conducting freewheeling current; at $\omega t = \alpha$ Q_1 is turned on and Q_3 is commutated. Q_1 and Q_4 conduct, supplying energy to the motor;

at $\omega t = \pi$ Q_2 is turned on and Q_4 is commutated as v_{ab} goes negative; Q_1 and Q_2 conduct freewheeling current;

at $\omega t = \pi + \alpha$ Q_3 is turned on and Q_1 is commutated; Q_2 and Q_3 conduct, supplying energy to the motor;

at $\omega t = 2\pi$ Q_4 is turned on, Q_2 is commutated, and the cycle recommences.

The gating signals for Q_1 and Q_3 can be moved to the right until $\alpha = \pi - \omega t_q$. The reason for this restriction is explained in the following. Equation 3.26 describes the relation between $\bar{v}_t$ and α for this first-quadrant operation.

Figure 3.21 shows the waveforms of the circuit variables for operation in the fourth quadrant of Fig. 2.6. Now the gating signals for Q_1 and Q_3 are fixed, whereas those for Q_2 and Q_4 may be moved along the ωt axis. Thyristor Q_2 is now the reference device, with signal i_{G2} commencing at $\omega t = \alpha$. Because signals i_{G1} and i_{G3} start ωt_q before the points $\omega t = \pi$ and $\omega t = 2\pi$, respectively, interval ωt_q is available to commutate Q_3 when Q_1 is turned on and to commutate Q_4 when Q_2 is turned on. Interval ωt_q must equal or exceed $\omega t_{off} + \mu$, where t_{off} is the specified turn-off time for the thyristors and μ is the angle of overlap. The sequence of events that occurs during the negative half-cycle of the supply pd is as follows. Q_2 and Q_3 are conducting at $\omega t = 0$. Because $v_t < 0$, energy is supplied by the armature circuit to the ac source of the converter:

at $\omega t = \alpha - \pi$ Q_4 is turned on and Q_2 is commutated; Q_3 and Q_4 conduct freewheeling current;

at $\omega t = \pi - \omega t_q$ Q_1 is turned on and Q_3 is commutated; Q_1 and Q_4 conduct, thus supplying energy to the ac source;

at $\omega t = \alpha$ Q_2 is turned on and Q_4 is commutated; Q_1 and Q_2 conduct freewheeling current;

at $\omega t = 2\pi - \omega t_q$ Q_3 is turned on, Q_1 is commutated, and the cycle recommences.

In theory the gating signals for Q_2 and Q_4 can be moved to the right until α approaches the point $\omega t = 2\pi$. In practice this degree of regeneration is never necessary and the range of α can be restricted. The relation between $\bar{v}_t$ and α for this fourth-quadrant operation is given by

$$\bar{v}_t = \frac{1}{\pi}\int_{\pi}^{\alpha} \sqrt{2}\,V\sin(\omega t)\,d(\omega t) = \frac{-\sqrt{2}\,V}{\pi}(1 + \cos\alpha)\ \text{V} \qquad (3.28)$$

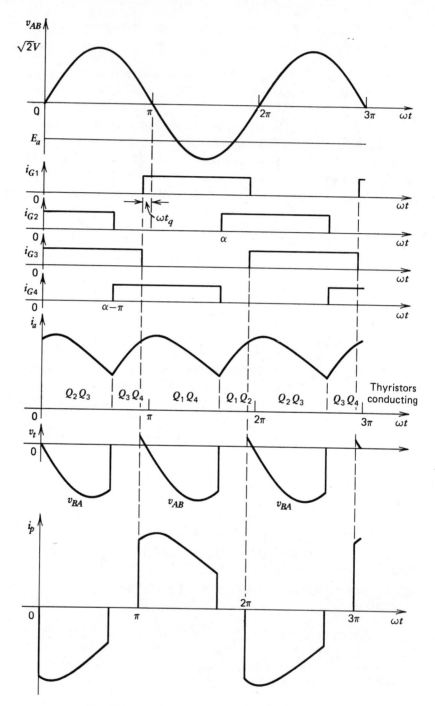

Fig. 3.21. Waveforms of variables in Fig. 3.19—$\bar{v}_t < 0$.

82

Equation 3.28 neglects the small positive part of the waveform of v_t shown in Fig. 3.21.

The firing control circuits for this converter are more complicated than those for the rectifier circuits discussed in the preceding sections, particularly if two converters are combined in a dual converter.

The power-circuit conditions that give rise to continuous-current operation are the same as those discussed in Section 3.3. The operation of this circuit, however, is liable to discontinuities that do not arise when freewheeling is not used,[3] and computer simulation of any projected system over the whole range of anticipated operating conditions is advisable.

Example 3.3

In the system in Example 3.1 the converter is replaced by a half-controlled rectifier. Will the armature current be continuous at constant, full-speed operation?

Solution

For steady-state operation (Example 3.1)

$$E_a = 209.6 \text{ V} \qquad \bar{v}_t = 214.9 \text{ V}$$

Substitution of the known numerical values and $\alpha = 0$ in Eq. 3.25 yields a result of 4.998 which indicates that continuous-current operation is possible. If indeed current is continuous, then from Eq. 3.26

$$214.9 = \frac{260\sqrt{2}}{\pi}(1 + \cos \alpha)$$

from which $\alpha = 33.27°$ or 0.5806 rad. Substitution of the known numerical values and this value of α in Eq. 3.25 yields a result of -10.77. Thus under the specified conditions continuous current is not obtained.

3.4. RECTIFIER TRANSFER FUNCTIONS

For the analysis of systems that incorporate controlled rectifiers it is desirable to obtain a linear transfer function that to a reasonable degree of approximation can be used to represent the rectifier. It has already been pointed out in Section 3.2 that this cannot usually be done for the rectifier without freewheeling because an unacceptable amount of inductance would have to be added to the motor armature circuit to produce continuous-current operation over the required working range. The discussion in this section is therefore confined to the rectifiers in Sections 3.3 and 3.3.1.

3.4.1. Half-Controlled Rectifier

The curve of $\bar{v}_t$ versus α described by Eq. 3.26 is shown in Fig. 3.22 and may be considered linear over the range $30° < \alpha < 150°$. From this "linear" range the gain of the converter may be expressed as

$$k = \frac{\Delta \bar{v}_t}{-\Delta \alpha} = \frac{2\sqrt{2}\, V}{\pi} \frac{(\cos 30° - \cos 150°)}{150 - 30°} = 0.0130 \text{ V/deg} \qquad (3.29)$$

Although the change in v_t can be considered to occur instantaneously when a gating signal is applied to a thyristor, the change in the average value $\bar{v}_t$ cannot be considered to do so. The reason is given in Fig. 3.23, in which at instant t_1 the delay angle is changed from α_1 to α_2. This change has no effect until at $\omega t = 2\pi + \alpha_2$ the next thyristor is turned on. Thus a dead time t_d occurs between the change of command and the change of response. The change in $\bar{v}_t$ that takes place is illustrated by the broken line in Fig. 3.23 but exactly *where* it takes place is arguable. Fortunately this point need not be decided precisely. Because the dead time can vary from zero to one-half the period of the ac source ($1/120$ s for 60 Hz) it is usually assumed to be one-quarter of the period; that is, the average value.

The time variation of $\bar{v}_t$ may be expressed by

$$\bar{v}_t = k(t - t_d) \text{ V} \qquad (3.30)$$

The Laplace transform of this function is

$$L\big[k(t - t_d)\big] = k\varepsilon^{-t_d s} \qquad (3.31)$$

Because t_d is small compared with the major mechanical time constants of the elements of a drive system, no significant inaccuracy results in expressing the

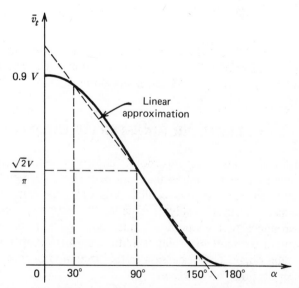

Fig. 3.22. $\bar{v}_t$ versus α for a half-controlled rectifier.

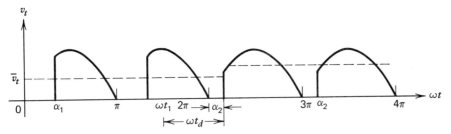

Fig. 3.23. Response of $\bar{v}_t$ to a change in α.

transfer function of the converter approximately as

$$G(s) = \frac{k}{1 + s\bar{t}_d} \qquad (3.32)$$

where $\bar{t}_d$ is the average value of t_d. In fact, this small time constant can usually simply be added to other small time constants of the system to yield a single first-order element when analysis of the dynamic behavior of the system is carried out.[2]

3.4.2. Rectifier with Regeneration

The curve of $\bar{v}_t$ versus α, described by Eqs. 3.26 and 3.28 and shown in Fig. 3.24, may, with acceptable accuracy, be considered linear over the entire range

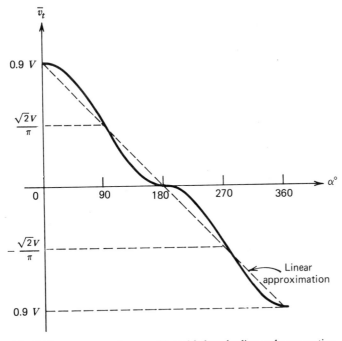

Fig. 3.24. $\bar{v}_t$ versus α for a rectifier with freewheeling and regeneration.

of $0 < \alpha < 360°$; therefore the gain of the converter may be expressed as

$$k = \frac{2\sqrt{2}\, V}{\pi} \frac{(\cos 0 + \cos 360°)}{360° - 0} = 0.005 \text{ V/deg} \qquad (3.33)$$

The transfer function will have the form of Eq. 3.32, with the value of t_d unchanged. This is obviously not so good an approximation as that for the half-controlled rectifier.

3.5. POWER IN LOAD AND SOURCE CIRCUITS

Because it is desirable to operate a rectifier-driven dc motor with continuous current, this is the condition that should be investigated for performance, including harmonics of current and pd, when the system is being designed.

3.5.1. Fully Controlled Rectifier

Continuous-current operation with a motor driven by a fully controlled rectifier is likely to be achieved only if the motor is large, operating at or near full load, and possibly with some additional inductance in the armature circuit.

For the fully controlled rectifier continuous-current operation with $\alpha > \eta$ is illustrated by the waveforms in Fig. 3.7. The condition for $\alpha < \eta$ does not differ significantly from the condition in Fig. 3.7 because the assumption is made that the current is not only continuous but also essentially constant.

The waveform of v_t may be described by a Fourier series in the form of

$$v_t = \bar{v}_t + \sum_{n=1}^{\infty} c_n \sin(n\omega t + \vartheta_n) \text{ V} \qquad (3.34)$$

The fundamental frequency of v_t is shown in Fig. 3.7 to be 2ω rad/s. Thus all harmonics of v_t must be in the order of $n = 2m$, where m is an integer. The coefficients and angles of the series in Eq. 3.34 are given by

$$c_n = \left[a_n^2 + b_n^2\right]^{1/2} \text{ V} \qquad (3.35)$$

$$\vartheta_n = \tan^{-1}\frac{a_n}{b_n} \text{ rad} \qquad (3.36)$$

where

$$a_n = \frac{2}{\pi}\int_0^{\pi} v_t \cos(n\omega t)\, d(\omega t) \text{ V} \qquad n = 2, 4, 6 \ldots$$

$$= \frac{2\sqrt{2}\, V}{\pi}\left[\frac{\cos(n+1)\alpha}{n+1} - \frac{\cos(n-1)\alpha}{n-1}\right] \text{ V} \qquad (3.37)$$

$$b_n = \frac{2}{\pi}\int_0^{\pi} v_t \sin(n\omega t)\, d(\omega t) \text{ V} \qquad n = 2, 4, 6 \ldots$$

$$= \frac{2\sqrt{2}\, V}{\pi}\left[\frac{\sin(n+1)\alpha}{n+1} - \frac{\sin(n-1)\alpha}{n-1}\right] \text{ V} \qquad (3.38)$$

Satisfactory results in the design of motor drives are obtained if only the harmonic of lowest frequency is taken into consideration. For this $n = 2$ and

$$a_2 = \frac{2\sqrt{2}\,V}{\pi}\left(\frac{\cos 3\alpha}{3} - \cos\alpha\right) V \qquad (3.39)$$

$$b_2 = \frac{2\sqrt{2}\,V}{\pi}\left(\frac{\sin 3\alpha}{3} - \sin\alpha\right) V \qquad (3.40)$$

Substitution in Eq. 3.35 then yields

$$c_2 = \frac{2\sqrt{2}\,V}{\pi}\left[\frac{10}{9} - \frac{2}{3}\cos 2\alpha\right]^{1/2} V \qquad (3.41)$$

The variation in c_2/V as a function of α is shown in Fig. 3.25. The amplitude of the second harmonic is a maximum when $\alpha = \pi/2$. This worst case therefore is used in the design procedure. For this condition

$$a_2 = 0 \qquad b_2 = c_2 = \frac{8\sqrt{2}\,V}{3\pi} = 1.20V \text{ V} \qquad \alpha = \frac{\pi}{2}\text{ rad} \qquad (3.42)$$

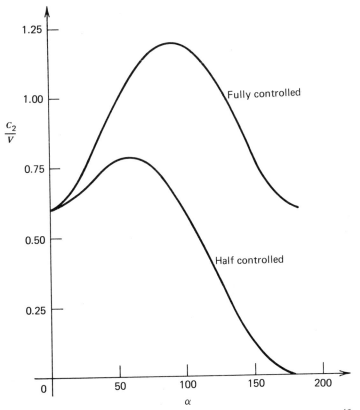

Fig. 3.25. Variation of c_2/V as a function of α for single-phase full-wave rectifiers.

If the armature-circuit parameters are such that $2\omega L_a \gg R_a$, the armature current can, to a good approximation, be described by

$$i_a \simeq \bar{i}_a - \frac{8\sqrt{2}\,V}{6\pi\omega L_a}\cos(2\omega t) = \bar{i}_a - \frac{0.6V}{\omega L_a}\cos(2\omega t)\ \text{A} \qquad (3.43)$$

The maximum output of the converter occurs when $\alpha = 0$, for which $b_2 = 0$, and

$$a_2 = c_2 = \frac{-4\sqrt{2}\,V}{3\pi}\ \text{V} \qquad \alpha = 0 \qquad (3.44)$$

This is the amplitude of the second harmonic obtained from a diode rectifier.

On the basis of the foregoing approximation, the rms magnitude of the second harmonic current at any value of α is

$$I_{R2} = \frac{c_2}{2\sqrt{2}\,\omega L_a}\ \text{A} \qquad (3.45)$$

The rms armature current is then

$$I_R = \left[\left(\bar{i}_a \right)^2 + I_{R2}^2 \right]^{1/2}\ \text{A} \qquad (3.46)$$

It remains to determine a design value for the current i_p drawn from the power supply. The waveform of this current contains no even harmonics. Although its harmonics can be determined from those of the armature circuit, the mathematics of doing so is complicated. A good approximation to the harmonics of i_p may be obtained by assuming that its waveform is rectangular and of amplitude $\hat{i}_p$, where

$$\hat{i}_p = \frac{N_s}{N_p} \bar{i}_a\ \text{A} \qquad (3.47)$$

This is equivalent to assuming that the inductance of the armature circuit is so large that i_a is virtually ripple free and of constant magnitude $\bar{i}_a$. This assumed rectangular wave of i_p lags that of v_{AN}, and consequently that of v_p, by α rad.

By use of the method of discontinuities explained in Appendix A this approximate primary-current waveform may be described by the series

$$i_p = \sum \frac{4}{n\pi} \frac{N_s}{N_p} \bar{i}_a \sin[n(\omega t - \alpha)] \qquad n = 1, 3, 5\ \text{A} \qquad (3.48)$$

Only the fundamental component of the primary current delivers energy to the converter and the rms magnitude of this component is

$$I_{p1} = \frac{2\sqrt{2}}{\pi} \frac{N_s}{N_p} \bar{i}_a\ \text{A} \qquad (3.49)$$

The rms value of the assumed rectangular wave of source current is

$$I_p = \frac{N_s}{N_p} \bar{i}_a \text{ A} \tag{3.50}$$

and the source-current ripple factor is

$$K_i = \frac{I_p}{I_{p1}} = \frac{\pi}{2\sqrt{2}} = 1.111 \tag{3.51}$$

The fundamental power factor of the system is

$$PF_1 = \cos \alpha \tag{3.52}$$

The power input is

$$P_{in} = V_p I_{p1} \cos \alpha = \frac{2\sqrt{2}}{\pi} \frac{N_s}{N_p} \bar{i}_a V_p \cos \alpha \text{ W} \tag{3.53}$$

Because losses in the transformer and converter have been neglected, the power developed at the armature terminals, neglecting current harmonics higher than the second, is

$$P_{in} = P_a = R_a I_R^2 + E_a \bar{i}_a = R_a \left[(\bar{i}_a)^2 + I_{R2}^2 \right]^{1/2} + k\Phi\Omega_m \bar{i}_a \text{ W} \tag{3.54}$$

The apparent power factor of the armature supply may be defined as the active power divided by the product of the source pd and the rms source current. Thus

$$\text{apparent } PF = \frac{P_{in}}{V_p(N_s/N_p)\bar{i}_a} = \frac{2\sqrt{2}}{\pi} \cos \alpha = 0.9 \cos \alpha \tag{3.55}$$

If delay angle α is increased to more than $\pi/2$ rad then, from Eq. 3.14, $\bar{v}_t < 0$. Because $\bar{i}_a$ can only be positive, this indicates that the energy flow in the system has been reversed. This may be determined from the waveforms of Fig. 3.7, for if $\alpha > \pi/2$ the fundamental component of i_p lags v_{AN} by more than 90° and energy is delivered to the power supply system from the armature. This confirms the conclusions already reached in Section 3.2.1, that the converter under these conditions acts as an inverter of fixed output frequency.

3.5.2. Rectifiers with Freewheeling

As explained in Section 3.3, continuous-current operation can be achieved with a relatively low value of armature-circuit inductance when freewheeling is used by selecting a half-controlled rectifier, fitting a freewheeling diode, or installing individual control of thyristors in the bridge rectifier discussed in Section 3.3.1. Whichever of these methods is adopted, Fig. 3.15 illustrates the waveforms of the circuit variables for operation in the first quadrant of the $\bar{v}_t$-$\bar{i}_a$ diagram.

In Fig. 3.15 the waveform of v_t is again defined and may be analyzed into the series of Eq. 3.34, where

$$a_n = \frac{\sqrt{2}\,V}{\pi}\left[\frac{1 + \cos(n + 1)\alpha}{n + 1} - \frac{1 + \cos(n - 1)\alpha}{n - 1}\right] V \qquad n = 2, 4, 6 \tag{3.56}$$

$$b_n = \frac{\sqrt{2}\,V}{\pi}\left[\frac{\sin(n + 1)\alpha}{n + 1} - \frac{\sin(n - 1)\alpha}{n - 1}\right] V \qquad n = 2, 4, 6\ldots \tag{3.57}$$

For the lowest-order harmonic

$$a_2 = \frac{\sqrt{2}\,V}{\pi}\left[\frac{1 + \cos 3\alpha}{3} - (1 + \cos\alpha)\right] V \tag{3.58}$$

$$b_2 = \frac{\sqrt{2}\,V}{\pi}\left[\frac{\sin 3\alpha}{3} - \sin\alpha\right] V \tag{3.59}$$

The delay angle $\alpha = \pi/3$ yields the waveform of v_t with the highest second harmonic. For this worst case

$$a_2 = -\frac{V}{\sqrt{2}\,\pi} \qquad b_2 = -\frac{\sqrt{3}\,V}{\sqrt{2}\,\pi} V \tag{3.60}$$

so that

$$c_2 = \frac{\sqrt{2}\,V}{\pi} = 0.450V \text{ V} \tag{3.61}$$

A comparison of this amplitude with that given in Eq. 3.44 shows the reduction in second-harmonic amplitude that results from freewheeling. The variation in c_2/V as a function of α is shown in Fig. 3.25.

From Eq. 3.36

$$\vartheta_2 = \tan^{-1}\frac{1}{\sqrt{3}} = 30° \tag{3.62}$$

If $2\omega L_a \gg R_a$ the armature current becomes

$$i_a \simeq \bar{i}_a + \frac{0.450}{\sqrt{2}\,\omega L_a}\cos(2\omega t + 30°) \text{ A} \tag{3.63}$$

where $\bar{i}_a$ is again obtained from Eq. 3.11.

The maximum output of the converter occurs when $\alpha = 0$, for which

$$b_2 = 0 \qquad a_2 = c_2 = \frac{-4\sqrt{2}\,V}{3\pi}\;\text{V} \qquad (3.64)$$

As expected, this is the same as the value given in Eq. 3.44 for the converter without freewheeling.

Equation 3.47 applies here also. From Fig. 3.15, however, the approximate waveform of i_p must now be defined by

$$i_p = 0\;\text{A} \qquad 0 < \omega t < \alpha \text{ rad}$$

$$i_p = \frac{N_s}{N_p} \bar{i}_a \;\text{A} \qquad \alpha < \omega t < \pi \text{ rad}$$

$$i_p = 0\;\text{A} \qquad \pi < \omega t < \pi + \alpha \text{ rad}$$

$$i_p = -\frac{N_s}{N_p}\bar{i}_a \;\text{A} \qquad \pi + \alpha < \omega t < 2\pi \text{ rad} \qquad (3.65)$$

This waveform may be described by the series

$$i_p = \sum \frac{4}{n\pi}\frac{N_s}{N_p}\bar{i}_a \cos\frac{n\alpha}{2}\sin\left[n\left(\omega t - \frac{\alpha}{2}\right)\right] \qquad n = 1, 3, 5\ldots \qquad (3.66)$$

The rms magnitude of the fundamental component is therefore

$$I_{p1} = \frac{2\sqrt{2}}{\pi}\frac{N_s}{N_p}\bar{i}_a \cos\frac{\alpha}{2}\;\text{A} \qquad (3.67)$$

A comparison of the waveforms of i_p in Figs. 3.7 and 3.15 will show that the harmonic content of the line current is greater for the converter with freewheeling. The rms value of the assumed rectangular wave of source current is

$$I_p = \frac{N_s}{N_p}\left(\frac{\pi - \alpha}{\pi}\right)^{1/2}\bar{i}_a \;\text{A} \qquad (3.68)$$

and the source-current ripple factor K_i is again given by the ratio I_p/I_{p1}. Thus when $\alpha = 0$ this yields the value given in Eq. 3.51.

The fundamental power factor of the system is

$$P_{F1} = \cos\frac{\alpha}{2} \qquad (3.69)$$

The power input is

$$P_{in} = V_p I_{p1} \cos\frac{\alpha}{2} = \frac{2\sqrt{2}}{\pi} \frac{N_s}{N_p} \bar{i}_a V_p \cos^2\frac{\alpha}{2} \text{ W} \qquad (3.70)$$

Again neglecting converter losses and current harmonics higher than the second, the power developed at the armature terminals is

$$P_a = P_{in} \text{ W} \qquad (3.71)$$

Then from Eqs. 3.68 and 3.70

$$\text{apparent } PF = \frac{P_{in}}{V_p I_p} = \left[\frac{2}{\pi(\pi - \alpha)}\right]^{1/2}(1 + \cos\alpha) \qquad (3.72)$$

Although line current harmonics are increased, armature current harmonics are reduced by freewheeling and the apparent power factor is increased.

Example 3.4

The 230 V, 500-rpm, frame-size 288 motor listed in Appendix B is to be driven with its armature excited from a 230-V, 60-Hz single-phase, ac source via a half-controlled rectifier. The ratio of the transformer between source and rectifier input is $N_p/N_s = 230/300$. The field current is supplied from a separate rectifier and maintained constant at the value required for rated operating conditions. The rotational losses of the motor may be assumed to be proportional to motor speed; when the motor is driven from a converter they are increased by 25%.

If the power delivered to the field winding is neglected determine the apparent power factor of the ac source and the motor efficiency when the average value of terminal pd and armature current are equal to the rated values.

Only the lowest order current harmonic need be considered.

Solution

Armature resistance = 1.33 Ω

Armature inductance = 36.0 mH

Rated current = 22 A

Output power = 3730 W

Under rated operating conditions:

$$\text{Motor speed} = 500 \text{ r/min} = 52.36 \text{ rad/s}$$

$$\text{Motor input} = 230 \times 22 = 5060 \text{ W}$$

$$\text{Armature copper loss} = 1.33 \times 22^2 = 644 \text{ W}$$

$$\text{Rotational losses} = 5060 - 3730 - 644 = 686 \text{ W}$$

$$E_a = 230 - 1.33 \times 22 = 200.7 \text{ V}$$

$$Z = [(120\pi \times 0.036)^2 + 1.33^2]^{1/2} = 13.64 \ \Omega$$

$$\tan \varphi = \frac{120\pi \times 0.036}{1.33} = 10.20$$

$$\varphi = 84.40° = 1.473 \text{ rad}$$

On the assumption that armature current is continuous, at rated speed and load

$$\bar{v}_t = 230 = \frac{300\sqrt{2}}{\pi}(1 + \cos\alpha)$$

from which

$$\alpha = 45.32° = 0.7910 \text{ rad}$$

Substitution in the left side of Eq. 3.25 yields $+3.279$. This positive value confirms that current is continuous.

$$I_p = \frac{N_s}{N_p}\left(\frac{\pi - \alpha}{\pi}\right)^{1/2} \times \bar{i}_a = \frac{300}{230}\left(\frac{\pi - 0.7910}{\pi}\right)^{1/2} \times 22 = 24.82 \text{ A}$$

The rms value of the fundamental component of primary current is

$$I_{p1} = \frac{2\sqrt{2}}{\pi}\frac{N_s}{N_p}\bar{i}_a\cos\frac{a}{2} = \frac{2\sqrt{2}}{\pi} \times \frac{300}{230} \times 22\cos\frac{45.32}{2} = 23.84 \text{ A}$$

$$PF_1 = \cos\frac{\alpha}{2} = \cos\frac{45.32}{2} = 0.9228$$

$$P_{in} = V_p I_{p1} \times PF_1 = 230 \times 23.84 \times 0.9228 = 5060 \text{ W}$$

which agrees with the value obtained earlier.

$$\text{Apparent } PF = \frac{P_{in}}{V_p I_p} = \frac{5060}{230 \times 24.82} = 0.8864$$

$$\text{Rotational losses} = 1.25 \times 686 = 858 \text{ W}$$

For the terminal pd v_t

$$a_2 = \frac{300\sqrt{2}}{\pi}\left[\frac{\sin(3 \times 45.32)}{3} - (1 + \cos 45.32)\right] = -198.7$$

$$b_2 = \frac{300\sqrt{2}}{\pi}\left[\frac{\sin(3 \times 45.32)}{3} - \sin 45.32\right] = -16.73$$

$$|c_2| = [198.7^2 + 16.73^2]^{1/2} = 209.0 \text{ V}$$

The second harmonic impedance is

$$Z_2 = \left[(120\pi \times 2 \times 0.036)^2 + 1.33^2\right] = 27.18 \ \Omega$$

The rms second harmonic of current is then

$$I_{R2} = \frac{209.0}{\sqrt{2} \times 27.18} = 5.438 \text{ A}$$

The approximate rms armature current is

$$I_R = (22^2 + 5.438^2)^{1/2} = 22.66 \text{ A}$$

Armature copper losses are

$$R_a I_a^2 = 1.33 \times 22.66^2 = 683 \text{ W}$$

Efficiency is

$$\eta = \frac{5060 - 858 - 683}{5060} = 0.6954$$

PROBLEMS

3.1. The 230-V, 500-rpm, frame-size 284 motor listed in Appendix B has its armature supplied by a converter of the type shown in Fig. 3.1a. The rectifier is supplied with 260 V at 60 Hz. The field current is fixed at the value that gives rated speed at rated load when $\bar{v}_t = 230$ V. Determine the range of α and Ω_m over which this motor can develop an internal torque equal to rated torque without the armature current becoming continuous.

3.2. The 230-V, 850-rpm, frame-size 283 motor listed in Appendix B is used to drive an antenna (the system in Example 3.1). The inertia of the antenna referred to the motor shaft is twice that of the motor. The loss torques of both motor and mechanism are directly proportional to speed; that of the mechanism is twice that of the motor. The gear ratio between motor and antenna is 500 to 1. The motor armature is supplied from a converter of the type shown in Fig. 3.1a and the ac supply is 260 V, 60 Hz. The motor field current is fixed at the value that gives rated speed at rated load when $\bar{v}_t = 230$ V. Motor speed, average values of armature current $\bar{i}_a$, and armature pd $\bar{v}_t$ may not exceed the rated values. If the converter is *not* to operate on continuous current determine the initial value of α required to accelerate the antenna to full speed, the time taken for this acceleration, and the angle through which the antenna has turned.

3.3. The system in Problem 3.2 is modified by replacing the single rectifier with a dual converter of the type shown in Fig. 3.12. The control of the gating signals is such that one set is blanked out when the armature current reaches zero and would reverse. Regenerative braking and final plugging is to be used to bring the antenna to standstill from full speed. The average value of armature current $\bar{i}_a$ and armature pd $\bar{v}_t$ may not exceed the rated values. Field current is maintained at the value obtaining in Problem 3.2. Determine

(a) whether the system will decelerate without going into continuous-current operation and the range of α required during deceleration;
(b) the time taken for deceleration;
(c) the angle turned through during deceleration;
(d) the time required to rotate the antenna through 180° from standstill to standstill (use the results in Example 3.1 and Problem 3.2).

3.4. In the system in Problem 3.2 the converter is replaced by a half-controlled rectifier:

(a) Will armature current be continuous at the start of acceleration and what value of α is required?
(b) Will the current be continuous at the end of acceleration and, if so, what value of α is required?

3.5. By obtaining expressions for $\bar{v}_t$ and $\bar{i}_a$ in the system in Example 3.3, for the conditions shown in Fig. 3.1b determine α and β for full-speed operation.

3.6. The 850-rpm, frame-size 286 motor of Appendix B is to be used to drive a hoist with separate field excitation; the armature supply is provided by a dual converter formed from two of the rectifiers illustrated in Fig. 3.12

to Fig. 3.21. The ac-source is 300 V at 60 Hz. The loss torque of the motor is assumed to be directly proportional to speed. The field flux under hoisting conditions is that for rated operation, but for regenerative braking it is increased by 25%. The maximum average armature terminal pd is not to exceed 250 V and the average armature current may not exceed 30 A. The thyristors may be assumed to be ideal with zero turn-off time. Determine the maximum permissible torque at the motor coupling and the corresponding values of speed and α for (a) hoisting, (b) regenerative braking during lowering.

3.7. The 230-V, 500-rpm, frame-size 288 motor listed in Appendix B is to be driven with its armature excited from a fully controlled rectifier supplied by a 300-V, 60-Hz source. The field current is maintained constant at the value required for rated operating conditions. The rotational losses of the motor are increased by 30% when it is driven from a converter:

   (a) Show that the armature current is continuous when it has an average value equal to the rated current for the motor.
   (b) Determine the derating factor that must be applied to this motor at rated speed (i.e., the ratio of the continuous power that it can deliver without overheating to the rated power). Only the lowest order harmonics need be considered.

3.8. The 230-V, 500-rpm, frame-size 288 motor listed in Appendix B is to be driven with its armature excited from a fully controlled rectifier. The rectifier is supplied from a 440-V, 60-Hz, single-phase source by a 440:300-V, step-down transformer. The mechanical load is to be driven over a speed range of 350 to 550 rpm and requires a constant driving torque of 0.75 times the rated motor torque throughout this speed range. The rotational losses of the motor may be assumed to be directly proportional to speed and are increased by 30% at all speeds due to the harmonics produced by the rectifier. The field current is held at the value required to provide rated operation on a 230-V, dc source.

   (a) Show that current is continuous over the entire speed range.
   (b) Determine the apparent power factor at the source at rated speed.
   (c) Determine the motor efficiency at rated speed.
   (d) Will the motor overheat if run continuously at rated speed?

Chapter 4

Three-Phase Rectifiers with Motor Load

4.1. THREE-PHASE BRIDGE RECTIFIER DRIVES

The circuit of the three-phase bridge converter, one of the most frequently used in motor-control systems, is shown in Fig. 4.1a. A half-controlled configuration, with three thyristors replaced by diodes, is possible, but it can operate only in the first quadrant of the $v_t - i_a$ diagram. In addition, it has the disadvantage of introducing even harmonics into the line-current waveforms and is therefore unsuitable for large power applications. Only the fully controlled rectifier is discussed here.

The three ac sources shown in Fig. 4.1a, whose pd waveforms appear in Fig. 4.1b, may represent the terminal pd's of the seconday windings in a three-phase transformer. The primary or secondary windings of the transformer (or both) should be connected in delta, so that triplen or zero-sequence harmonic components of the magnetizing currents can flow. (A delta-connected tertiary winding would also perform this function.) If the terminal pds of the ac supply and motor are suitably matched no transformer need be installed because the converter could be supplied directly from the three-phase supply system.

The thyristors in Fig. 4.1a are turned on in the sequence in which they are numbered. Two thyristors necessarily conduct at any instant; for example, when v_{ab} is at its peak positive value thyristors Q_1 and Q_6 conduct; when v_{ab} is at its peak negative value, Q_3 and Q_4 conduct. The gating of each thyristor initiates a pulse of load current; therefore this is a six-pulse rectifier. The waveforms of the circuit variables for continuous-current operation in the first quadrant of the $\bar{v}_t - i_a$ diagram are shown in Fig. 4.2. This system can also operate with discontinuous current, but the increased number of pulses, compared with the single-phase rectifier, confines such operation to a narrow range of delay angle α even when the inductance of the motor armature circuit is low.

It is relevant here to make clear the meaning of the term "delay angle α" and is best done by stating the effect of reducing α to zero. *The delay angle is zero when the rectifier supplying a purely resistive load circuit without emf,*

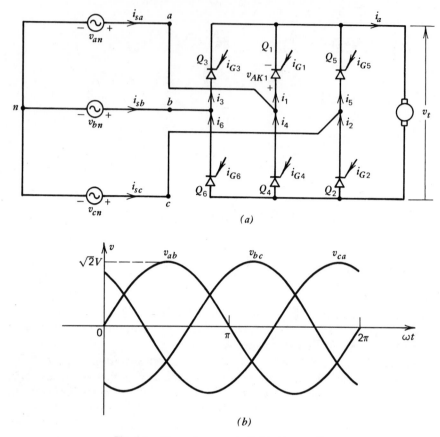

Fig. 4.1. Three-phase, controlled bridge rectifier.

delivers the maximum average load current. This means that the current through the resistive load circuit will, at any instant, be driven by the line-to-line pd in Fig. 4.1 that has the greatest absolute value. Thus the reference thyristor Q_1 must be turned on and begin to conduct at $\omega t = \pi/3$, at which instant Q_6 must already be turned on. The beginning of the gating signal for Q_1 is thus at $\omega t = \pi/3$ where $\alpha = 0$. In these circumstances each thyristor conducts for an interval of $2\pi/3$ rad, a condition that will persist with an increase in α to the value $\alpha = \pi/3$. At this point discontinuous current flows in the resistive load circuit and the current in Q_1 falls to zero at $\omega t = \pi$, again rising as Q_2 is turned on at this instant and falling to zero at $\omega t = 4\pi/3$.

The three-phase rectifier is also capable of inverter operation in the fourth quadrant of the $\bar{v}_t$–i_a diagram, as illustrated in Fig. 4.3. Thus two of these rectifiers connected as a dual converter provide a four-quadrant drive with regeneration in the second and fourth quadrants as described for the single-phase system in Section 3.2.2.

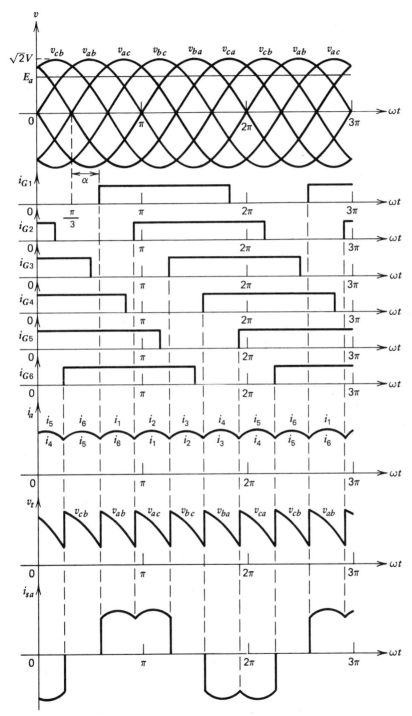

Fig. 4.2. Three-phase rectifier. First-quadrant operation.

99

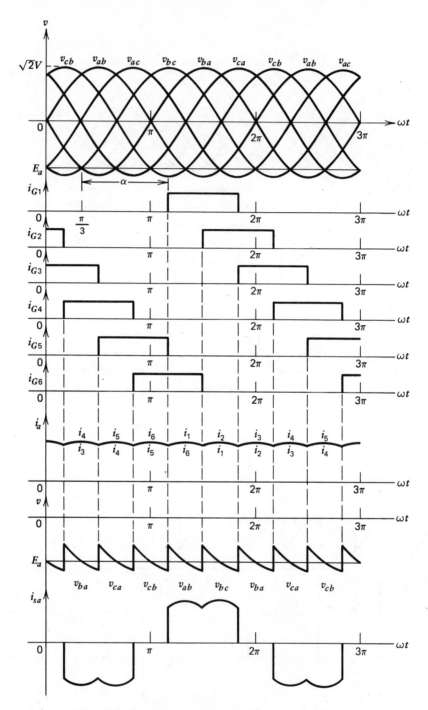

Fig. 4.3. Three-phase rectifier. Fourth-quadrant operation.

100

As shown by the waveform of v_t in Fig. 4.2, when $\alpha > \pi/2$, $\bar{v}_t < 0$. Construction of a waveform for pd v_{AK1} between the terminals of thyristor Q_1 permits the determination of interval ωt_q, illustrated for the single-phase system in Fig. 3.11. This is the time available for thyristor Q_1 to turn off and recover its forward-blocking capability. If α is increased to π on continuous-current operation this interval disappears. Thus operation in the range $\pi < \alpha < 7\pi/6$ is permissible for discontinuous current only. In practice, however, it is never necessary to use so large a value of α in a motor control system. Satisfactory system operation is obtained if the range of α is

$$0 < \alpha < \pi - \omega t_{\text{off}} - \mu \text{ rad} \tag{4.1}$$

where t_{off} is the specified time required by the thyristors to regain their forward-blocking capability[5] and μ is the angle of overlap.

Once more, $\bar{v}_t$ may be expressed as a function of α. Thus if

$$v_{ab} = \sqrt{2}\,V \sin \omega t \text{ V} \tag{4.2}$$

then

$$\bar{v}_t = \frac{3}{\pi} \int_{a+\pi/3}^{a+2\pi/3} \sqrt{2}\,V \sin(\omega t)\,d(\omega t) = \frac{3\sqrt{2}\,V}{\pi}\cos \alpha \text{ V} \tag{4.3}$$

When $\alpha = 0$, $\bar{v}_t = 1.35\,V$, and this is the relationship for a diode rectifier. The average value of armature current is again given by

$$\bar{i}_a = \frac{\bar{v}_t - k\Phi\Omega_m}{R_a} \text{ A} \tag{4.4}$$

The average torque is

$$\bar{T} = k\Phi\bar{i}_a \text{ N} \cdot \text{m} \tag{4.5}$$

Also

$$E_a = k\Phi\Omega_m = \bar{v}_t - R_a\bar{i}_a \text{ V} \tag{4.6}$$

and from Eqs. 4.5 and 4.6

$$\Omega_m = \frac{3\sqrt{2}\,V}{\pi k\Phi}\cos \alpha - \frac{R_a\bar{T}}{(k\Phi)^2} \text{ rad/s} \tag{4.7}$$

The characteristics of Ω_m versus $\bar{T}$ for this system are therefore similar to those of the single-phase rectifier drive with continuous-current operation.

A family of speed-torque characteristics for a three-phase drive similar to those shown in Fig. 3.8 for a single-phase drive may be constructed by a procedure similar to that described at the end of Section 3.2.

Equations 3.5 and 3.9 may be applied to discontinuous-current operation of a three-phase, bridge-rectifier drive, provided that α is replaced by $\alpha + \pi/3$ in both equations, and, for the point of transition from continuous to discontinuous-current operation, β is replaced by $\alpha + 2\pi/3$ in Eq. 3.9. This last equation may then be used to calculated Ω_m at transition for a series of values

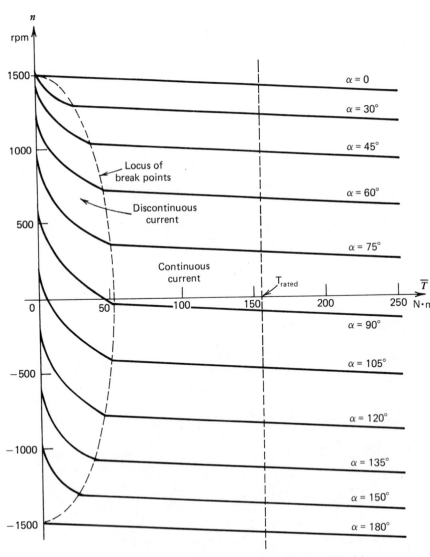

Fig. 4.4. Speed-torque characteristics for a three-phase rectifier drive.

of α. The corresponding values of $\bar{T}$ at transition may then be obtained from Eqs. 4.3 to 4.5. The point obtained lies on the straight line described by Eq. 4.7.

Once again, the point on the axis of Ω_m for $\bar{T} = 0$ may be obtained from

$$\hat{v}_t = \sqrt{2} V \text{ V} \qquad 0 < \alpha < \frac{\pi}{6} \text{ rad}$$

$$\hat{v}_t = \sqrt{2} V \sin\left(\alpha + \frac{\pi}{3}\right) \text{ V} \qquad \frac{\pi}{6} < \alpha < \pi \text{ rad} \qquad (4.8)$$

and

$$\Omega_m = \frac{\hat{v}_t}{k\Phi} \text{ rad/s} \qquad (4.9)$$

Figure 4.4 shows a family of calculated speed-torque characteristics for the 230-V, 25-hp, frame-size 366 motor listed in Appendix B with the armature excited by a three-phase bridge rectifier. Each characteristic is for a constant value of α. The rectifier was supplied with 208-V, line-to-line at 60 Hz and the field current was set at the value that would give rated operation on a 230-V, dc source. These characteristics show that over much of the normal operating range current is continuous. The curve drawn through the break points indicates that break-point torque $\bar{T}_{bp}$ is a maximum at approximately zero speed or at approximately $\alpha = 90°$.

Example 4.1

For the motor in Fig. 4.4 determine the effect on the maximum break-point torque of doubling the armature-circuit inductance.

Solution

The motor parameters are now $R_a = 0.155$ Ω, $L_a = 4.8$ mH. Rated current $I_R = 92$ A and

rated speed = 1150 rpm = 120.4 rad/s

$$k\Phi = \frac{230 - 92 \times 0.155}{120.4} = 1.792 \text{ N} \cdot \text{m/A}$$

$$Z = \left[(120\pi \times 4.8 \times 10^{-3})^2 + 0.155^2\right]^{1/2} = 1.816 \text{ } \Omega$$

$$\tan \varphi = \frac{120\pi \times 4.8 \times 10^{-3}}{0.155} = 11.67$$

$$\varphi = 85.10° = 1.485 \text{ rad}$$

When α is replaced by $\alpha + \pi/2$ and β, by $\alpha + 2\pi/3$ in Eq. 3.9 and the numerical values are inserted the following equation is obtained:

$$162.0 \sin(\alpha + 34.9) - 0.9923\Omega_m - 148.1 \sin(\alpha - 25.1) = 0$$

and expansion of the sine terms yields

$$155.5 \cos \alpha - 1.250 \sin \alpha - 0.9923\Omega_m = 0$$

There are two possible methods of obtaining the approximate maximum value of break-point torque. One is to assume that $\Omega_m = 0$, the other to assume that $\alpha = 90°$. The second is much simpler. Thus

$$\Omega_m = \frac{-1.250}{0.9923} = -1.260 \text{ rad/s}$$

$$\bar{v}_t = 0$$

$$\bar{i}_a = \frac{1.260 \times 1.792}{0.155} = 14.57 \text{ A}$$

$$\bar{T} = 1.792 \times 14.57 = 26.10 \text{ N} \cdot \text{m}$$

By adding 2.4 mH inductance to the armature circuit the maximum break-point torque is approximately halved.

4.2.   THREE-PHASE RECTIFIERS WITH FREEWHEELING

4.2.1.   Freewheeling Only

If a freewheeling diode is connected across the output terminals of the rectifier in Fig. 4.1 the circuit in Fig. 4.5 is obtained. In this circuit v_t cannot have a negative value, and the operation of the rectifier is confined to the first quadrant of the $\bar{v}_t$–$\bar{i}_a$ diagram. The waveforms of the circuit variables are shown in Fig. 4.6 for operating conditions under which current flows in the freewheeling diode and i_a is continuous. Since $\bar{v}_t$ is low, the motor is running at low speed.

In this circuit $v_D = -v_t$. Thus if current is continuous and $v_t > 0$ throughout the cycle no diode current flows and the operation of the converter is the same as it would be without the diode. These conditions will occur for $\alpha < \pi/3$ and, as in Eq. 4.3,

$$\bar{v}_t = \frac{3\sqrt{2} \, V}{\pi} \cos \alpha \text{ V} \qquad 0 < \alpha < \frac{\pi}{3} \text{ rad} \qquad (4.10)$$

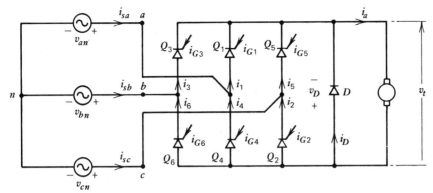

Fig. 4.5.   Three-phase bridge rectifier with freewheeling diode.

The analysis of Section 4.1 then applies. If, however, $\alpha > \pi/3$, then v_t and v_D become zero for interval $\pi < \omega t < \alpha + 2\pi/3$ and current flows in the diode, as illustrated in Fig. 4.6. Also it can be seen from this diagram that $\bar{v}_t = 0$ when $\alpha = 2\pi/3$. Thus for the operating condition illustrated

$$\bar{v}_t = \frac{3}{\pi} \int_{\alpha+\pi/3}^{\pi} \sqrt{2}\, V \sin(\omega t)\, d(\omega t)$$

$$= \frac{3\sqrt{2}\, V}{\pi}\left[1 + \cos\left(\alpha + \frac{\pi}{3}\right)\right]\,V \qquad \frac{\pi}{3} < \alpha < \frac{2\pi}{3}\ \text{rad} \qquad (4.11)$$

The control range for this converter is $0 < \alpha < 2\pi/3$ rad.

Equations 4.4 to 4.6 apply to this system also, but in the light of Eqs. 4.10 and 4.11 Eq. 4.7 must be replaced by

$$\Omega_m = \frac{\bar{v}_t}{k\Phi} - \frac{R_a \bar{T}}{(k\Phi)^2}\ \text{rad/s} \qquad (4.12)$$

Once more it is desirable to determine whether, under a given set of operating conditions, i_a would be continuous or discontinuous. A procedure similar to that used in Section 3.3 for the single-phase drive may be followed.

The boundary condition of operation between continuous and discontinuous current over the range $\pi/3 < \alpha < 2\pi/3$ may be visualized from Fig. 4.6, in which it would be illustrated if the load torque were so reduced that the waveform of i_a fell until its troughs just touched the horizontal axis. Below the corresponding level of average current two possible conditions of operation may be envisaged. If average current were extremely low the current pulse of i_a initiated by i_{G1} would fall to zero before the instant $\omega t = \pi$. No current would then flow in the diode. At somewhat higher average current the pulse of i_a

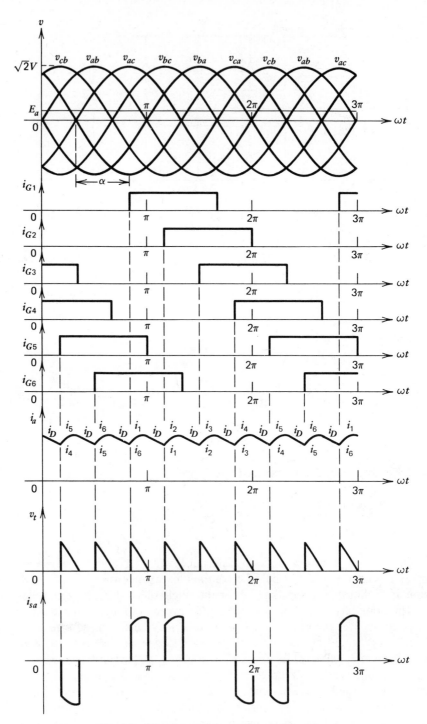

Fig. 4.6. Waveforms of the variables in Fig. 4.5.

initiated by i_{G1} would last through the interval $\alpha + \pi/3 < \omega t < \pi$ and would not have reached zero at the end of this interval. Diode current i_D would flow for all or part of the interval $\pi < \omega t < \alpha + 2\pi/3$, at the end of which i_{G2} initiates another pulse of i_a. Thus it must be determined whether i_D falls to zero before $\omega t = \alpha + 2\pi/3$. A procedure similar to that in Section 3.3 yields

$$i_a = \frac{\sqrt{2}\,V}{Z}\sin(\omega t - \varphi) - \frac{k\Phi\Omega_m}{R_a}$$

$$+ \left[\frac{k\Phi\Omega_m}{R_a} - \frac{\sqrt{2}\,V}{Z}\sin\left(\alpha + \frac{\pi}{3} - \varphi\right)\right]\varepsilon^{(\alpha+\pi/3-\omega t)/\tan\varphi}\ \mathrm{A}$$

$$\alpha + \frac{\pi}{3} < \omega t < \pi \ \mathrm{rad} \tag{4.13}$$

$$I_{a\pi} = \frac{\sqrt{2}\,V}{Z}\sin\varphi - \frac{k\Phi\Omega_m}{R_a}$$

$$+ \left[\frac{k\Phi\Omega_m}{R_a} - \frac{\sqrt{2}\,V}{Z}\sin\left(\alpha + \frac{\pi}{3} - \varphi\right)\right]\varepsilon^{(\alpha-2\pi/3)/\tan\varphi}\ \mathrm{A} \tag{4.14}$$

$$I_{a\pi b} = \frac{k\Phi\Omega_m}{R_a}\left[\varepsilon^{(\alpha-\pi/3)/\tan\varphi} - 1\right]\ \mathrm{A} \tag{4.15}$$

and for the boundary condition $I_{a\pi} - I_{a\pi b} = 0$; that is,

$$\frac{\sqrt{2}\,V}{Z}\sin\varphi - \frac{k\Phi\Omega_m}{R_a}\varepsilon^{(\alpha-\pi/3)/\tan\varphi}$$

$$+ \left[\frac{k\Phi\Omega_m}{R_a} - \frac{\sqrt{2}\,V}{Z}\sin\left(\alpha + \frac{\pi}{3} - \varphi\right)\right]\varepsilon^{(\alpha-2\pi/3)/\tan\varphi} = 0 \tag{4.16}$$

For a chosen value of α, Ω_m can be calculated from Eq. 4.16 and the breakpoint internal torque may then be obtained from Eq. 4.12. The point on the Ω_m axis for $\overline{T} = 0$ may be obtained from

$$\hat{v}_t = \sqrt{2}\,V\ \mathrm{V} \qquad 0 < \alpha < \frac{\pi}{6}$$

$$\hat{v}_t = \sqrt{2}\,V\sin\left(\alpha + \frac{\pi}{3}\right)\ \mathrm{V} \qquad \frac{\pi}{6} < \alpha < \frac{2\pi}{3} \tag{4.17}$$

$$\Omega_m = \frac{\hat{v}_t}{k\Phi}\ \mathrm{rad/s} \tag{4.18}$$

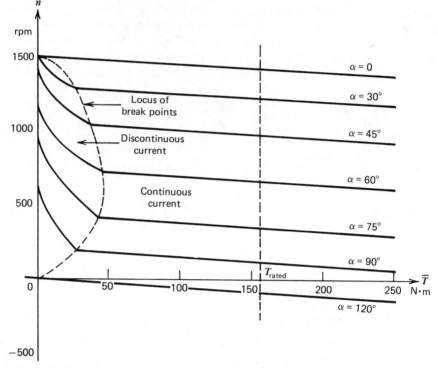

Fig. 4.7. Speed-torque characteristics for a rectifier drive with freewheeling.

The foregoing procedure has been carried out for a single-quadrant drive that consists of the system whose operation is illustrated in Fig. 4.4 but with a freewheeling diode added to the bridge rectifier. The results are shown in Fig. 4.7. The area of the first quadrant in which discontinuous current occurs is smaller than in Fig. 4.4 but the maximum break-point torque, which now occurs at about one-third rated speed, is only slightly reduced. However, the reduction in break-point torque at low speed might suit the load speed-torque characteristics of many loads and result in continuous-current operation over the entire speed range.

Example 4.2

The 230-V, 1750-rpm, frame-size 367 motor of Appendix B is driven with its armature excited by the three-phase bridge rectifier with a freewheeling diode. The ac source is 208 V line-to-line at 60 Hz. The loss torques of the motor and load mechanism are directly proportional to speed and that of the mechanism is 1.25 times that of the motor running on a 230-V, dc source. The loss torque of the motor is increased by 25% when it is operated from the rectifier. The field excitation is maintained at the value required for rated operation on a 230-V, dc source.

Determine whether the armature current will be continuous when the motor is running at 600 rpm and a working torque equal to 25% of rated motor torque is required in the driven mechanism.

Solution

The armature-circuit parameters are $R_a = 0.0415$ Ω, $L_a = 1.10$ mH, the full-load armature current is 117 A, and the rated output power is $50 \times 746 = 37.30$ kW:

$$\text{rated speed} = 1750 \text{ rpm} = 183.3 \text{ rad/s}$$

$$k\Phi = \frac{230 - 0.0415 \times 177}{183.3} = 1.215 \text{ N} \cdot \text{m/A}$$

$$Z = \left[(120\pi \times 1.10 \times 10^{-3})^2 + 0.0415^2\right]^{1/2} = 0.4168 \text{ Ω}$$

$$\tan\varphi = \frac{120\pi \times 1.10 \times 10^{-3}}{0.0415} = 9.993$$

$$\varphi = 84.29° = 1.471 \text{ rad}$$

$$\text{rated torque} = \frac{50 \times 746}{183.3} = 203.5 \text{ N} \cdot \text{m}$$

For nameplate operation

$$\text{power in} = 230 \times 177 = 40.71 \times 10^3 \text{ W}$$

$$\text{power out} = 50 \times 746 = 37.30 \times 10^3 \text{ W}$$

$$R_a I_a^2 = 0.0415 \times 177^2 = 1.3 \times 10^3 \text{ W}$$

$$\text{rotational losses} = (40.71 - 37.30 - 1.30) \times 10^3 = 2110 \text{ W}$$

$$\text{motor loss torque} = \frac{2110}{183.3} = 11.51 \text{ N} \cdot \text{m}$$

$$\text{mechanism loss torque} = 1.25 \times 11.51 = 14.39 \text{ N} \cdot \text{m}$$

$$\text{motor loss torque driven from rectifier} = 14.39 \text{ N} \cdot \text{m}$$

At rated speed

$$T_{\text{loss}} = 2 \times 14.39 = 28.78 \text{ N} \cdot \text{m}$$

$$28.78 = B \times 183.3$$

$$B = 0.1570$$

At any speed

$$T_{\text{loss}} = 0.1570\Omega_m \text{ N} \cdot \text{m}$$

At 600 rpm = 62.83 rad/s

$$\text{average internal torque } \bar{T} = 203.5 \times 0.25 + 0.1570 \times 62.83$$

$$= 60.74 \text{ N} \cdot \text{m}$$

$$\bar{i}_a = \frac{60.74}{1.215} = 49.99 \text{ A}$$

$$\bar{v}_t = 49.99 \times 0.0415 + 62.83 \times 1.215 = 78.41 \text{ V}$$

On the assumption that current is continuous and that $\alpha < \pi/3$, from Eq. 4.10

$$\alpha = \cos^{-1}\frac{78.41\pi}{3\sqrt{2} \times 208} = 73.79°$$

This assumption is not valid. From Eq. 4.11

$$\alpha = \cos^{-1}\left(\frac{78.41\pi}{3\sqrt{2} \times 208} - 1\right) - 60° = 76.12° = 1.329 \text{ rad}$$

To determine whether current is continuous substitute $\alpha = 76.12°$, $\Omega_m = 62.83$ rad/s, and the known numerical values in the left side of Eq. 4.16. This yields a result of $+45.99$, a positive value that indicates that current is continuous.

4.2.2. Freewheeling with Regeneration

As in the case of the single-phase bridge rectifier, freewheeling can be obtained in the first and fourth quadrants of the $\bar{v}_t$–$\bar{i}_a$ diagram without the need to fit a freewheeling diode. The required gating-current pulses must again be modified and are illustrated in Figs. 4.8 and 4.9.[4]

In Fig. 4.8 $\alpha = \pi/2$ and, with gating signals terminated as in Fig. 4.2, $\bar{v}_t$ and i_a would be zero. However, the effect of the prolonged gating signals shown in Fig. 4.8 is to provide freewheeling paths through two of the thyristors; therefore current no longer flows in the source line when v_t tends to go negative and the negative parts of the v_t waveform are eliminated. Thus, for example, at $\omega t = \alpha + \pi/3$ Q_1 is turned on and current flows from the source via Q_1, the motor armature, and Q_6. At $\omega t = \pi$ v_{ab} goes negative and because Q_4 is gated Q_6 is commutated. The load current then freewheels through Q_1 and Q_4 until $\omega t = \alpha + 2\pi/3$, when Q_2 is turned on, and, because $v_{ac} > 0$ Q_4 is commutated and current flows from the source through Q_1, the motor armature, and Q_2, and so on. The thyristor currents corresponding to i_a are

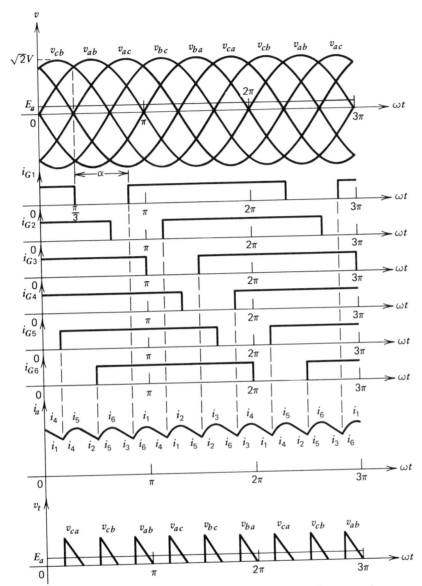

Fig. 4.8. Three-phase rectifier with freewheeling. First-quadrant operation.

marked on the waveform of i_a in Fig. 4.9, and the pd's driving the source current through the armature are marked on the waveform of v_t. The waveform of i_{sa} is identical to that shown in Fig. 4.6.

As in the circuit of Fig. 4.5, freewheeling is not possible for $0 < \alpha < \pi/3$ since for freewheeling to occur v_t must fall to zero before the end of the pulse of source current. Figure 4.2 shows that this does not take place. Thus for

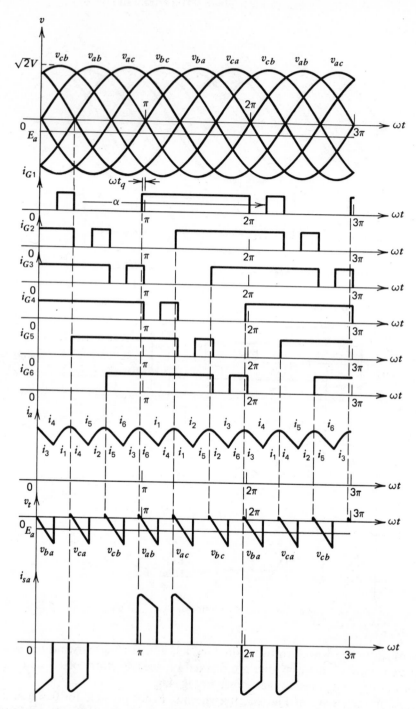

Fig. 4.9. Three-phase rectifier with freewheeling. Fourth-quadrant operation.

first-quadrant operation $\bar{v}_t$ is expressed as a function of α by Eqs. 4.10 and 4.11, except that for the 4.11 the range of α must be slightly reduced to $\pi/3 < \alpha < (2\pi/3 - \omega t_q)$. The reason for this upper limit is given when fourth-quadrant operation is discussed in the next paragraphs.

Operation with freewheeling in the fourth quadrant is illustrated in Fig. 4.9. The overall length of the gating signals is maintained constant at $(4\pi/3 + \omega t_q)$ but a break is introduced, commencing at $\pi/3$ from the end of each gating signal. Delay angle α now signifies the interval from instant $\omega t = \pi/3$ to the start of the second part of the i_{G1} signal. The length of the first part of the signal remains constant at $(\pi + \omega t_q)$.

At $\omega t = \pi - \omega t_q$ Q_1 is gated. Because $(v_{ab} + E_a) < 0$, Q_1 and Q_6 conduct. When Q_4 is turned on at $\omega t = \alpha - \pi$, $v_{ab} < 0$ and Q_6 is commutated. Thyristors Q_1 and Q_4 then conduct freewheeling current. When Q_2 is turned on $v_{ac} > 0$ for an interval ωt_q in length so that Q_4 is commutated; Q_5 then commutates Q_1 and so on. For this mode of operation the range of the delay angle as defined in the preceding paragraph, is $5\pi/3 < \alpha < 2\pi$. At the upper end of this range the second part of each gating signal disappears and freewheeling ceases.

If the brief interval $(2\pi - \omega t_q) < \omega t < 2\pi$, when $v_t > 0$ is neglected then

$$\bar{v}_t = \frac{3}{\pi} \int_{2\pi}^{\alpha+\pi/3} \sqrt{2}\, V \sin(\omega t + \pi)\, d(\omega t)$$

$$= \frac{3\sqrt{2}\, V}{\pi}\left[\cos\left(\alpha + \frac{\pi}{3}\right) - 1\right] V \qquad \frac{5\pi}{3} < \alpha < 2\pi \text{ rad} \qquad (4.19)$$

Operation in the fourth quadrant without freewheeling has already been illustrated in Fig. 4.3 and Eq. 4.10 applies over the range $2\pi/3 < \alpha < \pi - \omega t_q$.

Speed-torque characteristics for a drive that incorporates the converter in Figs. 4.8 and 4.9 could be constructed and would form a diagram with a first quadrant similar to that in Fig. 4.7 and with a second quadrant similar to the fourth quadrant in Fig. 4.4 rotated through 180°.

4.3.   RECTIFIER TRANSFER FUNCTIONS

Approximate linear transfer functions for the three-phase rectifier similar to that for the single-phase rectifier in Eq. 3.32 can be obtained. Because this is a six-pulse converter, the dead time t_d is only one-third of that for the two-pulse, single-phase converter. For each of the three configurations discussed in the preceding sections a gain factor can be determined.

4.3.1.   Rectifier Without Freewheeling

For the configuration represented in Figs. 4.1 to 4.3 Eq. 4.3 describes the relation between $\bar{v}_t$ and α for the entire range of $0 < \alpha < \pi - \omega t_q$. A satisfactory linear approximation is obtained if the range of α is restricted to

$30° < \alpha < 150°$. Then

$$k = \frac{\Delta \bar{v}_t}{-\Delta \alpha} = \frac{3\sqrt{2}\,V}{\pi}\frac{(\cos 30° - \cos 150°)}{150° - 30°} = 0.0195V \text{ V/deg} \quad (4.20)$$

4.3.2. Rectifier with Freewheeling Diode

For the configuration in Figs. 4.5 and 4.6 Eqs. 4.3 and 4.10 represent the relation between $\bar{v}_t$ and α for the range $0 < \alpha < \pi/3$, whereas Eq. 4.11 supplies the relation for the range $\pi/3 < \alpha < 2\pi/3$. The curve of $\bar{v}_t$ as a function of α for the entire operating range is shown in Fig. 4.10. Provided that it is not necessary for the operation of drive to reduce $\bar{v}_t$ smoothly to zero, a satisfactory linear approximation is obtained if the range of α is restricted to $\pi/6 < \alpha < \pi/2$. Then from Eqs. 4.10 and 4.11

$$k = \frac{\Delta \bar{v}_t}{-\Delta \alpha} = \frac{3\sqrt{2}\,V}{\pi}\frac{\left[\cos 30° - (1 + \cos 150°)\right]}{90° - 30°} = 0.0165V \text{ V/deg}$$

$$(4.21)$$

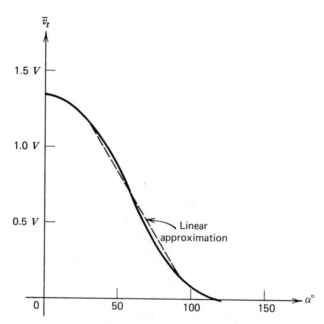

Fig. 4.10. $\bar{v}_t$ as a function of α for the rectifier with freewheeling diode.

4.3.3. Rectifier with Freewheeling and Regeneration

For the configuration in Figs. 4.1, 4.8, and 4.9 the relation between $\bar{v}_t$ and α as defined in Figs. 4.8 and 4.9, is a discontinuous function that cannot be described approximately by a linear relationship. The gating signals for this configuration, however, are so complicated that they are most readily produced with the aid of a microprocessor. With this resource available, there is little

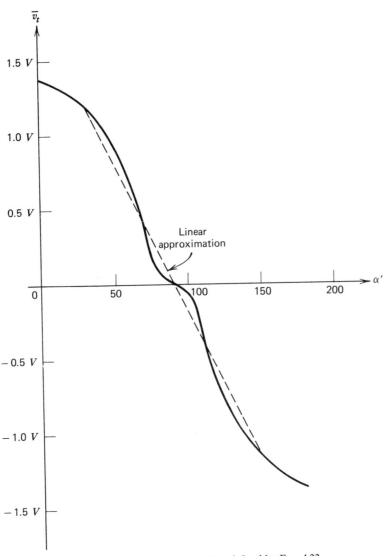

Fig. 4.11. $\bar{v}_t$ as a function of α' as defined by Eqs. 4.22.

difficulty in defining a variable α' in terms of α such that $\bar{v}_t$ can be represented approximately as a linear function of α'. The necessary relationships between α' and α are

$$0 < \alpha < \frac{\pi}{3} \qquad \alpha' = \alpha \qquad 0 < \alpha' < \frac{\pi}{3}$$

$$\frac{\pi}{3} < \alpha < \frac{2\pi}{3} \qquad \alpha' = \frac{\alpha}{2} + \frac{\pi}{6} \qquad \frac{\pi}{3} < \alpha' < \frac{\pi}{2}$$

$$\frac{5\pi}{3} < \alpha < 2\pi \qquad \alpha' = \frac{\alpha}{2} - \frac{\pi}{3} \qquad \frac{\pi}{2} < \alpha' < \frac{2\pi}{3}$$

$$\frac{2\pi}{3} < \alpha < \pi \qquad \alpha' = \alpha \qquad \frac{2\pi}{3} < \alpha' < \pi$$

$$(4.22)$$

With this definition of α' the curve of $\bar{v}_t$ versus α' is as shown in Fig. 4.11.

An acceptable linear approximation is obtained if the range of α' is restricted to $\pi/6 < \alpha' < 5\pi/6$ and this approximation yields the same transfer function as that obtained for the rectifier without freewheeling, with the exception that

$$k = \frac{\Delta\bar{v}_t}{-\Delta\alpha'} \text{ V/deg} \qquad (4.23)$$

4.4.   POWER IN LOAD AND SOURCE CIRCUITS

The characteristics of Fig. 4.4 show that a motor with its armature supplied from a six-pulse converter will draw continuous armature current over a large part of its operating range. This feature can be improved by freewheeling and even more by the addition of a small amount of inductance to the armature circuit. It is therefore appropriate to base a general appraisal of the performance of these drives on their behavior with continuous armature current. Indeed, as in the case of the single-phase converter, the assumption is made that the current is not only continuous but also essentially constant.

4.4.1.   Rectifier Without Freewheeling

The waveform of v_t in Figs. 4.2 and 4.3 may be described by the series

$$v_t = \bar{v}_t + \sum_{n=1}^{\infty} c_n \sin(n\omega t + \vartheta_n) \text{ V} \qquad (4.24)$$

The fundamental frequency of v_t in this six-pulse converter is 6ω rad/s. Thus all harmonics of v_t must be of order $n = 6m$, where m is an integer.
   The coefficients and angles of the series in Eq. 4.24 are given by

$$c_n = [a_n^2 + b_n^2]^{1/2} \text{ V} \tag{4.25}$$

$$\vartheta_n = \tan^{-1}\frac{a_n}{b_n} \text{ rad} \tag{4.26}$$

where

$$a_n = \frac{6}{\pi}\int_{\alpha+\pi/3}^{\alpha+2\pi/3} v_t \cos(n\omega t)\, d(\omega t) \text{ V} \qquad n = 6,12,18\ldots \tag{4.27}$$

$$b_n = \frac{6}{\pi}\int_{\alpha+\pi/3}^{\alpha+2\pi/3} v_t \sin(n\omega t)\, d(\omega t) \text{ V} \qquad n = 6,12,18\ldots \tag{4.28}$$

For the harmonic of lowest frequency $n = 6$ and

$$a_6 - \frac{6\sqrt{2}\,V}{\pi}\left(\frac{\cos 7\alpha}{14} - \frac{\cos 5\alpha}{10}\right) \text{ V} \tag{4.29}$$

$$b_6 = \frac{6\sqrt{2}\,V}{\pi}\left(\frac{\sin 7\alpha}{14} - \frac{\sin 5\alpha}{10}\right) \text{ V} \tag{4.30}$$

The variation in c_6/V as a function of α is shown in Fig. 4.12. A comparison with Fig. 3.25 shows that the amplitude of this sixth harmonic is much less than that of the second harmonic for the single-phase rectifier drive.
   As in a fully controlled, single-phase system, the harmonics are greatest when $\alpha = \pi/2$. For this worst case

$$a_6 = 0 \qquad b_6 = c_6 = -0.463V \text{ V} \qquad \alpha = \frac{\pi}{2} \text{ rad} \tag{4.31}$$

If $6\omega L_a \gg R_a$ the armature current can to a good approximation be described by

$$i_a \simeq \bar{i}_a + \frac{0.463V}{6\omega L_a}\cos 6\omega t \text{ A} \tag{4.32}$$

The maximum output of the converter occurs when $\alpha = 0$, for which condition $b_6 = 0$, and

$$a_6 = c_6 = -0.0772V \text{ V} \qquad \alpha = 0 \tag{4.33}$$

This amplitude is again much less than that of the second harmonic in the

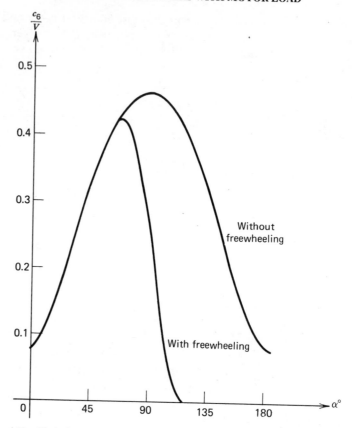

Fig. 4.12. Variation of c_6/V as a function of α for three-phase bridge rectifiers.

single-phase system. Equation 4.33 gives the sixth harmonic amplitude obtained from a diode rectifier.

On the basis of the foregoing approximations, the rms magnitude of the sixth harmonic at any value of α is

$$I_{R6} = \frac{c_6}{6\sqrt{2}\,\omega L_a} \text{ A} \qquad (4.34)$$

The rms armature current is then

$$I_R = \left[(\bar{i}_a)^2 + I_{R6}^2 \right]^{1/2} \text{ A} \qquad (4.35)$$

It remains to determine a design value for the line current i_{sa} drawn from the power supply. The waveform of this current, shown in Fig. 4.2, has alternating symmetry and therefore contains no even harmonics. The approximation used for the single-phase rectifier of considering the armature current constant and of magnitude $\bar{i}_a$ may be applied here with even more justification. Thus the waveform of i_{sa} will be considered to consist of rectangles of amplitude $\bar{i}_a$ and duration $2\pi/3$ rad. The first positive half-wave of i_{sa} in Fig. 4.2 has duration $\alpha + \pi/3 < \omega t < \alpha + 2\pi/3$. Again by using the method of discontinuities explained in Appendix A, this approximate line-current waveform may be described by the series

$$i_{sa} = \sum_n \frac{4\bar{i}_a}{n\pi}\cos\frac{n\pi}{6}\sin\left[n\left(\omega t - \alpha - \frac{\pi}{6}\right)\right] \text{ A} \qquad n = 1,3,5\ldots \quad (4.36)$$

The rms magnitude of the fundamental component of i_{sa} is

$$I_{sa1} = \frac{\sqrt{6}}{\pi}\bar{i}_a \text{ A} \qquad (4.37)$$

The rms magnitude of the approximate waveform of i_{sa} is

$$I_{sa} = \left[\frac{2}{\pi}\int_0^{\pi/3}(\bar{i}_a)^2\,d(\omega t)\right]^{1/2} = \sqrt{\frac{2}{3}}\,\bar{i}_a \text{ A} \qquad (4.38)$$

and the line-current ripple factor is

$$K_i = \frac{I_{sa}}{I_{sa1}} = \frac{\pi}{3} = 1.047 \qquad (4.39)$$

The cosine of the phase angle between the line-to-neutral pd v_{an} and the fundamental component of i_{sa} is the fundamental power factor of the system. Because the phase angle in Eq. 4.36 is that between the line-to-line pd v_{ab} and the current component, it follows that

$$PF_1 = \cos\alpha \qquad (4.40)$$

The power input is thus

$$P_{in} = \sqrt{3}\,VI_{sa1}\cos\alpha = \frac{3\sqrt{2}}{\pi}\bar{i}_a V\cos\alpha \text{ W} \qquad (4.41)$$

The power developed at the armature-circuit terminals is

$$P_a = \bar{v}_t\bar{i}_a = \frac{3\sqrt{2}}{\pi}V\bar{i}_a\cos\alpha = P_{in} \text{ W} \qquad (4.42)$$

Thus

$$\text{apparent } PF = \frac{\bar{v}_t\bar{i}_a}{\sqrt{3}\,VI_{sa}} = \frac{\bar{v}_t}{\sqrt{2}\,V} = \frac{3}{\pi}\cos\alpha = 0.955\cos\alpha \qquad (4.43)$$

Again, energy flow is reversed if $\alpha > \pi/2$.

4.4.2. Rectifiers with Freewheeling

Figures 4.6 and 4.8 show waveforms of rectifiers that operate with freewheeling in the first quadrant of the $\bar{v}_t - \bar{i}_a$ diagram. The waveform of v_t may again be analyzed into the series of Eq. 4.24 where, for $\alpha > \pi/3$,

$$a_n = \frac{6}{\pi} \int_{\alpha+\pi/3}^{\pi} v_t \cos(n\omega t)\, d(\omega t)\ \text{V} \qquad n = 6, 12, 18\ldots \qquad (4.44)$$

$$b_n = \frac{6}{\pi} \int_{\alpha+\pi/3}^{\pi} v_t \sin(n\omega t)\, d(\omega t)\ \text{V} \qquad n = 6, 12, 18\ldots \qquad (4.45)$$

Thus for the lowest-frequency harmonic,

$$a_6 = \frac{3\sqrt{2}\,V}{\pi}\left[\frac{1 + \cos 7(\alpha + \pi/3)}{7} - \frac{1 + \cos 5(\alpha + \pi/3)}{5}\right]\text{V} \quad (4.46)$$

$$b_6 = \frac{3\sqrt{2}\,V}{\pi}\left[\frac{\sin 7(\alpha + \pi/3)}{7} - \frac{\sin 5(\alpha + \pi/3)}{5}\right]\text{V} \qquad (4.47)$$

The variation in c_6/V as a function of α is shown in Fig. 4.12.

Because of the increased number of pulses, the freewheeling diode has markedly less effect on the operation of the three-phase bridge converter than on the single-phase converter.

Conduction by the freewheeling diode affects the waveform of the source-line current, as illustrated for current i_{sa} in Fig. 4.6. If the assumption is again made that the armature current is constant and of magnitude $\bar{i}_a$, the waveform of i_{sa} may be described by the series

$$i_{sa} = \sum_{n=1,3,5\ldots} \frac{4\bar{i}_a}{n\pi}\left[\cos\frac{n\alpha}{2} - \cos n\left(\frac{2\pi}{3} - \frac{\alpha}{2}\right)\right] \times \sin n\left(\omega t - \frac{\alpha}{2} - \frac{\pi}{3}\right)\text{A}$$

$$(4.48)$$

The rms magnitude of the fundamental component of i_{sa} is

$$I_{sa1} = \frac{2\sqrt{6}\cdot \bar{i}_a}{\pi}\cos\left(\frac{\alpha}{2} + \frac{\pi}{6}\right)\text{A} \qquad (4.49)$$

The rms magnitude of the approximate waveform of i_{sa} is

$$I_{sa} = \left[\frac{2}{\pi}\int_{\alpha-\pi/3}^{\pi/3}(-\bar{i}_a)^2\, d(\omega t)\right]^{1/2} = \left[\frac{2}{\pi}\left(\frac{2\pi}{3} - \alpha\right)\right]^{1/2}\bar{i}_a\ \text{A} \quad (4.50)$$

and the line-current ripple factor is

$$K_i = \frac{I_{sa}}{I_{sa1}} = \frac{(2\pi/3 - \alpha)^{1/2}}{2\sqrt{3}/\sqrt{\pi}\,\cos(\alpha/2 + \pi/6)} \qquad (4.51)$$

As might be expected from the waveform of i_{sa}, this ripple factor is increased by the presence of the freewheeling circuit. Thus at $\alpha = \pi/2$ $K_i = 1.430$, compared with the constant value of 1.047 obtained for the rectifier without freewheeling.

The cosine of the phase angle between the line-to-neutral pd v_{an} and the fundamental component of i_{sa} is the fundamental power factor of the system. Because the phase angle in Eq. 4.48 is that between the line-to-line pd v_{ab} and the current component, it follows that

$$PF_1 = \cos\left(\frac{\alpha}{2} + \frac{\pi}{6}\right) \tag{4.52}$$

The power input is thus

$$P_{in} = \sqrt{3} \cdot VI_{sa1}\cos\left(\frac{\alpha}{2} + \frac{\pi}{6}\right)$$

$$= \frac{3\sqrt{2} \cdot V \cdot i_a}{\pi}\left[1 + \cos\left(\alpha + \frac{\pi}{3}\right)\right] \text{ W} \tag{4.53}$$

The power developed at the armature-circuit terminals is

$$P_a = \bar{v}_t i_a = \frac{3\sqrt{2} \cdot V \cdot i_a}{\pi}\left[1 + \cos\left(\alpha + \frac{\pi}{3}\right)\right] = P_{in} \text{ W} \tag{4.54}$$

The apparent power factor is given by

$$\text{apparent } PF = \frac{\bar{v}_t i_a}{\sqrt{3} \, VI_{sa}} \tag{4.55}$$

The foregoing analysis can also be applied to operation with freewheeling in the fourth quadrant of the $\bar{v}_t$–i_a diagram.

Example 4.3

The 230-V, 1150-rpm, frame-size 367 motor of Appendix B has its armature circuit supplied from a three-phase bridge rectifier. The ac source is 208 V, line-to-line at 60 Hz. The field current is held constant at the value that gives rated performance on a 230-V, dc source. The rotational loss torque may be assumed to be proportional to speed and increased by 15% when the motor is driven from the rectifier.

If 0.75 rated torque must be delivered at the coupling between ±1000 rpm plot curves in the motoring and regenerating regions of $\bar{T}$, i_a, α, and apparent PF as functions of n, which is to be the variable shown on the vertical axis of the diagram.

Solution

For this motor $R_a = 0.0963\Omega$, $I_R = 108$ A

$$1150 \text{ rpm} = 120.4 \text{ rad/s}$$

$$k\Phi = \frac{230 - 0.0963 \times 108}{120.4} = 1.824 \text{ N} \cdot \text{m/A}$$

$$0.75T_R = \frac{0.75 \times 30 \times 746}{120.4} = 139.4 \text{ N} \cdot \text{m}$$

For rated operation

$$\text{input power} = 230 \times 108 = 24.84 \times 10^3 \text{ W}$$

$$\text{output power} = 30 \times 746 = 22.38 \times 10^3 \text{ W}$$

$$R_a I_R^2 = 0.0963 \times 108^2 = 1.12 \times 10^3 \text{ W}$$

$$\text{rotational losses} = (24.84 - 22.38 - 1.12) \times 10^3 = 1.34 \times 10^3 \text{ W}$$

Loss torque at 1150 rpm when operated from the rectifier is

$$T_{\text{loss}} = 1.15 \times \frac{1.34 \times 10^3}{120.4} 12.80 \text{ N} \cdot \text{m}$$

$$T_{\text{loss}} = \frac{12.80}{120.4}\Omega_m = 0.1063\Omega_m \text{ N} \cdot \text{m}$$

Internal torque to be developed is thus

$$\bar{T} = 139.4 + 0.1063\Omega_m \text{ N} \cdot \text{m}$$

The required expressions to calculate the quantities required may be obtained from this expression for $\bar{T}$ and

$$\bar{i}_a = \frac{\bar{T}}{k\Phi}$$

$$\bar{v}_t = R_a\bar{i}_a + k\Phi\Omega_m = \frac{3\sqrt{2}\,V}{\pi}\cos\alpha$$

$$PF = \frac{3}{\pi}\cos\alpha$$

The required curves are shown in Fig. 4.13.

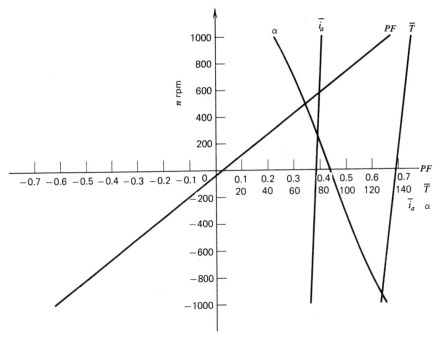

Fig. 4.13. Diagram for Example 4.3.

PROBLEMS

4.1. The 230-V, 1750-rpm, frame-size 288 motor of Appendix B is separately excited with the armature supplied from a 208-V, line-to-line, 60-Hz source by a three-phase bridge rectifier. Motor rotational losses may be neglected and the armature inductance assumed high enough to give continuous current under all required operating conditions.

   If the motor is delivering full-load torque and the field excitation is that required to give rated operation on a 230-V, dc source determine the speed for (a) $\alpha = 45°$, (b) $\alpha = 135°$.

4.2. A 230-V, 50-rpm, 3.75-kW motor has a full-load current of 18.3 A and an armature-circuit resistance of $R_a = 1.36$ Ω. It is separately excited with its armature supplied from a dual converter composed of 2 three-phase bridge rectifiers. The ac source is 208 V, line-to-line at 60 Hz. The field excitation is adjusted to the value required for rated operation on a 230-V source. The rotational losses of the motor may be neglected and the armature-circuit inductance assumed to be great enough to give continuous-current operation under all required conditions. The coupling torque presented by the driven mechanism is equal to the rated torque of the motor and opposes rotation at all speeds. The drive operates on the following work cycle:

(a) constant speed of 900 rpm;
(b) deceleration to 600 rpm, followed by constant speed;
(c) reversals to −600 rpm, followed by constant speed;
(d) reversal to 900 rpm, followed by (a).

The permissible acceleration and deceleration of the system are equal to 1.5 times the acceleration achieved when rated torque is developed by the motor.

(a) On a diagram of speed n versus torque $\overline{T}$ show the steady-state operating points and draw through them the steady-state, speed-torque characteristics that correspond to each control setting. Indicate which converter is operating in each of the quadrants of the diagram and in which mode, rectifying or inverting.
(b) Draw diagrams of speed n and armature current i_a as functions of time for the entire work cycle (only short periods of constant speed need be shown and, because inertia is not given, an arbitrary acceleration may be assumed). Show the value of delay angle α before and after all points at which it is abruptly changed.

4.3. A transformer is installed between the ac source and the converter input in Fig. 4.4, raising the converter input pd to 250-V line-to-line. What is the effect of this change on the diagram in Fig. 4.4 and, in particular, on the discontinuous-current area of that diagram?

4.4. The 1150-rpm, frame-size 503, 50-hp (37.3-kW) motor in Appendix B has its armature supplied by a three-phase bridge rectifier. The ac source is 208 V, line-to-line at 60 Hz. The steady-state torque presented to the motor coupling by the driven mechanism is 100 N · m at standstill and rises in a straight line to 250 N · m at 1000 rpm. The rotational inertia of the mechanical system is 2.20 kg · m² when referred to the motor coupling. The loss torque of the motor is directly proportional to speed and is increased by 25% at all speeds when the motor is driven from the rectifier. The system is to be accelerated from standstill to 1000 rpm, with an average armature current equal to the rated motor current. The field excitation is to be maintained at the value required to give nameplate performance.

(a) Is the current continuous throughout acceleration?
(b) What is the time required to accelerate the system from standstill to 1000 rpm?
(c) Derive an expression for α as a function of speed during acceleration.
(d) What is the value of α at a steady speed of 1000 rpm?

4.5. A dual converter that consists of two rectifiers of the type illustrated in Figs. 4.8 and 4.9 is used to supply the armature of the 230-V, 25-hp (18.6-kW), frame-size 366 motor in Appendix B whose characteristics are illustrated in Figs. 4.4 and 4.7. The ac source in this case is also 208 V, line-to-line at 60 Hz. The loss torque of this motor is increased by 20% when it is driven from the rectifiers and may then be described by the equation

$$T_L = k_1 + k_2\Omega_m \ \text{N} \cdot \text{m}$$

The two components of T_L are of equal magnitude at rated speed. The field excitation is to be that required for rated operation from a 230-V, dc source. The torque presented by the load is directly proportional to speed and is equal to 0.75 of rated motor torque at rated motor speed. The inertia of the load referred to the motor shaft is 0.595 kg · m². The work cycle of the system requires that it be smoothly accelerated to 1000 rpm in 2.5 s and then smoothly decelerated to standstill in the same time. Disregarding any transients occurring at the commencement of acceleration or deceleration, draw curves of speed versus torque for this operation from standstill back to standstill and, by superimposing on them the boundary operation curves from Figs. 4.4 and 4.7, determine whether there are any speed ranges over which discontinuous current occurs and what they are. Is the freewheeling feature of this drive effective in preventing discontinuous current operation?

4.6. The 230-V, 1750-rpm, frame-size 368 motor in Appendix B is to be driven with the armature circuit supplied from a three-phase bridge rectifier. The ac source is 208 V, line-to-line at 60 Hz and the motor is separately excited with a field current that would give nameplate operation of the motor from a 230-V, dc source. The rotational loss torque of the motor is directly proportional to speed and is increased by 15% when the motor is driven from the rectifier. The converter and motor form elements of a speed-control system in which speed feedback is provided by a tachometer that gives an output of 25 V/1000 rpm.

(a) If the speed reference input signal is set to give rated speed at 0.75 rated torque determine k_1, the regulator/logic/converter gain required to ensure that the speed will rise only 10 rpm when the load torque is removed.

(b) With this value of k_1, determine the speed reference input pd to give the conditions in (a) and the change in this reference pd required to give a speed reduction of 5% from rated speed.

4.7. In the system in Problem 4.4 the ac source pd is found to vary considerably.

(a) If the field circuit and the control logic are supplied from a stabilized power source calculate the change of speed that results from an increase of 20% in the ac source pd.

(b) If a permanent-magnet feedback tachometer that gives 20 V/1000 rpm and a regulator supplied from the stabilized power source and giving a k_1 gain (Fig. 2.11) of 50 at normal ac source pd are fitted, calculate the speed change that results from a 20% increase in ac source pd.

4.8. The 230-V, 750-rpm, frame-size 284, 10-hp (7.46-kW), motor in Appendix B is to be driven with its armature supplied from a three-phase bridge converter. The ac source is 208 V at 60 Hz. The rotational loss torque may be assumed to be directly proportional to speed and to be increased by 15% when the motor is driven from the rectifier. The field is separately excited from an independent field rectifier and the field current is set at the value that yields nameplate performance on a 230-V, dc source. All harmonics higher than the sixth may be neglected. Determine

(a) The efficiency of the motor at 0.75 × rated torque when operating from a 230-V, dc source; field power should be included in the calculation.

(b) For operation from the rectifier at 0.75 × rated torque and rated speed, calculate

(i) RMS armature current;
(ii) motor efficiency;
(iii) RMS ac line current;
(iv) fundamental source power factor;
(v) apparent source power factor.

Chapter 5

Chopper Drives

5.1. INTRODUCTION

If a supply of direct current at appropriate potential difference is available, it may be controlled by a dc-to-dc converter or chopper and used to supply the armature circuit of a separately excited dc motor. Because the use of dc is widespread in electric transportation systems, chopper drives find a ready application in that field.

Because the line-to-line or line-to-ground (steel rail) potential difference in a dc supply system is low in comparison with that used in a typical ac supply system, direct current is relatively high for a given power. Thus the harmonic content of the line current may result in high amplitude current harmonics that can cause serious interference with communication systems. The chopper on the vehicle and the rectifier at the substation are the sources of these harmonics, and although the supply from the substation will have the expected harmonics coming from six- or 12-pulse rectifiers the contribution of the chopper may be reduced by making its chopping frequency as high as possible. If a filter is then fitted at the input of the chopper, consisting usually of a series inductance in one line and a parallel capacitance across the chopper input terminals, the line harmonics will be much reduced and the chopper may be considered to operate from a constant-potential source. The resonant frequency of the filter should be as far below the chopper working frequency as feasible; that is, the inductor and capacitor should be large. Harmonics can also be reduced effectively by two or more choppers operating at staggered pulse frequencies from a common filter.

Choppers may be classified according to the number of quadrants of the $\bar{v}_t - \bar{i}_a$ diagram in which they are capable of operating. A classification that is convenient for the discussion that follows is shown in Fig. 5.1.

5.2. CLASS A CHOPPER

Figure 5.2a illustrates the basic power circuit of a step-down single-quadrant chopper. The model of the motor armature circuit is shown as three separate circuit elements. The term *step-down* signifies that the average terminal pd of

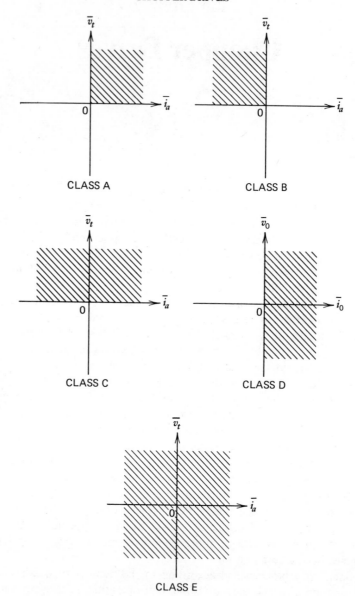

Fig. 5.1. Classification of choppers by quadrants of operation.

the armature circuit is less than that of the source. The term *single-quadrant* signifies that the armature circuit variables $\bar{v}_t$ and $\bar{i}_a$ occur only in the first quadrant of the $\bar{v}_t$–$\bar{i}_a$ diagram. The operation of this system may be understood from a consideration of the waveforms of the circuit variables shown in Figs. 5.2b and c. When thyristor Q_1 is turned on the source pd appears at the terminals of the armature circuit and, if this state of affairs were to continue,

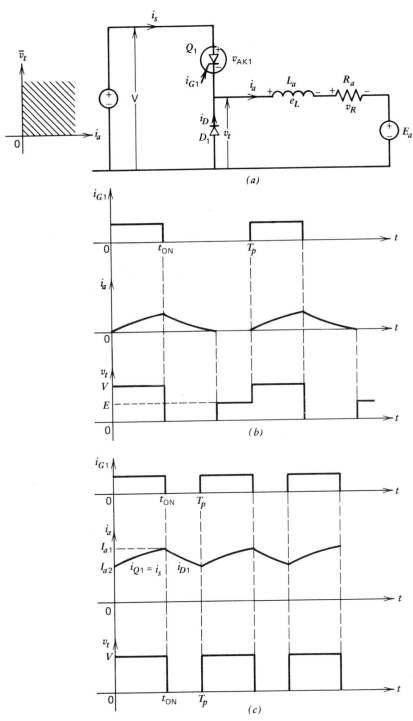

Fig. 5.2. Basic principles of a Class A, step-down, single-quadrant chopper.

the armature current would increase until it reached the steady-state magnitude expressed by

$$i_a = \frac{V - E_a}{R_a} \text{ A} \tag{5.1}$$

The average current in the armature circuit can be controlled by commutating thyristor Q_1 before the current has reached the value in Eq. 5.1 and allowing it to decay through diode D_1 either to zero, as shown in Fig. 5.2b, or to some lower value than it had attained while Q_1 was conducting (Fig. 5.2c). If this process of turning Q_1 on and off is repeated at regular intervals, the average value of i_a is controlled. The corresponding waveform of v_t illustrates the reason for the popular name "chopper" (dc-to-dc converter).

The requirement that Q_1 shall be turned off while still subjected to a positive terminal pd v_{AK1} has not been met in rectifiers in which each thyristor is commutated by the next in sequence to be turned on. Auxiliary circuitry is required to commutate Q_1 by momentarily subjecting it to a negative terminal pd after the gating signal i_{G1} has been removed. This procedure is called *forced commutation* and may be done in a variety of ways, the details of which are not given here. The fact that Q_1 can be commutated is indicated by enclosing its circuit symbol in a circle. It is therefore assumed that as the gating current i_{G1} is removed the commutation circuit comes into operation and Q_1 is turned off in a time interval that is negligibly small in the scale of the diagrams in Fig. 5.2.

The average value of i_a may be controlled in three different ways. These are

(a) by varying the duration of t_{ON} before Q_1 is commutated and keeping the period T_p of the pulse constant; this is pulse-width modulation;

(b) by varying T_p and keeping t_{ON} constant; this is frequency modulation;

(c) by a combination of the methods in (a) and (b).

If t_{ON} is short in relation to T_p (Fig. 5.2b) discontinuous current will result and the current waveform will consist of a series of pulses that, when steady-state conditions have been reached, will be identical. If t_{ON} is longer in relation to T_p the load current will not decay to zero during the interval $t_{ON} < t < T_p$ but will merely decrease until Q_1 is again turned on. In the steady state, therefore, the current will vary in a regular manner (Fig. 5.2c). The pulsing frequency of the chopper is high (typically 200–500 Hz), so that even with armature circuits of low inductance the no-load losses of motor and mechanism result in continuous current in the steady state. Under transient conditions, however, current may become discontinuous.[6]

Because continuous-current operation will normally occur, this is the condition that must be analyzed when a system is to be designed. For the right-hand mesh of the circuit in Fig. 5.2a

$$v_t = e_L + v_R + E_a \text{ V} \tag{5.2}$$

from which

$$\frac{di_a}{dt} + \frac{R_a i_a}{L_a} = \frac{v_t - E_a}{L_a} \text{ A/s} \tag{5.3}$$

When Q_1 is turned on at $t = 0$, $v_t = V$ and $i_a = I_{a2}$. From Eq. 5.3 and these initial conditions

$$i_a = \frac{V - E_a}{R_a}(1 - \varepsilon^{-t/\tau_a}) + I_{a2}\varepsilon^{-t/\tau_a} \text{ A} \qquad 0 \le t \le t_{\text{ON}} \text{ s} \tag{5.4}$$

where

$$\tau_a = \frac{L_a}{R_a} \text{ s} \tag{5.5}$$

At $t = t_{\text{ON}}$ when Q_1 is commutated

$$i_a = I_{a1} = \frac{V - E_a}{R_a}(1 - \varepsilon^{-t_{\text{ON}}/\tau_a}) + I_{a2}\varepsilon^{-t_{\text{ON}}/\tau_a} \text{ A} \tag{5.6}$$

When Q_1 is commutated i_a continues to freewheel through diode D_1 so that $v_t = 0$; from Eq. 5.3

$$\frac{di_a}{dt'} + \frac{R_a i_a}{L_a} = -\frac{E_a}{L_a} \text{ A/s} \tag{5.7}$$

where

$$t' = t - t_{\text{ON}} \text{ s} \tag{5.8}$$

At $t' = 0$, $i_a = I_{a1}$. From Eq. 5.7 and these initial conditions

$$i_a = -\frac{E_a}{R_a}\left(1 - \varepsilon^{-t'/\tau_a}\right) + I_{a1}\varepsilon^{-t'/\tau_a} \text{ A} \qquad t_{\text{ON}} \le t \le T_p \text{ s} \tag{5.9}$$

At $t' = t - t_{\text{ON}}$ or $t = T_p$ when Q_1 is again turned on

$$i_a = I_{a2} = -\frac{E_a}{R_a}(1 - \varepsilon^{-(T_p - t_{\text{ON}})/\tau_a}) + I_{a1}\varepsilon^{-(T_p - t_{\text{ON}})/\tau_a} \text{ A} \tag{5.10}$$

Equations 5.6 and 5.10 may be solved simultaneously to yield

$$I_{a1} = \frac{V}{R_a} \cdot \frac{(1 - \varepsilon^{-t_{\text{ON}}/\tau_a})}{(1 - \varepsilon^{-T_p/\tau_a})} - \frac{E_a}{R_a} \text{ A} \tag{5.11}$$

$$I_{a2} = \frac{V}{R_a} \cdot \frac{(\varepsilon^{t_{\text{ON}}/\tau_a} - 1)}{(\varepsilon^{T_p/\tau_a} - 1)} - \frac{E_a}{R_a} \text{ A} \tag{5.12}$$

When Q_1 is continuously turned on so that $t_{ON} = T_p$ both I_{a1} and I_{a2} have the value of i_a given by Eq. 5.1.

The waveform of v_t in Fig. 5.2c may be described by the Fourier series

$$v_t = \bar{v}_t + \sum_{n=1}^{\infty} c_n \sin(n\omega_0 t + \vartheta_n) \text{ V} \tag{5.13}$$

where ω_0 is the angular chopping frequency defined by

$$\omega_0 = \frac{2\pi}{T_p} \text{ rad/s} \tag{5.14}$$

and the average value of v_t is

$$\bar{v}_t = \frac{t_{ON}}{T_p} V \text{ V} \tag{5.15}$$

Use of the method of discontinuities discussed in Appendix A yields

$$c_n = \frac{2V}{n\pi} \sin \frac{n\omega_0 t_{ON}}{2} \text{ V} \tag{5.16}$$

and

$$\vartheta_n = \frac{\pi}{2} - \frac{n\omega_0 t_{ON}}{2} \text{ rad} \tag{5.17}$$

From Eq. 5.16 the amplitudes of the harmonics are greatest when $t_{ON} - T_p/2$ s. The harmonic of lowest frequency is the first or fundamental for which the maximum amplitude is thus $2V/\pi$ V.

The average value of the armature current is

$$i_a = \frac{\bar{v}_t - E_a}{R_a} = \frac{1}{R_a}\left[\frac{t_{ON}}{T_p}V - E_a\right] \text{ A} \tag{5.18}$$

Assuming that $\omega_0 L_a \gg R_a$, the fundamental component of the armature current from Eqs. 5.13, 5.16 and 5.17 is

$$i_{a1} = \frac{2V}{\pi\omega_0 L_a} \sin \frac{\omega_0 t_{ON}}{2} \sin\left(\omega_0 t - \frac{\omega_0 t_{ON}}{2}\right) \text{ A} \tag{5.19}$$

The rms value of this fundamental component is

$$I_{R1} = \frac{\sqrt{2}\,V}{\pi\omega_0 L_a} \sin \frac{\omega_0 t_{ON}}{2} \text{ A} \tag{5.20}$$

The armature current can be described to a good approximation by the sum of the two components given in Eqs. 5.18 and 5.19. The rms armature current is then

$$I_R = \left[\left(\bar{i}_a \right)^2 + I_{R1}^2 \right]^{1/2} \text{ A} \tag{5.21}$$

If necessary the magnitude of this rms current may be reduced by additional inductance in the armature circuit but only a limited improvement in motor performance is obtained.

The relation between the source current and the armature current is defined by

$$i_s = i_a \text{ A} \qquad 0 \le t < t_{ON} \text{ s}$$

$$i_s = 0 \qquad t_{ON} < t \le T_p \text{ s} \tag{5.22}$$

The harmonics of the waveform of i_s could be obtained from those of i_a but a good approximation to the line-current harmonics may be obtained by assuming that, because $\omega_0 L_a \gg R_a$, the armature current is constant at magnitude $\bar{i}_a$. In these circumstances the source current becomes a series of pulses of magnitude $\bar{i}_a$, duration t_{ON}, and periodic time T_p. This may be analyzed in the same way as the waveform of v_t, yielding an approximate expression for the line current

$$i_s = \frac{t_{ON}}{T_p} \bar{i}_a + \sum_{n=1}^{\infty} \frac{2\bar{i}_a}{n\pi} \sin \frac{n\omega_0 t_{ON}}{2} \sin\left(n\omega_0 t + \frac{n\omega_0 t_{ON}}{2} \right) \text{ A} \tag{5.23}$$

Once again, the amplitudes of the harmonics are greatest when $t_{ON} = T_p/2$ s.

If the further assumption is made that i_s may be represented approximately by the average value and first harmonic of the expression in Eq. 5.23 the rms source current is

$$I_s = \bar{i}_a \left[\left(\frac{t_{ON}}{T_p} \right)^2 + \left(\frac{\sqrt{2}}{\pi} \sin \frac{\omega_0 t_{ON}}{2} \right)^2 \right]^{1/2} \text{ A} \tag{5.24}$$

The average value of i_s in Eq. 5.23 is

$$\bar{i}_s = \frac{t_{ON}}{T_p} \bar{i}_a \text{ A} \tag{5.25}$$

From Eqs. 5.15 and 5.25 it may then be seen that

$$P_a = \bar{v}_t \bar{i}_a = \frac{t_{ON}}{T_p} V \bar{i}_a = V \bar{i}_s = P_{in} \text{ W} \tag{5.26}$$

Example 5.1

The 230-V, 500-rpm, frame-size 283 motor in Appendix B is driven with its armature supplied from a Class A chopper and a 240-V, dc source. The field current is held constant at the value that gives rated operation on 230 V. The chopping frequency is constant at 500 Hz. The minimum load torque anticipated is 5 N · m.

(a) Determine the value of t_{ON} for minimum load torque at 500 rpm.
(b) Determine whether i_a is continuous for the conditions in (a).
(c) Determine the minimum value of t_{ON} for which the current is continuous at 500 rpm and the corresponding coupling torque.

Solution

For this motor I_{rated} = 4.1 A, R_a = 7.56 Ω, L_a = 55.0 mH. For rated operating conditions

$$\text{speed} = 500 \text{ rpm} = 52.36 \text{ rad/s}$$

$$k\Phi = \frac{E_a}{\Omega_m} = \frac{230 - 7.56 \times 4.1}{52.36} = \frac{199.0}{52.36} = 3.801 \text{ N} \cdot \text{m/A}$$

$$\text{armature power in} = 230 \times 4.1 = 943 \text{ W}$$

$$\text{coupling power out} = 746 \text{ W}$$

$$R_a I_{\text{rated}}^2 = 7.56 \times 4.1^2 = 127 \text{ W}$$

$$\text{rotational losses} = (943 - 746 - 127) = 70 \text{ W}$$

At 500 rpm

$$T_{\text{LOSS}} = \frac{70}{52.36} = 1.337 \text{ N} \cdot \text{m}$$

(a) For minimum load torque at 500 rpm the average internal torque is

$$\bar{T} = 5 + 1.337 = 6.337 \text{ N} \cdot \text{m}$$

$$\bar{i}_a = \frac{6.337}{3.801} = 1.667 \text{ A}$$

$$\bar{v}_t = 199.0 + 7.56 \times 1.667 = 211.6 \text{ V}$$

On the assumption that current is continuous

$$t_{\text{ON}} = \frac{\bar{v}_t}{V} T_p = \frac{211.6}{240} \times \frac{1}{500} = 1.763 \times 10^{-3} \text{ s}$$

(b) The boundary condition between continuous and discontinuous current arises when $I_{a2} = 0$ in Fig. 5.2c.

$$\tau_a = \frac{L_a}{R_a} = \frac{55 \times 10^{-3}}{7.56} = 7.275 \times 10^{-3} \text{ s}$$

Substitution of the known value for all other quantities than t_{ON} in Eq. 5.12 yields

$$0 = \frac{240}{7.56} \frac{\left(\varepsilon^{10^3 t_{ON}/7.275} - 1\right)}{\left(\varepsilon^{2/7.275} - 1\right)} - \frac{199.0}{7.56}$$

from which

$$t_{ON} = 1.695 \times 10^{-3} \text{ s}$$

Because this is less than the value of t_{ON} obtained in (a), the assumption that current is continuous is justified.

(c) The value of t_{ON} obtained in (b) is the minimum giving continuous current. Under these conditions

$$T_p = \frac{1}{500} = 2 \times 10^{-3} \text{ s}$$

$$\bar{v}_t = \frac{t_{ON}}{T} V = \frac{1.695}{2} \times 240 = 203.4 \text{ V}$$

$$\bar{i}_a = \frac{203.4 - 199.0}{7.56} = 0.582 \text{ A}$$

$$\bar{T} = 0.582 \times 3.801 = 2.212 \text{ N} \cdot \text{m}$$

minimum coupling torque $= 2.212 - 1.337 = 0.875 \text{ N} \cdot \text{m}$

Example 5.2

The 230-V, 1750-rpm, frame-size 288 motor in Appendix B is driven with its armature supplied from a Class A chopper and a 240-V, dc source. The field current is held constant at the value giving rated operation on 230 V. The chopping frequency is constant at 500 Hz. If the average armature current is equal to the rated value and t_{ON} is at the setting that gives the largest harmonic content determine

(a) the speed of the motor;
(b) the rms armature current;
(c) the armature current and line-current ripple factors defined as

$$\text{ripple factor} = \frac{\text{rms value of fundamental}}{\text{average value of current}}$$

Solution

For this motor $I_{rated} = 74$ A, $R_a = 0.180$ Ω. For rated operating conditions

$$\text{speed} = 1750 \text{ rpm} = 183.3 \text{ rad/s}$$

$$k\Phi = \frac{230 - 0.180 \times 74}{183.3} = 1.182 \text{ N} \cdot \text{m/A}$$

(a) For $t_{ON} = T_p/2$

$$\bar{v}_t = 0.5 \times 240 = 120 \text{ V}$$

$$\bar{i}_a = 74 = \frac{120 - E_a}{0.180} \text{ A}$$

$$E_a = 106.7 \text{ V}$$

$$\Omega_m = \frac{106.7}{1.182} = 90.27 \text{ rad/s} = 862.0 \text{ rpm}$$

(b) The angular chopping frequency is

$$\omega_0 = 2\pi \times 500 = 1000\pi \text{ rad/s}$$

At $t_{ON} = T_p/2$ from Eq. 5.20

$$I_{R1} = \frac{\sqrt{2} \times 240}{\pi_2 \times 2.93} = 11.74 \text{ A}$$

$$I_R = (74^2 + 11.74^2)^{1/2} = 74.93 \text{ A}$$

(c) The armature-current ripple factor is

$$\frac{11.74}{74} = 0.1586$$

The average value of source current is

$$\bar{i}_s = \frac{t_{ON}}{T_p} \bar{i}_a = \frac{74}{2} = 37 \text{ A}$$

From Eq. 5.23 the rms value of the lowest harmonic component of source current at $t_{ON} = T_p/2$ is

$$I_{Rs1} = \frac{\sqrt{2}\,\bar{i}_a}{\pi} = \frac{\sqrt{2} \times 74}{\pi} = 33.31 \text{ A}$$

The source-current ripple factor is

$$\frac{33.31}{37} = 0.9003$$

This result confirms the desirability of a filter at the chopper input.

5.3. CLASS B CHOPPER

A Class B chopper steps up the output terminal pd of a regenerating motor to feed energy back to the dc source. It may be formed from the components of the Class A chopper rearranged by switching. Thus in a system in which a switching interval between driving the motor by Class A action and regenerating is acceptable the components and firing circuit of the Class A converter will suffice for both purposes. A typical application is the chopper drive of a subway train.

The basic power circuit for Class B operation is shown in Fig. 5.3a. The symbols and reference directions of the variables are the same as in Fig. 5.2, so that the system is operating in the second quadrant of the $\bar{v}_t$-i_a diagram and $v_t = v_{AK2}$. Operation with discontinuous current is possible, but once again only continuous-current operation in the steady state is analyzed.

If thyristor Q_2 is never turned on and $V > E_a$ i_a and i_s are zero; therefore the circuit is completely inactive. If Q_2 is turned on and off during regular intervals of period T_p emf E_a stores energy in inductance L_a whenever the thyristor is conducting and part of that stored energy is delivered to source V by current through D_2 when Q_2 is commutated. If the gating signals to Q_2 are such as are shown in Fig. 5.3 the operation of the circuit may be analyzed to give the waveforms of the other variables. For reasons that will become apparent when the Class C chopper is described *the interval during which D_2 conducts is designated t_{ON}*. Thus a cycle of operation commences at $t = 0$ in Fig. 5.3 at the instant that Q_2 is *commutated*.

At $t = 0$ let i_a have negative magnitude I_{a2}. For interval $0 < t < t_{ON}$ D_2 conducts and $v_{AK2} = V$. During this interval

$$\frac{di_a}{dt} + \frac{R_a i_a}{L_a} = \frac{V - E_a}{L_a} \text{ A/s} \tag{5.27}$$

The solution to Eq. 5.27 for the stated initial conditions is

$$i_a = \frac{(V - E_a)}{R_a}(1 - \varepsilon^{-t/\tau_a}) + I_{a2}\varepsilon^{-t/\tau_a} \text{ A} \tag{5.28}$$

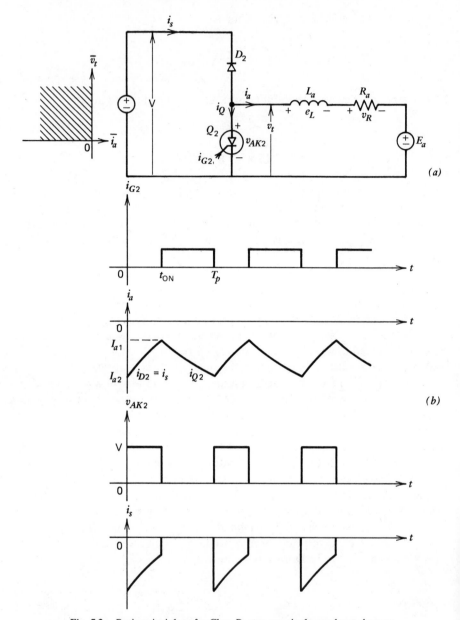

Fig. 5.3. Basic principles of a Class B, step-up, single-quadrant chopper.

138

At $t = t_{ON}$ I_a has reached a magnitude I_{a1}, where $I_{a2} < I_{a1} < 0$. Thus from Eq. 5.28

$$I_{a1} = \frac{(V - E_a)}{R_a}\left(1 - \varepsilon^{-t_{ON}/\tau_a}\right) + I_{a2}\varepsilon^{-t_{ON}/\tau_a} \text{ A} \qquad (5.29)$$

At $t = t_{ON}$ Q_2 is turned on and at t_{ON}^+ v_{AK2} becomes zero and $i_a = I_{a1}$.
  During the interval $t_{ON} < t < T_p$

$$\frac{di_a}{dt'} + \frac{R_a i_a}{L_a} = -\frac{E_a}{L_a} \text{ A/s} \qquad (5.30)$$

where

$$t' = t - t_{ON} \text{ s} \qquad (5.31)$$

The solution to Eq. 5.30 for the stated initial conditions is

$$i_a = -\frac{E_a}{R_a}\left(1 - \varepsilon^{-t'/\tau_a}\right) + I_{a1}\varepsilon^{-t'/\tau_a} \text{ A} \qquad (5.32)$$

Thus at the end of the cycle when $t = T_p$, or $t' = T_p - t_{ON}$, i_a must have returned to its initial value I_{a2}; from Eq. 5.32

$$I_{a2} = -\frac{E_a}{R_a}\left(1 - \varepsilon^{-(T_p - t_{ON})/\tau_a}\right) + I_{a1}\varepsilon^{-(T_p - t_{ON})/\tau_a} \text{ A} \qquad (5.33)$$

Equations 5.29 and 5.33 are identical to Eqs. 5.6 and 5.10; therefore they may be solved simultaneously to yield Eqs. 5.11 and 5.12. It must be borne in mind, however, that for the step-up chopper currents i_a and i_s are always negative and operation takes place in the second quadrant of the $\bar{v}_t-i_a$ diagram.
  Fourier analysis of the waveforms of currents i_a and i_s may be carried out as for Class A operation.

5.4. CLASS C TWO-QUADRANT CHOPPER

Although switching from a Class A to a Class B configuration is a satisfactory method of obtaining regenerative braking for some applications, in others a smooth transition from driving to braking is essential. This is frequently the case in machine-tool drives, for example. A combination of the circuits of Figs. 5.2 and 5.3 provides the required drive and is shown in Fig. 5.4a.
  In the circuit of Fig. 5.4a each of the thyristors may be commutated immediately after its gating signal has been removed. It is clear that both thyristors may not be turned on simultaneously because that would short-circuit source V. They are turned on alternately, as shown by the gating signal

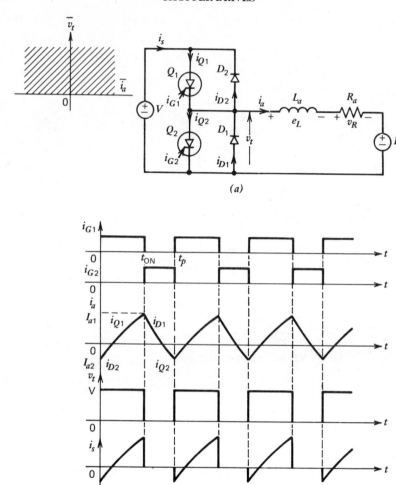

Fig. 5.4.   Basic principles of a Class C, two-quadrant chopper.

waveforms in Fig. 5.4*b*, and a short interval (typically about 100 μs), too brief to be shown on the time scale in Fig. 5.4*b*, is allowed to elapse between the removal of one signal and the application of the other. This gives time for the commutated thyristor to recover its forward-blocking capability.

For first-quadrant operation, Q_1 and D_1 perform the functions discussed in Section 5.2, and if the average armature current $\bar{i}_a$ is high enough Q_2 and D_2 do not conduct, even though Q_2 receives a gating signal. The waveforms of v_t and i_a in this case are shown in Fig. 5.2*c*.

For second-quadrant operation Q_2 and D_2 perform the functions discussed in Section 5.3, and if the average load current $\bar{i}_a$ has a sufficiently large negative value Q_1 and D_1 do not conduct, even though Q_1 receives a gating signal. The waveforms of v_t and i_a in this case are shown in Fig. 5.3*b*.

The circuit parameters and value of t_{ON} may be such as would result in discontinuous current in the single-quadrant step-down chopper. Current in the Class C chopper, however, cannot be discontinuous because under these conditions Q_2 and D_2 conduct for part of the cycle. When the current in D_1 falls to zero emf E_a drives negative current through Q_2 to store energy in inductance L_a. When Q_2 is commutated the fall in this stored energy induces a negative emf e_L, which, in conjunction with emf E_a, supplies energy to source V until the negative current becomes zero and the energy in inductance L_a is exhausted. Positive load current i_a then resumes through Q_1. The device current for each part of the cycle is indicated on the waveform of i_a in Fig. 5.4b. The waveform of source current i_s is also shown.

The analysis of Section 5.2 may be applied directly to this two-quadrant chopper, the only new feature being that I_{a1} and I_{a2} in Eqs. 5.11 and 5.12 may be positive or negative. The quadrant in which the converter is operating may be determined by Eq. 5.15, which states

$$\bar{v}_t = \frac{t_{ON}}{T_p} V \text{ V} \tag{5.34}$$

If $\bar{v}_t > E_a$ then $\bar{i}_a > 0$ and net energy is delivered to the armature circuit. On the other hand, if $\bar{v}_t < E_a$ then $\bar{i}_a < 0$ and the net energy flow is to source V. When $t_{ON} = T_p$ and Q_1 conducts continuously

$$\bar{i}_a = I_{a1} = I_{a2} = \frac{V - E_a}{R_a} \text{ A} \tag{5.35}$$

When $t_{ON} = 0$ and Q_2 conducts continuously

$$\bar{i}_a = I_{a1} = I_{a2} = -\frac{E_a}{R_a} \text{ A} \tag{5.36}$$

but this is a state in which all regenerated energy is dissipated in the armature-circuit resistance.

Because the thyristors and diodes are considered ideal,

$$V\bar{i}_s = \bar{v}_t\bar{i}_a \text{ W} \tag{5.37}$$

The results of the Fourier analysis in Section 5.2 may also be applied to the Class C converter.

5.5.   CLASS D TWO-QUADRANT CHOPPER

The basic power circuit of the Class D chopper is shown in Fig. 5.5. There is no advantage to using this converter as a source for a dc motor armature because first and second quadrant or four-quadrant operation is required for

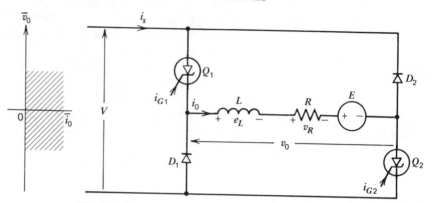

Fig. 5.5. Power circuit of a Class D, two-quadrant chopper.

that purpose. It is of advantage, however, in controlling the field current of a dc (or synchronous) machine when rapid change of that current is required because it can short-circuit its load circuit and rapidly reduce the field current. It is also useful as a dc source for other converters, notably the current-source inverter. Thus, although a source of emf is included in the load circuit in Fig. 5.5, there may not be an emf present.

The operation of the circuit may be understood with the help of the waveforms in Fig. 5.6a and b. It will be noted that the two thyristors are turned on alternately, their gating signals terminating at fixed points on the time axis and commencing at controllable points; the delay time for thyristor Q_1 is designated t_α. If both thyristors are continuously turned on the load current rises to a constant magnitude expressed by

$$i_O = \frac{V - E}{R} \text{ A} \tag{5.38}$$

The periodic time of the gating signals is T_p and there are two modes of operation: one for which $t_\alpha < T_p/2$ and the two gating signals overlap; the other for which $t_\alpha > T_p/2$ and only one thyristor is turned on at any instant. These modes of operation are analyzed for continuous current i_O, although each may result in discontinuous current.

5.5.1. Mode 1 Operation: $t_\alpha < T_p/2$

For steady-state operation in this mode it is necessary that $V > E$. When both thyristors are turned on source pd V is applied to the load circuit and current i_O increases. When only one thyristor is turned on that thyristor and one of the diodes short-circuit the load branch and provide a path in which some of the energy stored in inductance L may be dissipated in maintaining a decreasing load current i_O. Because one cycle of the load-circuit variables takes place in

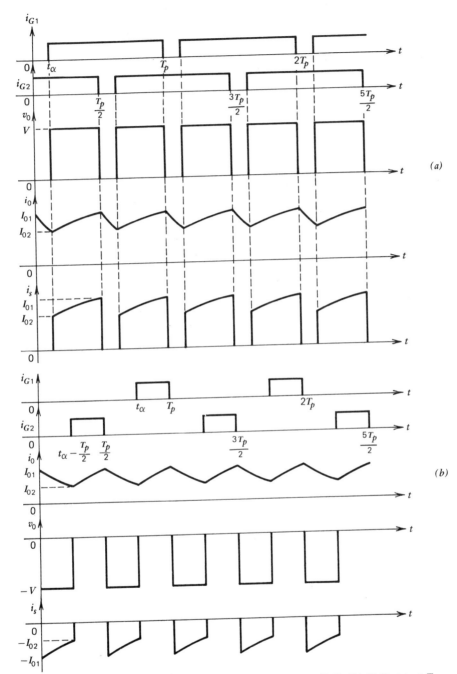

Fig. 5.6. Waveforms of the variables in Fig. 5.5. (a) $0 < t_\alpha < T_p/2$; (b) $T_p/2 < t_\alpha < T_p$.

time $T_p/2$, two intervals are to be considered. The first is interval $0 < t < t_\alpha$. Continuous current is assumed; therefore at $t = 0$ let $i_O = I_{O1}$. Only thyristor Q_2 is turned on and consequently current flows through Q_2 and D_1; the equation for the circuit mesh is

$$Ri_O = \frac{Ldi_O}{dt} + E = 0 \text{ V} \tag{5.39}$$

For the stated initial conditions

$$i_O = -\frac{E}{R}(1 - \varepsilon^{-t/\tau}) + I_{O1}\varepsilon^{-t/\tau} \text{ A} \qquad 0 < t < t_\alpha \text{ s} \tag{5.40}$$

where

$$\tau = \frac{L}{R} \text{ s} \tag{5.41}$$

At $t = t_\alpha$, $i_O = I_{O2}$ and substitution in Eq. 5.40 yields

$$I_{O2} = -\frac{E}{R}(1 - \varepsilon^{-t_\alpha/\tau}) + I_{O1}\varepsilon^{-t_\alpha/\tau} \text{ A} \tag{5.42}$$

The second interval is $t_\alpha < t < T_p/2$ s. Let

$$t' = t - t_\alpha \text{ s} \tag{5.43}$$

Both thyristors are turned on; consequently

$$Ri_O + \frac{Ldi_O}{dt'} + E = V \text{ V} \tag{5.44}$$

and for the stated initial conditions for this interval

$$i_O = \frac{(V - E)}{R}(1 - \varepsilon^{-t'/\tau}) + I_{O2}\varepsilon^{-t'/\tau} \text{ A} \qquad t_\alpha < t < \frac{T_p}{2} \text{ s} \tag{5.45}$$

At $t = T_p/2$ or $t' = T_p/2 - t_\alpha$, $i_O = I_{O1}$ and substitution in Eq. 5.45 yields

$$I_{O1} = \frac{(V - E)}{R}(1 - \varepsilon^{-(T_p/2-t_\alpha)/\tau}) + I_{O2}\varepsilon^{-(T_p/2-t_\alpha)/\tau} \text{ A} \tag{5.46}$$

Equations 5.42 and 5.46 may be solved simultaneously to yield

$$I_{O1} = \frac{V}{R} \cdot \frac{(1 - \varepsilon^{-(T_p/2-t_\alpha)/\tau})}{(1 - \varepsilon^{-T_p/2\tau})} - \frac{E}{R} \text{ A} \tag{5.47}$$

$$I_{O2} = \frac{V}{R} \cdot \frac{(\varepsilon^{(T_p/2-t_\alpha)/\tau} - 1)}{(\varepsilon^{T_p/2\tau} - 1)} - \frac{E}{R} \text{ A} \tag{5.48}$$

5.5.2. Mode 2 Operation: $T_p/2 < t_\alpha < T_p$

For steady-state operation in this mode it is necessary that $E < 0$ and $-E > V$. Thus steady-state operation with a passive load circuit, such as the field winding of a dc machine, is not possible in this mode.

Two thyristors are not turned on simultaneously. When either one is turned on the load circuit terminals are shorted and the load current builds up because $E < 0$. When neither thyristor is turned on the two diodes conduct and the load circuit supplies energy to source V. Again two intervals are to be considered. The first is $0 < t < t_\alpha - T_p/2$. Continuous current is assumed; therefore at $t = 0$, $i_O = I_{O1}$. No thyristor is turned on and

$$Ri_O + \frac{L\,di_O}{dt} + E = -V \text{ V} \qquad (5.49)$$

For the stated initial conditions of this interval

$$i_O = \frac{-(V+E)}{R}(1 - \varepsilon^{-t/\tau}) + I_{O1}\varepsilon^{-t/\tau} \text{ A} \qquad 0 < t < \frac{T_p}{2} - \alpha \text{ s} \quad (5.50)$$

At $t = t_\alpha - T_p/2$, $i_O = I_{O2}$ and substitution in Eq. 5.50 yields

$$I_{O2} = \frac{-(V+E)}{R}(1 - \varepsilon^{-(t_\alpha - T_p/2)/\tau}) + I_{O1}\varepsilon^{-(t_\alpha - T_p/2)/\tau} \text{ A} \quad (5.51)$$

The second interval is $(t_\alpha - T_p/2) < t < T_p/2$. Let

$$t' = t - \left(t_\alpha - \frac{T_p}{2}\right) \text{ s} \qquad (5.52)$$

Thyristor Q_2 is turned on and current flows through Q_2 and D_1; the equation for the mesh is

$$Ri_O + \frac{L\,di_O}{dt'} + E = 0 \text{ V} \qquad (5.53)$$

Because at $t' = 0$, $i_O = I_{O2}$, for this interval

$$i_O = -\frac{E}{R}(1 - \varepsilon^{-t'/\tau}) + I_{O2}\varepsilon^{-t'/\tau} \text{ A} \qquad \left(t_\alpha - \frac{\pi}{2}\right) < t < \frac{T_p}{2} \text{ s} \quad (5.54)$$

At $t = T_p/2$ or $t' = T_p - t_\alpha$, $i_O = I_{O1}$ and substitution in Eq. 5.54 yields

$$I_{O1} = -\frac{E}{R}(1 - \varepsilon^{-(T_p - t_\alpha)/\tau}) + I_{O2}\varepsilon^{-(T_p - t_\alpha)/\tau} \text{ A} \qquad (5.55)$$

Equations 5.51 and 5.55 may be solved simultaneously to yield

$$I_{O1} = -\frac{V}{R} \cdot \frac{\left(\varepsilon^{(t_\alpha - T_p/2)/\tau} - 1\right)}{\left(\varepsilon^{T_p/2\tau} - 1\right)} - \frac{E}{R} \quad \text{A} \tag{5.56}$$

$$I_{O2} = -\frac{V}{R} \cdot \frac{\left(1 - \varepsilon^{-(t_\alpha - T_p/2)/\tau}\right)}{\left(1 - \varepsilon^{-T_p/2\tau}\right)} - \frac{E}{R} \quad \text{A} \tag{5.57}$$

5.5.3. Power in the Load and Source Circuits

The waveforms of v_O in Fig. 5.6a and b may be described by the Fourier series

$$v_O = \bar{v}_O + \sum_{n=1}^{\infty} c_n \sin(n\omega_0 t + \vartheta_n) \quad \text{V} \tag{5.58}$$

where n is a positive integer and ω_0 is defined by

$$\omega_0 = \frac{4\pi}{T_p} \quad \text{rad/s} \tag{5.59}$$

The definition in eq. 5.59 is based on the fact that one cycle of v_O takes place in $T_p/2$ s.

The average value of v_O is

$$\bar{v}_O = \left(1 - \frac{2t_\alpha}{T_p}\right)V \quad \text{V} \tag{5.60}$$

By the usual methods

$$c_n = \frac{4V}{n\pi} \sin^2 \frac{n\omega_0 t_\alpha}{2} = \frac{4V}{n\pi} \sin^2 \frac{2n\pi t_\alpha}{T_p} \quad \text{V} \tag{5.61}$$

$$\vartheta_n = \frac{\pi}{2} - \frac{n\omega_0 t_\alpha}{2} = \frac{\pi}{2} - \frac{2n\pi t_\alpha}{T_p} \quad \text{rad} \tag{5.62}$$

The amplitude of the fundamental frequency in the waveform of v_O is

$$c_1 = \frac{4V}{\pi} \sin \frac{\omega_0 t_\alpha}{2} = \frac{4V}{\pi} \sin \frac{2\pi t_\alpha}{T_p} \quad \text{V} \tag{5.63}$$

Amplitude c_1 has its maximum value when $\omega_0 t_\alpha = \pi$ or 3π; that is, $t_\alpha/T_p = 0.25$ or 0.75. The second value in each case corresponds to operation in the fourth quadrant, as illustrated in Fig. 5.6b.

The average value of the load current is

$$i_O = \frac{\bar{v}_O - E}{R} = \frac{1}{R}\left[\left(1 - \frac{2t_\alpha}{T_p}\right)V - E\right] \text{ A} \tag{5.64}$$

Assuming that $\omega_0 L \gg R$, the rms value of the fundamental component of current is

$$I_{R1} = \frac{2\sqrt{2}\,V}{\pi\omega_0 L}\sin\frac{2\pi t_\alpha}{T_p} = \frac{VT_p}{\sqrt{2}\,\pi^2 L}\sin\frac{2\pi t_\alpha}{T_p} \text{ A} \tag{5.65}$$

The rms load current, to a close approximation, is

$$I_R = \left[\left(i_O\right)^2 + I_{R1}^2\right]^{1/2} \text{ A} \tag{5.66}$$

On the assumption that i_O is constant at magnitude $\bar{i}_O$, the waveform of the source current i_s is similar to that of v_O, the pulses of i_s having magnitude $\bar{i}_O$. This waveform may therefore be analyzed by the method already used with that of v_O. Thus by analogy with Eq. 5.60

$$\bar{i}_s = \left(1 - \frac{2t_\alpha}{T_p}\right)\bar{i}_O \text{ A} \tag{5.67}$$

and the output power is

$$P_O = \bar{v}_O \bar{i}_O = \left(1 + \frac{2t_\alpha}{T_p}\right)V\bar{i}_O = V\bar{i}_s = P_{in} \text{ W} \tag{5.68}$$

Example 5.3

A separately excited dc motor has a field winding with resistance $R_f = 190\ \Omega$ and inductance $L_f = 40.8$ H. The field is supplied from a 240-V, dc source and a Class D two-quadrant chopper. The periodic time of the gating signals $T_p = 1/400$ s. If the motor is running in the steady state with an average field current of 0.9 A determine the (approx.) rms field current and the average and rms source current.

Solution

The average field current is $\bar{i}_f = 0.9$ A. Because there is no emf in this load circuit, from Eq. 5.64

$$i_f = \frac{1}{R_f}\left(1 - \frac{t_\alpha}{T_p}\right)V$$

where $T_p = 1/400$ s. Thus

$$\frac{t_\alpha}{T_p} = \left(1 - \frac{190 \times 0.9}{240}\right) = 0.2875$$

From Eq. 5.65 the rms value of the fundamental component of field current is

$$I_{R1} = \frac{240}{\sqrt{2}\,\pi^2 \times 40.8 \times 400}\sin(2\pi \times 0.2875) = 1.02 \times 10^{-3}\text{ A}$$

This is negligible in comparison with $\bar{i}_f$; therefore the rms value of the field current is

$$I_R = 0.9\text{ A}$$

From Eq. 5.67 the average value of the source current is

$$\bar{i}_s = \left(1 - \frac{2t_\alpha}{T_p}\right)\bar{i}_O = (1 - 2 \times 0.2875)0.9 = 0.3825\text{ A}$$

Assuming that the source current consists of pulses of amplitude $\bar{i}_O$, by analogy with Eq. 5.63 the rms value of the fundamental component of source current is

$$I_{Rs1} = \frac{1}{\sqrt{2}} \cdot \frac{4\bar{i}_O}{\pi}\sin\frac{2\pi t_\alpha}{T_p}$$

$$= \frac{1}{\sqrt{2}} \times \frac{4 \times 0.9}{\pi}\sin(2\pi \times 0.2875) = 0.7879\text{ A}$$

The approximate rms source current is thus

$$I_{Rs} = (0.3825^2 + 0.7879^2)^{1/2} = 0.8758\text{ A}$$

This result clearly shows the need for an input filter.

5.6. CLASS E FOUR-QUADRANT CHOPPER

The power circuit of a chopper that can operate in all four quadrants of the $\bar{v}_t - \bar{i}_a$ diagram is shown in Fig. 5.7a. If thyristor Q_4 is turned on continuously the antiparallel-connected pair of devices Q_4 and D_3 constitute a short circuit. Thyristor Q_3 may not be turned on at the same time as Q_4 because that would short circuit source V. Moreover, because under these conditions the terminal

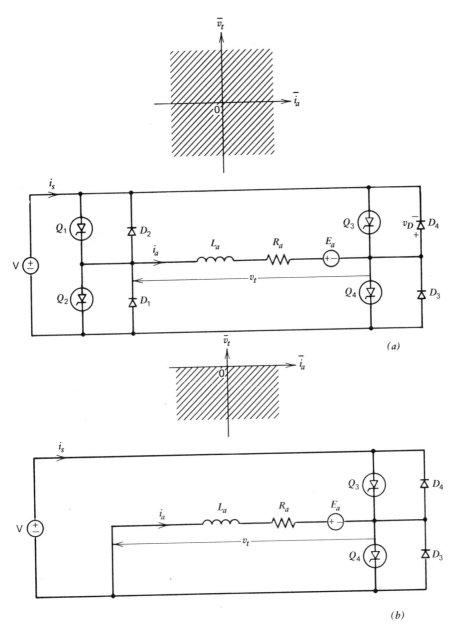

Fig. 5.7. Basic principles of the Class E, four-quadrant chopper.

pd of diode D_4 is always negative, the pair of devices Q_3 and D_4 is equivalent to an open circuit. Continuous turn-on of Q_4 thus produces a circuit equivalent to that of Fig. 5.4a and operation in the first and second quadrants is possible.

If, on the other hand, thyristor Q_2 is turned on continuously the equivalent circuit in Fig. 5.7b results. In this circuit $\bar{v}_t$ is negative and operation in the third and fourth quadrants is possible.

The analysis of Section 5.4 may be applied to this converter, which could be considered equally well as a combination of the circuit in Fig. 5.5 with one of the same configuration but giving a negative value of i_a.

Example 5.4

The 230-V, 1750-rpm, frame-size 366 motor in Appendix B is separately excited and driving a pure inertia load at 1500 rpm. The armature circuit, resistance 0.067 Ω, is supplied from a 240-V source by a Class E four-quadrant chopper. The chopping frequency is 400 Hz. The field current is held constant at a value for which $k\Phi = 1.28$ N $\cdot$ m/A. It is required to reverse the motor and load as rapidly as possible from this steady-state condition until they are running at 500 rpm in the reverse direction. Motor and load rotational losses may be neglected. The maximum permissible armature current is 290 A.

(a) Assuming that the circuit variables change the instant a change in thyristor gating signals is made, sketch and dimension the locus of the operating point in the speed-torque diagram for this transition.

(b) Sketch and dimension the gating signals for the four transistors in Fig. 5.7 in each of the following conditions:

At constant forward speed.
Immediately after deceleration begins.
At zero speed.
Immediately before reverse acceleration ends.
At constant reverse speed.

Solution

(a) Initial speed = $1500 \times 2\pi/60 = 157$ rad/s.
Initial torque = 0.
Decelerating torque = $k\Phi i_a = -1.28 \times 290 = -371$ N $\cdot$ m.
Final speed = $-500 \times 2\pi/60 = -52.4$ rad/s.
Final torque = 0.

The locus of the operating point is shown in Fig. 5.8a.

(b) At constant speed current is negligible and

$$E_a = \bar{v}_t = k\Phi\Omega_m = 1.28 \times 1500 \times \frac{2\pi}{60} = 201.1 \text{ V}$$

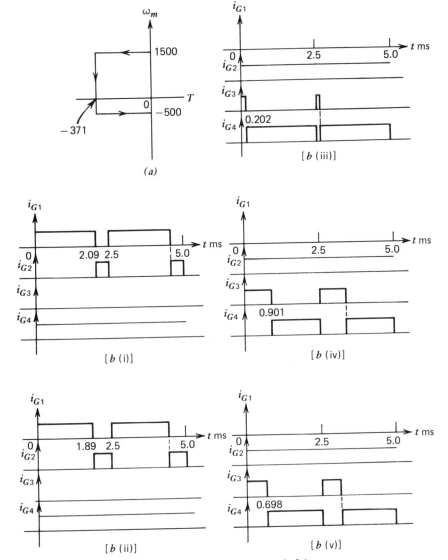

Fig. 5.8. Solution to Example 5.4.

Because $\bar{V}_t = t_{ON}/T_p$ V and $T = 1/400$ s,

$$t_{ON} = \frac{201.1}{400 \times 240} = 2.095 \text{ ms}$$

Operation is in the first quadrant; therefore Q_4 must be continuously gated and Q_3 continuously blocking. The gating signals are shown in

Fig. 5.8b(i). For the period of deceleration

$$i_a = -290 \text{ A}$$

To produce this current $\bar{v}_t$ must be reduced initially to

$$\bar{v}_t = E_a + R_a i_a = 201.1 - 0.067 \times 290 = 181.7 \text{ V}$$

Because $\bar{v}_t > 0$ and $i_a < 0$ the chopper is operating in the second quadrant. Thus when deceleration begins

$$t_{ON} = \frac{\bar{v}_t}{V} T_p = \frac{181.7}{240 \times 400} = 1.893 \text{ ms}$$

The gating signals are shown in Fig. 5.8b(ii). At zero speed $E_a = 0$ and

$$\bar{v}_t = R_a i_a = -0.067 \times 290 = -19.43 \text{ V}$$

Operation is now in the third quadrant, for which Q_2 must be continuously gated and Q_1 continuously blocking. Time t_{ON} now refers to the gating signal applied to thyristor Q_3:

$$t_{ON} = \left| \frac{-19.43}{240} \times \frac{1}{400} \right| = 0.2024 \text{ ms}$$

The gating signals are shown in Fig. 5.8b(iii). At the end of reverse acceleration operation is still in the third quadrant:

$$E_a = k\Phi\Omega_m = 1.28\left(-500 \times \frac{2\pi}{60} \right) = -67.02 \text{ V}$$

$$\bar{v}_t = E_a + R_a i_a = -67.02 - 0.067 \times 290 = -86.45 \text{ V}$$

$$t_{ON} = \left| \frac{-86.45}{240} \times \frac{1}{400} \right| = 0.9005 \text{ ms}$$

The gating signals are shown in Fig. 5.8b(iv). For driving at constant speed in the reverse direction the motor again takes negligible current and $\bar{v}_t = E_a$. Thus

$$t_{ON} = \left| \frac{-67.02}{240} \times \frac{1}{400} \right| = 0.6981 \text{ ms}$$

The gating signals are shown in Fig. 5.8b(v).

5.7. CHOPPER TRANSFER FUNCTIONS

In four of the classes of chopper discussed (the exception is Class D) the average output terminal pd $\bar{v}_t$ is proportional to t_{ON}. This linear relationship is expressed in Eq. 5.15, from which the gain of the converter may be expressed as

$$k = \frac{\Delta \bar{v}_t}{\Delta t_{ON}} = \frac{V}{T_p} \text{ V/s} \qquad (5.69)$$

For the Class D chopper $\bar{v}_O$ is governed by the value of t_α in an inverse linear relationship expressed in Eq. 5.60. From this equation the gain of the converter may be expressed as

$$k = \frac{\Delta \bar{v}_0}{-\Delta t_\alpha} = \frac{2V}{T_p} \text{ V/s} \qquad (5.70)$$

The effect of a change in t_{ON} or t_α is subject to a dead time, as shown in Figs. 5.2c and 5.6. This dead time may vary over the range $0 < t_d < T_p$ for all except Class D, for which $0 < t_\alpha < T_p/2$.

Thus t_d for any chopper of normal chopping frequency will be substantially smaller than that for a three-phase bridge rectifier. Once again, therefore, the effect of the dead time may be approximated by that of a time constant equal to the average dead time and the transfer function for a chopper may be written as

$$G(s) = \frac{k}{1 + s\bar{t}_d} \qquad (5.71)$$

5.8. CHOPPER SOURCE FILTERS

A simple filter that may be fitted in the dc supply line to reduce harmonics in the line is shown in Fig. 5.9. The filter output current may now be considered as the chopper "source" current, as distinct from the "line" current entering the filter.

If it is assumed that the inductance of the armature circuit is high enough to make i_a effectively constant and equal to $\bar{i}_a$, then from the waveform of i_a in Fig. 5.2 it may be seen that i_s consists of rectangular pulses of magnitude $\bar{i}_a$, duration t_{ON}, and frequency $1/T_p$. Thus

$$\bar{i}_s = \left(\frac{t_{ON}}{T_p} \right) \bar{i}_a \text{ A} \qquad (5.72)$$

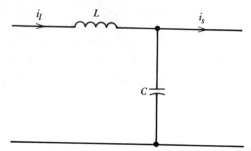

Fig. 5.9. Chopper source filter.

The relationship between the phasors of the nth harmonics of line and source current is, from Fig. 5.9,

$$\frac{\bar{I}_{ln}}{\bar{I}_{sn}} = \frac{\bar{Z}_L}{\bar{Z}_L + \bar{Z}_c} = \frac{1/j\omega_0 nC}{j\omega_0 nL + 1/j\omega_0 nC} = \frac{1}{1 - \omega_0^2 n^2 LC} \qquad (5.73)$$

where $\omega_0 = 2\pi/T_p$ and is the angular chopping frequency. For this ratio to be small it is necessary that $\omega_0^2 n^2 LC \gg 1$; that is

$$\frac{\omega_0^2}{\omega_f^2} \gg 1 \qquad (5.74)$$

where ω_f is the resonant frequency of the filter. If ω_f is to be small, then both inductor and capacitor must be made as large as possible. Their size will be limited by cost, weight, and the space available. If inequality 5.74 is satisfied the ratios of the harmonic amplitudes in the line and source currents are given approximately by

$$\frac{\hat{i}_{ln}}{\hat{i}_{sn}} = \frac{1}{\omega_0^2 n^2 LC} \qquad (5.75)$$

PROBLEMS

5.1. The 230-V, 1150-rpm, frame-size 365 motor in Appendix B has its armature supplied from a Class A chopper and a 300-V, dc source. The chopping frequency is constant at 250 Hz and the field current is set at the value for rated operation on a 230-V, dc source. Rotational loss torque may be assumed to be constant and increased by 10% when the motor is driven from the chopper. Rate of heat dissipation is independent of speed.

(a) Determine the maximum load torque that can be driven continuously with $t_{ON}/T_p = 0.5$ without overheating. Only the lowest harmonic of current need be considered.

(b) Determine the speed at which this torque is delivered.

5.2. The 230-V, 1150 rpm, frame-size 284 motor in Appendix B has its armature supplied from a Class A chopper and a 300-V, dc source. The chopping frequency is constant at 250 Hz and the field current is set at the value for rated operation on a 230-V, dc source. When the motor is driven from the rectifier the rotational loss torque T_{loss} varies according to the relationship

$$T_{loss} = \left(0.3 + \frac{0.8\Omega_m}{\Omega_{rated}}\right) T_{LOSS} \text{ N} \cdot \text{m}$$

where T_{LOSS} is the loss torque under rated operating conditions. The motor must deliver rated torque at all speeds. Rate of heat dissipation may be considered independent of speed and only the lowest harmonic of current need be taken into consideration.

(a) Plot curves of motor armature I^2R losses and total armature losses versus speed from standstill up to 1500 rpm, and determine over what speed range this drive may be operated without the losses exceeding those for rated operation.

(b) Repeat (a) with the addition of a 10 mH inductor in the motor armature circuit.

5.3. A drive comprised of a 230-V, dc motor and a Class A chopper supplied from a 300-V, dc source is required to operate continuously without overheating the motor at speeds of 100 to 1000 rpm and load torques anywhere in this speed range of 25 to 500 N · m. The chopping frequency is 250 Hz.

Select a suitable 1150 or 850 rpm motor from Appendix B for this application after considering its operation under the sets of conditions that would be expected to produce maximum heating of the motor. The following assumptions may be made:

(a) Field current is at the rated value.

(b) The rotational loss torque of the motor is directly proportional to speed.

(c) Only the lowest frequency harmonic of armature current need be considered.

(d) Heat dissipation is independent of speed.

5.4. The 230-V, 750-rpm, frame-size 286 motor in Appendix B is driven from a Class A chopper that may be switched to Class B configuration. The dc source is 250 V and the chopping frequency is 400 Hz. The motor is driving a load that possesses inertia and is developing rated torque at rated speed when the circuit is switched to provide regenerative braking which, after transients, produces negative rated torque at the coupling. It may be considered that the motor speed does not change during the time required for the switching operation and the establishment of a steady-state cycle of circuit variables in the Class B mode of operation before deceleration begins. Field excitation is not changed during switching. Determine

(a) t_{ON}, $\bar{i}_a$, I_{a1} and I_{a2} before switching;
(b) the same quantities as in (a) before deceleration begins.

5.5. The train of Example 1.2 is accelerated at 1.25 m/s² up to speed of 50 km/h, runs at that speed for 50 m, and then decelerates at 1.5 m/s² to a speed of 2 km/h by regenerative braking. The motors are driven from a 600-V, dc source with the armatures supplied by Class C choppers. Motor data are $J_m = 3.25$ kg · m², $R_a = 0.053\Omega$, and $k\Phi$ for rated operation = 6.58 N · m/A.

Draw curves of $\bar{i}_a$ and t_{ON}/T_p versus distance s for one of the motors and a curve of train speed v versus s on the same axes. The following assumptions should be made:

(a) Field flux is increased by 15% during acceleration and deceleration.
(b) Current is continuous at all speeds.
(c) Motor loss torque may be neglected.
(d) The train resistance formula in Eq. 1.23 may be employed. It includes the mechanical losses in gears.
(e) The torques calculated in Example 1.2 may be used.

5.6. A Class D chopper supplied from a 300-V, dc source is used to excite the field circuit of a large dc motor. The periodic time of the gating signals $T_p = 1/500$ s. The field resistance is 27 Ω and the inductance, 31 H. The field current at base speed is 6.30 A and at top speed, 2.62 A. Field current changes must be made as rapidly as possible to enable the motor to satisfy the work cycle.

(a) Disregarding current harmonics, determine the minimum time in which the reduction in current can take place and the values of t_a/T_p to be used before, during, and after this change.
(b) Determine the minimum time in which the change in (a) can be reversed.
(c) Determine the amplitude of the fundamental frequency of field current for each steady-state condition.

5.7. The 230-V, 1150-rpm, frame-size 504 motor in Appendix B is selected to drive the system in Problem 2.6. The gear ratio between motor and winch drum is $N_2/N_1 = 24$. Rotational losses of motor and mechanism may be neglected except when determining the rated value of $k\Phi$, when motor losses should be included. The armature circuit of the motor is supplied from a Class E chopper and a 300-V, dc source. The chopping frequency is 500 Hz. Acceleration and deceleration in the up direction is to take place with field flux increased to 1.25 of the rated value. For constant

speed up the flux is the rated value; for the entire down trip it is half the
rated value. Changes in flux may be considered as taking place instantaneously. The current during acceleration and deceleration is to be twice
the rated value. Prepare diagrams of the chopper gating signals for the
following:

(a) Start and end of acceleration up.
(b) Constant speed up.
(c) Start and end of deceleration up.
(d) Start and end of acceleration down.
(e) Constant speed down.
(f) Start and end of deceleration down.

The results of Problem 2.6 should be used when necessary.

5.8. For the system and operating condition of Example 5.2, determine the
approximate line current ripple factor, as there defined, if a filter with
$L = 0.5$ mH and $C = 2$ mF is fitted at the input to the chopper.
Compare the result with the factor obtained in Example 5.2.

Chapter 6

Three-Phase Induction Motors

6.1. INTRODUCTION

Three-phase induction motors are robust, inexpensive compared with dc machines (particularly if they are squirrel-cage motors), require little maintenance, and have a high power-weight ratio. Until recently they have been little used for speed control because by classical methods[1] they become increasingly inefficient as speed is reduced below the synchronous value. They have been regarded chiefly as constant-speed machines that operate on a source of constant frequency and potential difference. The evolution of power semiconductor converters has now reached a stage at which induction motors may be considered as serious rivals to dc machines in many speed-control systems.

The power-electronic equipment needed to control the speed of an induction motor satisfactorily is relatively complicated, bulkier, and more expensive than that needed for a dc machine, but the overall reliability and convenience of the power supply for converter-driven induction motors outweigh this disadvantage for many applications. In these applications the energy source, as it appears at the motor terminals, may have

- (a) constant frequency and controlled terminal pd (Chapter 7);
- (b) constant frequency and terminal pd (Chapter 8);
- (c) controlled frequency and controlled terminal pd (Chapter 9);
- (d) controlled frequency and controlled line current (Chapter 10).

It is necessary to provide a range of models to represent the induction motor under these varied conditions. The basic models are derived in this chapter from that for a wound-rotor motor; the squirrel-cage motor is considered a special case of that machine. The models developed here are suitable only for determining the steady-state operation of an induction motor drive system under balanced conditions.

6.2. EQUIVALENT CIRCUITS

A per-phase equivalent circuit of a wound-rotor induction motor is shown in Fig. 6.1.[1] In modeling the physical system of fields and coupled circuits a number of small approximations have been made to account for distributed physical phenomena by lumped circuit elements. These approximations do not cause significant discrepancies between predictions of performance from the model and the actual performance of the motor at constant terminal pd and frequency. Thus the model in Fig. 6.1 may, without severely straining the truth, be called an "exact" equivalent circuit. The following frequency/speed relationship applies to this model:

$$\omega_r = \omega_s - \frac{p}{2}\omega_m \text{ rad/s} \tag{6.1}$$

where ω_r = rotor angular frequency
ω_s = stator angular frequency
ω_m = angular speed of rotation
p = number of poles

Slip s is defined by

$$s = \frac{\omega_r}{\omega_s} = \frac{\omega_s - (p/2)\omega_m}{\omega_s} \text{ pu} \tag{6.2}$$

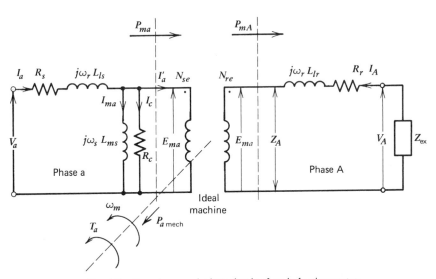

Fig. 6.1. Per-phase equivalent circuit of an induction motor.

If N_{re} and N_{se} are the effective number of rotor and stator turns per phase, respectively, then

$$\frac{E_{mA}}{E_{ma}} = s\frac{N_{re}}{N_{se}} \tag{6.3}$$

$$\frac{I_A}{I_a'} = \frac{N_{se}}{N_{re}} \tag{6.4}$$

A rotor-circuit impedance $\overline{Z}_A$, as it is "seen" by the source supplying the stator, is an equivalent impedance $\overline{Z}_A'$, where

$$\frac{\overline{Z}_A'}{\overline{Z}_A} = s\left(\frac{N_{re}}{N_{se}}\right)^2 \tag{6.5}$$

From the preceding relationships it can be shown that the ratio of the power developed per phase in the rotor and stator circuits is

$$\frac{P_{mA}}{P_{ma}} = s \tag{6.6}$$

Thus the three-phase power converted to mechanical form is

$$P_{mech} = 3(P_{ma} - P_{mA}) = 3(1-s)P_{ma} = 3\frac{p}{2}\frac{\omega_m}{\omega_s}P_{ma} \text{ W} \tag{6.7}$$

The air-gap torque exerted on the rotor is

$$T = \frac{P_{mech}}{\omega_m} = 3\left(\frac{p}{2}\right)\left(\frac{P_{ma}}{\omega_s}\right) \text{ N} \cdot \text{m} \tag{6.8}$$

In some converter-motor systems with wound-rotor motors it is necessary to use a motor model incorporating the ideal machine of Fig. 6.1. For squirrel-cage motors, in which no question of connection of an external circuit to the rotor arises, reference of all parameters and variables to the stator side of the air gap by Eqs. 6.3 to 6.5 yields the equivalent circuit in Fig. 6.2. In this circuit

$$P_{ma} = \frac{R_r'}{s}(I_a')^2 = R_r'(I_a')^2 + \frac{(1-s)}{s}R_r'(I_a')^2 \text{ W} \tag{6.9}$$

and because $R_r'(I_a')^2$ is clearly the per-phase resistive loss in the rotor it follows that

$$P_{mech} = \frac{3(1-s)}{s}R_r'(I_a')^2 \text{ W} \tag{6.10}$$

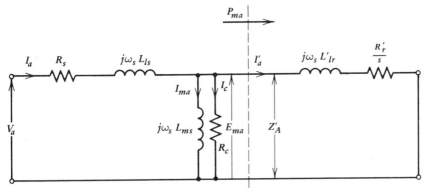

Fig. 6.2. Equivalent circuit referred to the stator.

6.2.1. Constant Terminal Potential Difference and Frequency

The circuit in Fig. 6.2 is again an exact equivalent circuit but it is inconvenient for some performance calculations. At this point, therefore, further approximations are made and in making them it must be borne in mind that modeling of the entire system in which the motor model is incorporated is unavoidably approximate.

The per-phase stator leakage impedance $R_s + j\omega_s L_{ls}$ is small, and even with large stator currents the difference between V_a and E_{ma} is small. Furthermore the per-phase magnetizing reactance $\omega_s L_{ms}$ is large and resistance R_c much larger. Thus I_{ma} and I_c are both small in comparison with I_a and are not greatly changed if the elements $X_{ms} = \omega_s L_{ms}$ and R_c are moved to the stator terminals as shown in Fig. 6.3. Since the variations in value of X_{ms} and R_c with changes in V_a/ω_s are also small, these elements may be shown as constant

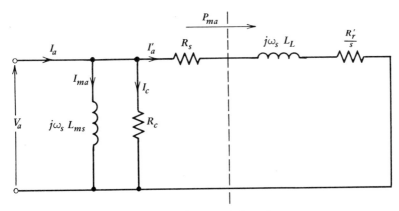

Fig. 6.3. Approximate equivalent circuit.

circuit parameters. In the rotor circuit

$$L_L = L_{ls} + L'_{lr} \ \text{H} \tag{6.11}$$

The resistance R_c, although it may be used to calculate the values of other circuit parameters, may be omitted from the model for the purpose of system calculations. The resulting equivalent circuit may be used over comparatively wide ranges of terminal pd and frequency, provided that the ratio V_a/ω_s is maintained constant. This is necessary; otherwise the value of I_{ma} would become excessive at low frequencies and X_{ms} would vary because of the varying degree of magnetic saturation in the motor.

The relation between motor internal torque and speed may also be obtained from Fig. 6.3, in which

$$P_{ma} = \frac{R'_r}{s}(I'_a)^2 \ \text{W} \tag{6.12}$$

Also

$$\bar{I}'_a = \frac{\bar{V}_a}{R_s + R'_r/s + j\omega_s L_L} \ \text{A} \tag{6.13}$$

This equation shows that for constant terminal pd at small slip $R'_r/s \gg R_s$ or $\omega_s L_L$; therefore I'_a is directly proportional to slip.

From Eqs. 6.7, 6.12, and 6.13

$$T = \frac{3}{\omega_s} \cdot \frac{p}{2} \cdot \frac{R'_r}{s} \cdot \frac{V_a^2}{\left(R_s + R'_r/s\right)^2 + \left(\omega_s L_L\right)^2} \ \text{N} \cdot \text{m} \tag{6.14}$$

and it may be seen that at small slip internal torque T is directly proportional to slip.

The only variable on the right side of Eq. 6.14 is slip s. The maximum magnitudes of positive and negative torque and the slips at which they occur can therefore be determined by setting $dT/ds = 0$. The slips are then

$$s = \pm \frac{R'_r}{\left(R_s^2 + \omega_s^2 L_L^2\right)^{1/2}} \simeq \pm \frac{R'_r}{\omega_s L_L} \ \text{pu} \tag{6.15}$$

The approximation in Eq. 6.15 applies to machines of more than 1 kW rating at normal power-system frequencies. Substitution of this approximate value of s in Eq. 6.14 yields

$$|T_{\max}| = \frac{3p}{4} \cdot \frac{V_a^2}{\omega_s^2 L_L} \ \text{N} \cdot \text{m} \tag{6.16}$$

Substitution of $s = 1$ in Eq. 6.14 gives the starting torque of the wound-rotor motor as

$$T_s = \frac{3}{\omega_s} \cdot \frac{p}{2} \cdot \frac{R_r' V_a^2}{\left(R_s + R_r'\right)^2 + \left(\omega_s L_L\right)^2} \quad \text{N} \cdot \text{m} \tag{6.17}$$

This relationship does not apply, however, to class B and C squirrel-cage motors for reasons explained in Section 6.4.

If R_c in Fig. 6.3 is considered large enough to constitute an open circuit the power input to the motor is

$$P_{in} = 3\left(R_s + \frac{R_r'}{s}\right)(I_a')^2 \quad \text{W} \tag{6.18}$$

The power factor at which the motor is operating is given by the cosine of the angle of the input impedance, which is

$$\overline{Z}_{in} = \frac{-\omega_s^2 L_L L_{ms} + j\omega_s L_{ms}\left(R_s + R_r'/s\right)}{R_s + R_r'/s + j\omega_s\left(L_{ms} + L_L\right)} \quad \Omega \tag{6.19}$$

From Eq. 6.19

$$\underline{/Z_{in}} = \pi - \tan^{-1}\frac{R_s + R_r'/s}{\omega_s L_L} - \tan^{-1}\left[\frac{\omega_s\left(L_{ms} + L_L\right)}{R_s + R_r'/s}\right] \text{rad} \quad (6.20)$$

The operating power factor is

$$PF = \cos\underline{/Z_{in}} \tag{6.21}$$

and the motor line current is

$$I_a' = \frac{P_{in}}{3V_a(PF)} \quad \text{A} \tag{6.22}$$

6.2.2. Constant Line Current and Frequency

The performance of a motor supplied with constant current differs markedly from that of the same motor supplied at constant terminal pd. The most striking difference may be illustrated by using the equivalent circuit in Fig. 6.2 in which for some purposes the stator impedance $R_s + j\omega_s L_{ls}$ may be ignored because I_a is constant. However, a complication arises because the ratio V_a/ω_s varies widely over the operating range, which means that L_{ms} and R_c vary as well.

If R_c is again omitted from the equivalent circuit, then, from Fig. 6.2,

$$\bar{I}'_a = \frac{j\omega_s L_{ms} \bar{I}_a}{R'_r/s + j\omega_s \left(L_{ms} + L'_{lr}\right)} \text{ A} \tag{6.23}$$

From Eqs. 6.8, 6.9, and 6.23 the air-gap torque is given by

$$T = \frac{3p}{2} \cdot \frac{R'_r}{s} \cdot \frac{\omega_s \left(L_{ms} I_a\right)^2}{\left(R'_r/s\right)^2 + \omega_s^2 \left(L_{ms} + L'_{lr}\right)^2} \text{ N} \cdot \text{m} \tag{6.24}$$

If L_{ms} is assumed to be constant, then at constant line current and frequency the only variable on the right side of Eq. 6.24 is slip s. Once again the slips at which the maximum magnitudes of positive and negative torque occur can be determined by setting $dT/ds = 0$. If this is done, the solution is

$$s = -x \pm \sqrt{x^2 + x} \tag{6.25}$$

where

$$x = \frac{\left(R'_r\right)^2}{\omega_s^2 \left(L_{ms} + L'_{lr}\right)^2} \tag{6.26}$$

Because the ratio x is small for a normal induction motor, from Eqs. 6.25 and 6.26

$$s \simeq \pm \frac{R'_r}{\omega_s \left(L_{ms} + L'_{lr}\right)} \text{ pu} \tag{6.27}$$

If Eq. 6.27 is compared with Eq. 6.15 it is seen that the slip at which breakdown torque is reached is much smaller for a motor driven at constant line current than it is for the same motor driven at constant terminal pd.

For performance calculations it is convenient to use the equivalent circuit of Fig. 6.3 in which R_c is regarded as an open circuit. Thus

$$\bar{I}'_a = \frac{j\omega_s l_{ms} I_a}{\left(R_s + R'_r/s\right) + j\omega_s \left(L_{ms} + L_L\right)} \text{ A} \tag{6.28}$$

From Eqs. 6.8, 6.9, and 6.28

$$T = \frac{3p}{2\omega_s} \cdot \frac{R'_r}{s} \cdot \frac{\left(\omega_s L_{ms} I_a\right)^2}{\left(R_s + R'_r/s\right)^2 + \omega_s^2 \left(L_{ms} + L_L\right)^2} \text{ N} \cdot \text{m} \tag{6.29}$$

The impedance of the motor at any slip may be written

$$\overline{Z}_{in} = R_{in} + jX_{in} \; \Omega \tag{6.30}$$

where

$$R_{in} = \frac{(\omega_s L_{ms})^2 (R_s + R'_r/s)}{(R_s + R'_r/s)^2 + \omega_s^2 (L_{ms} + L_L)^2} \; \Omega \tag{6.31}$$

$$X_{in} = \frac{\omega_s L_{ms}\left[(R_s + R'_r/s)^2 + \omega_s^2 L_L (L_{ms} + L_L)\right]}{(R_s + R'_r/s)^2 + \omega_s^2 (L_{ms} + L_L)^2} \; \Omega \tag{6.32}$$

$$Z_{in} = \left(R_{in}^2 + X_{in}^2\right)^{1/2} \; \Omega \tag{6.33}$$

$$\angle Z_{in} = \tan^{-1}\frac{X_{in}}{R_{in}} \; \text{rad} \tag{6.34}$$

$$PF = \cos\angle Z_{in} \tag{6.35}$$

$$V_a = Z_{in} I_a \; \text{V} \tag{6.36}$$

and

$$P_{in} = 3 V_a I_a (PF) \; \text{W} \tag{6.37}$$

Figure 6.4 shows calculated curves of developed torque, power factor, and input power plotted as functions of slip for a 15-kW wound-rotor motor. In Fig. 6.4a, where the terminal pd and frequency are constant, a curve of line current I_a is plotted. In Fig. 6.4b, where the line current and frequency are constant, a curve of line-to-neutral terminal pd V_a is plotted. It must be pointed out, however, that L_{ms} is also assumed to be constant despite the wide variation in V_a. The rated full-load slip of this motor is approximately 0.03, and in the case of the current source supplying a line current approximately equal to the motor full-load current the operating point for rated operating conditions lies on the unstable (i.e., positive slope) part of the torque-slip curve. There is no question of operating at this current on the stable part of the torque-slip curve because V_a would be unacceptably high and the magnetic system would be heavily saturated. It is therefore clear that a current source could not be used in a system without a speed feedback loop. The two curves of power factor versus slip are, of course, identical.

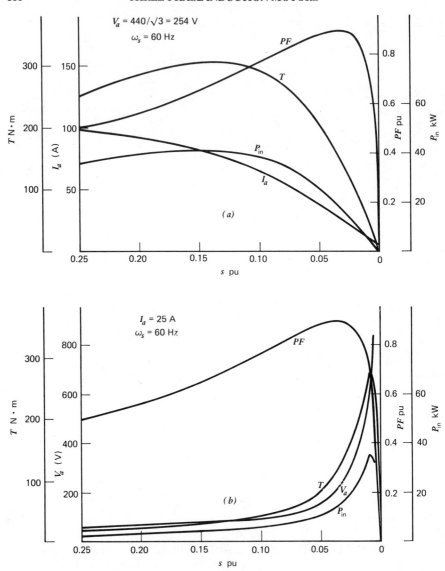

Fig. 6.4. Induction-motor characteristics.

6.3. SPEED CONTROL OF INDUCTION MOTORS

Speed control of induction motors has long been seen to be desirable, and numerous methods of obtaining stepped or continuous speed change have been evolved, some of which have resulted in complicated ac machines (Schrage motor) and some in the use of auxiliary machines (Scherbius and Kraemer systems). Few of these systems have been very efficient and all have required more maintenance than the induction motor alone. The basic principles of those classical methods of speed control that are relevant to systems using power semiconductor converters are discussed briefly in this section.

6.3.1. Variation of Rotor-Circuit Resistance

The attraction of the wound-rotor motor, as opposed to the cheaper squirrel-cage machine, has lain in the possibility of controlling the speed of the loaded motor by introducing additional resistance into the rotor circuit. This technique also made it possible to keep the motor current low during starting without sacrificing starting torque; therefore when repeated starting was necessary or a high-inertia load required a long time to reach operating speed the wound-rotor motor was able to perform this service without danger of overheating. The circuit of a motor with variable external resistances in the rotor circuit is illustrated in Fig. 6.5a.

Equation 6.15 shows that if the rotor-circuit resistance is varied the slip at which breakdown torque occurs will also vary and may become greater than unity. A family of speed-torque curves for various values of rotor-circuit resistance is shown in Fig. 6.5b. Stable operation will occur at the intersections of the curves of internal torque with that representing the load torque at the motor shaft coupling plus that due to the motor's own rotational losses. If the rotor-circuit resistance is made sufficiently large the load may drive the motor backward at an operating point such as p in Fig. 6.5b. At this point the motor torque is opposing rotation. Thus reversing the phase sequence of supply to the motor produces braking by "plugging" the machine in the second quadrant of Fig. 6.5b. Current is very high, however, unless large rotor resistance is introduced, and the braking torque per ampere of rotor current is low. This method is therefore permissible only for a short period of rapid braking or a longer period of slow braking. It should also be noted that on no load effective speed control of the motor is not obtained because the speed approaches the synchronous speed, no matter how much resistance is included in the rotor circuit.

If the slip in Eq. 6.14 becomes negative, that is, if the motor is driven at more than synchronous speed by the coupled mechanical system (e.g., by a vehicle going downhill), the developed torque becomes negative and regenerative braking is obtained where energy is fed back into the ac supply system.

An alternative method of varying the per-phase, effective rotor-circuit resistance is shown in Fig. 6.6. Here the rotor output is rectified and applied to a single variable resistor. This arrangement eliminates any danger of unbalance due to inequality of the three resistors shown in Fig. 6.5a. The system in Fig. 6.6 could be elaborated by introducing a chopper between the diode rectifier and the resistor, which could then have a fixed value. This is a system to which a feedback loop could be added to give speed control independent of load

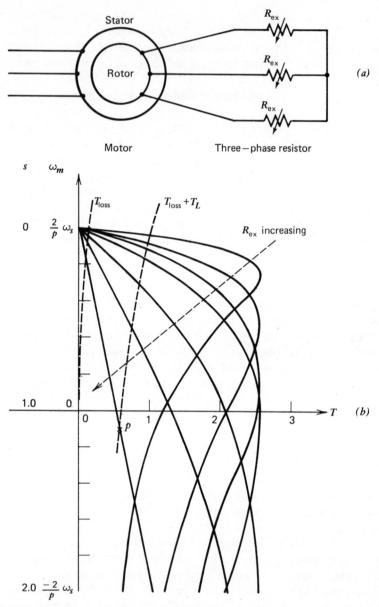

Fig. 6.5. Speed control of a wound-rotor induction motor by variation of external rotor-circuit resistance R_{ex}.

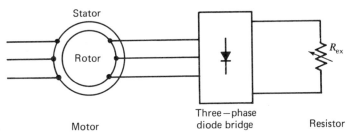

Fig. 6.6. Alternative method of varying rotor-circuit resistance.

torque. A disadvantage of the rectifier in the rotor circuit is that the rotor currents are not sinusoidal and the resulting harmonics are transformed through the motor into the supply system.

6.3.2. Variable Terminal Potential Difference

Because developed torque is proportional to the square of the applied terminal pd, a measure of speed control of a loaded motor can be obtained by varying the terminal pd. For this purpose it is necessary to use a Class D squirrel-cage motor with a high-resistance cage or a wound-rotor motor with some fixed external resistance in the rotor circuit. In either case the speed-torque curves would have the form shown in Fig. 6.7. The wound-rotor motor has the advantage that the heat generated in the rotor-circuit resistance is for the most part produced outside the machine and is easily dissipated. The motor is therefore smaller than the squirrel-cage machine for the same service. The squirrel-cage drive has the advantage of simplicity.

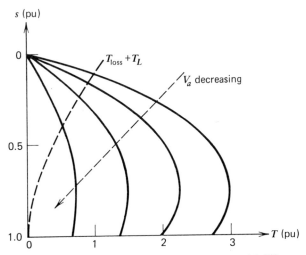

Fig. 6.7. Speed control by variation of source potential difference.

6.3.3. Variation of Source Frequency

The synchronous speed of an induction motor is given by

$$\omega_{\text{syn}} = \frac{2}{p}\omega_s \text{ rad/s} \tag{6.38}$$

Thus if the source frequency ω_s can be varied so also can the speed of the motor, loaded or unloaded. In some special applications the installation necessary was justifiable, even before the introduction of power semiconductor converters. A source for this purpose, for instance, could be obtained by driving an ac generator by a speed-controlled dc motor. The speed-torque characteristics obtainable from such a system are illustrated in Fig. 6.8. The base characteristic is that for which the source frequency is equal to the standard power-system frequency ω_b for which the motor has been designed. These characteristics show that control down to zero speed is possible and that by reduction of the source frequency a coupled inertia load may be decelerated by regenerative braking in the second quadrant of the speed-torque diagram.

If the magnetic system of the motor is not to become oversaturated (it is designed to operate with some degree of saturation) the equivalent circuits in

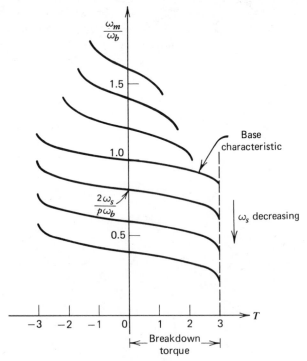

Fig. 6.8. Induction motor. Variable-frequency operation.

Figs. 6.1 and 6.2 show that V_a must be increased or decreased with ω_s. If the effect of stator winding resistance and leakage inductance is ignored maintenance of a constant ratio V_a/ω_s will result in a constant value of I_{ma} and this will result in a constant degree of saturation and a constant amplitude of the flux density wave in the air gap. Only at low frequencies does the effect of R_s become large in comparison with that of L_{ls}, thus necessitating an increase in the ratio V_a/ω_s.

Equation 6.16 shows that as long as the ratio of V_a/ω_s is held constant and ω_s is not very low the breakdown torque is constant. Furthermore Eq. 6.15 shows that, subject to the approximation by which R_s is neglected, the product $s\omega_s$ at the breakdown torque is also constant. This results in the parallel characteristics shown in the lower part of Fig. 6.8.

The basic characteristic is obtained at the rated frequency and terminal pd. For speeds exceeding those obtained under these conditions ω_s may be increased further, but the terminal pd may not be increased, either because of supply limitation or a limit imposed by stator insulation. If the ratio of V_a/ω_s decreases so also will the breakdown torque, but not the product $s\omega_s$ at which it occurs. Thus at frequencies higher than the rated value the characteristics in the upper part of Fig. 6.8 are obtained. This corresponds to the "field weakening" range of operation of a separately excited dc motor, and indeed this expression "field weakening" may also be appropriately applied to the induction motor because with the fall in the magnitude of ratio V_a/ω_s the amplitude of the rotating flux wave in the air gap is reduced.

6.4. MOTOR RATINGS

The diagram in Fig. 6.8 is for positive direction of rotation in the motoring and regenerating mode of operation. If that diagram were rotated through 180° and the result added to Fig. 6.8 the composite diagram obtained would apply to negative as well as positive directions of rotation. The imposition of a speed limit for mechanical reasons would result in horizontal boundaries across the top and bottom of the composite diagram and the addition of a contour touching the points of breakdown torque on all curves would result in an outline similar to that shown for a dc machine in Fig. 2.6. This outline represents a boundary that could not be crossed by the motor operating point under any circumstances, for if it were the motor would be brought to a standstill or driven up to an uncontrolled speed in the second quadrant.

If the points for permissible motor current were marked on each curve and joined up to form a boundary similar in shape to the outline but completely enclosed within it they would form a boundary enclosing all points of permissible *continuous* operation. This boundary may be crossed for limited periods of time. Permissible continuous current is determined by the rms magnitude of that current and the magnitude of the accompanying flux variations.

When the stator terminals of a squirrel-cage motor are connected to a power semiconductor converter the current and flux variations in the motor are not sinusoidal functions of time but contain harmonics to an extent that depends on the nature of the converter and the operating conditions. The harmonics give rise at a given power output to losses greater than those occurring at the same output in a conventionally operated machine excited by a sinusoidal voltage source.

Class B and C squirrel-cage motors are designed for constant-speed drives and, to obtain high starting torque with low starting current, are provided with deep slots or double cages. The result is that the equivalent circuit parameters of the motor vary with speed. Speed variation in a squirrel-cage motor also results in variation of the cooling effect of the fan on the shaft or of the flingers on the rotor. Reduced cooling down to approximately half speed in variable frequency systems is compensated by reduced core losses at the lower stator frequencies. At about twice rated speed and frequency the increased cooling is insufficient to dissipate the increased losses. Thus for operation over a wide speed range at variable frequencies Class B or C induction motors may have to be derated by up to 20% if they are not to overheat. (Class A motors are rarely used and Class D motors form a special case discussed in Chapter 7.)

The wound-rotor motor may be operated with the stator or rotor terminals connected to a converter. In both cases current and flux harmonics occur, and this motor must also be derated if the speed range is to be wide.

6.5. INDUCTION-MOTOR TESTS

Much information on induction motors is normally obtainable from the manufacturer. For a wound-rotor machine or for Class A or D squirrel-cage motors it may include the results of no-load and locked-rotor tests, the winding resistances measured by dc, and, in the case of the wound-rotor motor, some indication of the stator-to-rotor turns ratio N_s/N_r. It may not be sufficient to obtain the *effective* turns ratio N_{se}/N_{re}. The method of obtaining this additional information is described elsewhere.[1]

The information made available by the manufacturer on Class B or C squirrel-cage induction motors differs from that provided for a wound-rotor motor because preparation of an equivalent circuit is not normally envisaged. This information usually refers to operation of the motor on starting, full load, and no load. To predict the performance of a squirrel-cage motor in a variable-speed system, however, an equivalent circuit is required. Because in such systems rotor frequency at all speeds is usually kept constant at about the value that occurs at rated speed on rated stator frequency, the full-load and no-load information must be used to determine an equivalent circuit that at this rotor frequency may be applied at all speeds. Manufacturers' test data on typical squirrel-cage motors are given in Appendix C.

The results of the further test to determine the variations in L_{ms} and R_c mentioned in Section 6.2.2 are shown in Fig. 6.9 for a 550-V, 40-kW,

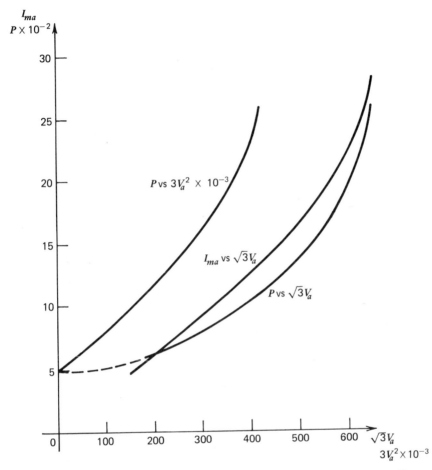

Fig. 6.9. Results of a loss test on a 550-V, 40-kW, six-pole, wound-rotor motor at 60 Hz.

wound-rotor motor. This test consists of running the motor on no load over a wide range of terminal pd above and below the rated value while taking readings of terminal pd, line current, and input power. A negligible proportion of the input power is absorbed in resistance losses and the power reading effectively gives the power dissipated in core losses and friction and windage losses. As the terminal pd is reduced so also are the core losses, but because the speed falls very little the friction and windage losses do not change. The curve of P vs $\sqrt{3} V_a$ is shown in Fig. 6.9. The intercept of this curve extrapolated to the vertical axis (where the core losses are zero) gives the friction and windage losses P_{FW}. The minimum power reading is obtained when the terminal pd is so low that the breakdown torque of the motor is just sufficient to overcome the friction and windage losses and occurs at $\sqrt{3} V_a = 150$ V for this 550-V motor. The intercept can be obtained quite accurately by plotting the curve of power versus the square of the terminal pd in Fig. 6.9. The friction and windage losses thus determined may be considered constant for the entire test.

If it is now assumed that the no-load equivalent circuit of the motor consists solely of circuit elements L_{ms} and R_c in parallel these quantities may be calculated for each set of readings. Because on no load $V_a \simeq E_{ma}$, the saturation curve of the motor may also be determined.

The calculated results are shown in Figs. 6.10 and 6.11, where, for this particular motor, the variation in L_{ms} for values of E_{ma} below the rated terminal line-to-neutral potential difference of 315 V is less than 20% of the value at rated pd, while the variation in R_c is even less. This justifies the use of an equivalent circuit with a constant value of L_{ms}. The curve of $\omega_s L_{ms}$ in Fig. 6.11 could be plotted against values of E_{ma}/ω_s and applied to calculations of performance when ω_s is varied. However, if variation of P_{FW} and R_c with source frequency is required, no-load tests must be performed for a range of frequencies.

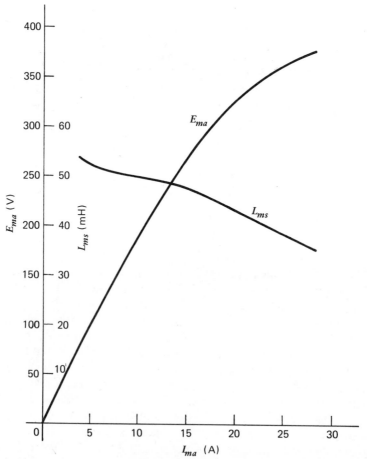

Fig. 6.10. Saturation curve and curve of L_{ms} versus I_{ma} from the test results of Fig. 6.9.

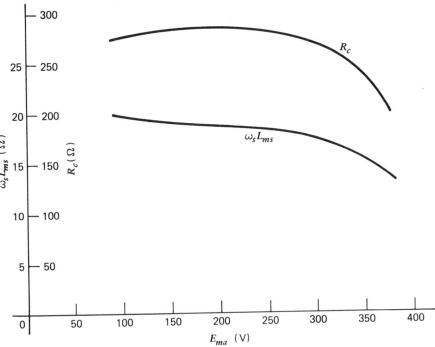

Fig. 6.11. Variation of R_c and $\omega_s L_{ms}$ as functions of E_{ma} at 60 Hz from the test results of Fig. 6.9.

The method of obtaining the equivalent circuit of a wound-rotor motor or a Class A or D squirrel-cage motor is well known.[1] A method of obtaining the full-speed equivalent circuit of a Class B or C squirrel-cage motor from data like those in Appendix C is best illustrated by a numerical example.

Example 6.1

For the 460-V, 25-hp (18.7-kW), 1765 rpm motor in Appendix C determine the equivalent circuit parameters of Fig. 6.3 in which R_c is considered infinite.

Solution

The relevant data for this motor are

$$P_{FL} = 21070 \text{ W} \qquad P_{FW} = 100 \text{ W}$$

$$I_{rated} = 32.4 \text{ A} \qquad R_s = 0.320 \; \Omega$$

$$I_{NL} = 13.0 \text{ A} \qquad V_a = 400/\sqrt{3} \text{ V}$$

$$n = 1765 \text{ rpm} = 184.8 \text{ rad/s} = \omega_m$$

The full load power factor is

$$PF_{FL} = \frac{P_{FL}}{460\sqrt{3} \times I_{\text{rated}}} = \frac{21070}{460\sqrt{3} \times 32.4} = 0.8162$$

$$\bar{I}_a = 32.4 \underline{/\cos^{-1}PF_{FL}} = 32.4\underline{/-35.29°} = 26.44 - j18.72 \text{ A}$$

$$\bar{I}_{ma} = I_{NL}\underline{/-90°} \text{ A}$$

$$\bar{I}'_a = \bar{I}_a - \bar{I}_{ma} = 26.44 - j18.72 + j13.0$$

$$= 26.44 - j5.72 = 27.05\underline{/-12.21°} \text{ A}$$

$$\omega_s L_{ms} = \frac{460}{\sqrt{3}\,I_{NL}} = \frac{460}{13\sqrt{3}} = 20.43 \text{ }\Omega$$

coupling torque $T_L = \dfrac{746 \times 25}{184.8} = 100.9 \text{ N} \cdot \text{m}$

$$T_{FW} = \frac{P_{FW}}{\omega_m} = \frac{100}{184.4} = 0.5411 \text{ N} \cdot \text{m}$$

air-gap torque $T = T_L + T_{FW} = 101.4 \text{ N} \cdot \text{m}$

from which it may be seen that T_{FW} in a squirrel-cage motor may very well be neglected.

$$3P_{ma} = T\omega_{\text{syn}} = 101.4 \times 60\pi = 19110 \text{ W}$$

$$s = \frac{1800 - 1765}{1800} = 0.01944$$

$$3P_{ma} = \frac{3R'_r}{s}\left(I'_a\right)^2 = \frac{3R'_r \times 27.05^2}{0.01944}$$

$$R'_r = \frac{19110 \times 0.01944}{3 \times 27.05^2} = 0.1692$$

$$\bar{Z}_r = R_s + \frac{R'_r}{s} + j\omega_s L_L = 0.320 + \frac{0.1692}{0.01944} + j\omega_s L_L$$

$$= 9.02 + j\omega_s L_L$$

$$\frac{\omega_s L_L}{9.024} = \tan\underline{/I'_a} = \tan 12.21°$$

$$\omega_s L_L = 9.024 \tan 12.21° = 1.953 \text{ }\Omega$$

At this point it should be remarked that if the full-load equivalent circuit for a squirrel-cage induction motor obtained by the method described in Example 6.1 is used to calculate the breakdown torque from Eq. 6.16 a ratio of breakdown to full-load torque substantially greater than the typical value of 2 will be obtained. The reason is that the full-load equivalent circuit applies only at low slip. It is therefore inaccurate at the relatively high slip at which breakdown occurs and at which rotor leakage flux is significantly greater than that under rated operating conditions.

Example 6.2

The 50-hp (37.3-kW), six-pole, squirrel-cage motor in Appendix C is to be driven from a source of variable pd and frequency. Draw curves of line current and slip as functions of source frequency from 60 Hz down to 10 Hz, making the following assumptions:

(a) The coupling torque is constant at the rated value.

(b) Friction and windage torque is negligible.

(c) Ratio V_a/ω_s is maintained constant at the rated value.

(d) Core and stray load losses are negligible.

Solution

The method in Example 6.1 with P_{FW} neglected yields the following equivalent circuit parameters:

$$R_s = 0.191\ \Omega, \qquad R'_r = 0.0704\ \Omega \qquad L_{ms} = 44.87\ \text{mH}, \qquad L_L = 2.986\ \text{mH}$$

At rated speed

$$\omega_m = 1181 \times \frac{2\pi}{60} = 123.7\ \text{rad/s}$$

$$T = \frac{746 \times 50}{123.7} = 301.5\ \text{N} \cdot \text{m}$$

At frequency f

$$V_a = \frac{f}{60} \times \frac{460}{\sqrt{3}}\ \text{V}$$

$$\omega_s L_L = 2\pi \times 0.002986 f\ \Omega$$

$$\omega_s = 2\pi f\ \text{rad/s}$$

If in Eq. 6.14 the quantity R'_r/s is replaced by x and the values for torque, known parameters, and the quantities for V_a and ω_s given above are substituted the following quadratic equation in x is obtained:

$$x^2 - (0.09308f - 0.382)x + 0.03648 + (0.01876f)^2 = 0$$

Two values for x, therefore for s, are obtained from this equation. One value for s represents a point of operation on the stable part of the speed-torque curve. When R'_r/s is known I'_a may be calculated from Eq. 6.13 and

$$I_a = \left[(I'_a)^2 + I^2_{NL} \right]^{1/2} \text{ A}$$

The results of a series of calculations are shown in Fig. 6.12.

It will be noted from Fig. 6.12 that slip and line current increase as source frequency, and consequently speed, is reduced and that at low speed the line

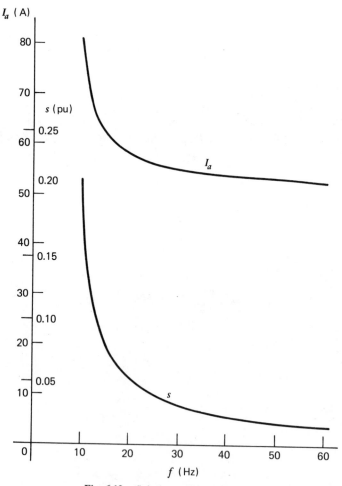

Fig. 6.12. Solution to Example 6.2.

current exceeds the rated value of 59.0 A. The increased heating of the motor due to resistive losses at low speed will to some extent be offset by reduced core, stray-load, and friction and windage losses. At low speed, however, cooling of the motor is relatively ineffective; therefore in drives demanding a wide speed range forced cooling or derating of the motor may be required. The calculated line currents at high speed are somewhat less than the rated value; this discrepancy may be attributed to the neglect of all losses in the motor other than resistive losses.

Example 6.3

The 20-hp (14.9-kW), six-pole, squirrel-cage induction motor in Appendix C is driven from a current source of 20 A in a closed-loop system.

Neglecting all losses other than copper losses and assuming that inductance L_{ms} remains constant at the value for rated full-load operation, determine the speed and terminal pd of the motor when the source frequency is 45 Hz and the coupling torque is equal to the rated value.

Solution

The relevant data for this motor are

$$P_{FL} = 17310 \text{ W} \qquad R_s = 0.420 \ \Omega$$

$$I_{\text{rated}} = 26.2 \text{ A} \qquad V_a = 460/\sqrt{3} \text{ V}$$

$$I_{NL} = 12.1 \text{ A} \qquad n = 1760 \text{ rpm}$$

When these data are used in the method in Example 6.1 to determine the equivalent-circuit parameters in Fig. 6.3 the following parameter values are obtained:

$$L_L = 2.955 \text{ mH}, \qquad L_{ms} = 58.22 \text{ mH}, \qquad R'_r = 0.2341 \ \Omega,$$

$$\omega_m = 184.3 \text{ rad/s} \qquad T = \frac{20 \times 746}{184.3} = 80.95 \text{ N} \cdot \text{m}$$

At 45 Hz $\omega_s = 90\pi$ rad/s

$$3P_{ma} = 80.95 \times 90\pi \times 2/6$$

$$P_{ma} = \frac{R'_r}{s} \left(I'_a \right)^2 = 2543 \text{ W}$$

From Eq. 6.28

$$\left(I'_{ma}\right)^2 = \frac{(90\pi \times 0.05822 \times 20)^2}{\left(0.420 + R'_r/s\right)^2 + [90\pi(0.05822 + 0.002955)]^2}$$

$$= \frac{329.2^2}{\left(0.420 + R'_r/s\right)^2 + 299.2}$$

Substitution in the expression for P_{ma} yields

$$2543 = \frac{329.2^2\left(R'_r/s\right)}{\left(0.420 + R'_r/s\right)^2 + 299.2}$$

If R'_r/s is given the symbol x this yields the quadratic equation

$$x^2 - 41.78x + 299.4 = 0$$

from which

$$\frac{R'_r}{s} = 32.59 \text{ or } 9.186 \ \Omega$$

and

$$s = 0.007183 \quad \text{or} \quad 0.02548$$

The larger slip represents operation on the unstable part of the speed-torque curve; thus

$$n = \frac{(1 - 0.02548) \times 45}{60} \times 1200 = 877.1 \text{ rpm}$$

From Eqs. 6.31 to 6.34

$$Z_{in} = 8.021 \underline{/34.01°} \ \Omega$$

$$\sqrt{3} \ V_a = \sqrt{3} \times 8.021 \times 20 = 277.9 \text{ V}$$

6.5.1. Distribution of Leakage Reactance in Squirrel-Cage Motors

For some purposes (see Chapter 9) it is convenient to use the equivalent circuit in Fig. 6.2 for squirrel-cage induction motors, usually with the omission of element R_c. This necessitates dividing the combined leakage inductance L_L

obtained from the tests described in Section 6.5 into two parts; one, the stator leakage inductance, the other, the rotor leakage inductance referred to the stator. There is no method of doing this other than relying on the results of accumulated design experience of the motor manufacturer. If no information is available for a particular machine, the following table may be used:

Motor	Stator	Rotor
Class B	$L_{ls} = 0.4L_L$	$L'_{lr} = 0.6L_L$
Class C	$L_{ls} = 0.3L_L$	$L'_{lr} = 0.7L_L$

Because the behavior of an induction motor depends much more on the total leakage inductance than on its distribution, the use of an approximate distribution makes little difference to predictions of performance.

PROBLEMS

6.1. For a 460-V, 25-hp (18.7-kW), 1720-rpm wound-rotor motor the values of the parameters of the equivalent circuit in Fig. 6.1 are the following:

$$R_s = 0.225\ \Omega \qquad L_{ls} = 1.89\ \text{mH} \qquad \frac{N_{se}}{N_{re}} = 1.88$$

$$R_r = 0.126\ \Omega \qquad L_{lr} = 0.536\ \text{mH}$$

$$R_c = 262\ \Omega \qquad L_{ms} = 73.7\ \text{mH} \qquad P_{FW} = 225\ \text{W}$$

If the rotor terminals are short-circuited calculate the line current, rotor current, and air-gap torque at rated terminal pd and the given nameplate speed. Is the nameplate speed too high or too low?

6.2. For the motor in Problem 6.1 calculate the breakdown torque of the motor and the speed and rotor-circuit frequency at which it occurs.

6.3. (a) Determine the full-load equivalent circuit for the 75-hp (56.0-kW), four-pole, squirrel-cage motor in Appendix C.
  (b) Compare the full-load efficiency calculated from the data with that calculated from the equivalent circuit.
  (c) Determine the core and stray-load losses that are neglected in the equivalent circuit.

6.4. The motor in Problem 6.3 is running from a 460-V, 60-Hz source and exerting half-rated torque at the coupling. Assuming that the friction and windage torque is the same as for full-load operation, determine the speed of the motor under these conditions.

6.5. The 30-hp (22.4-kW), four-pole, squirrel-cage motor in Appendix C is to be driven from a source of variable pd and frequency. Determine the speed and efficiency of the motor at a source frequency of 45 Hz when producing rated output torque on the basis of the following assumptions:

(a) Ratio V_a/ω_s is maintained constant.
(b) Losses other than resistive losses are proportional to the square of the stator terminal pd.

6.6. For the motor in Problem 6.5 draw the first-quadrant envelope to a family of speed torque curves similar to those in Fig. 6.8 but with the vertical axis scaled in rpm. The following assumptions should be made:

(a) The permitted speed range is $600 < n < 3600$ rpm.
(b) Maximum permitted terminal pd is 460 V.
(c) Below rated speed V_a/ω_s is maintained constant.
(d) Losses other than copper losses may be neglected.

6.7. The 75-hp, (56.0-kW), two-pole, squirrel cage induction motor in Appendix C is to be used in a system in which the amplitude of the air-gap flux-density wave is to be held constant at all speeds at the value occurring for rated operation while the source frequency is varied. Assuming that all losses other than resistive losses may be neglected and that the motor is to deliver rated torque at the coupling from standstill

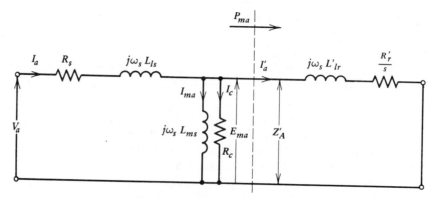

Fig. 6.13. Diagram for Problem 6.7.

up to rated speed,

(a) determine the equivalent circuit of Fig. 6.13, assuming $L'_{lr} = 2L_{ls}$ and $R_c \rightarrow \infty$;

(b) use the equivalent circuit of (a) to plot a curve to show the ratio V_a/ω_s over the speed range from $n = 0$ to the rated value.

6.8. For the motor in Problem 6.7 use the equivalent circuit in Fig. 6.13 to plot curves of torque versus slip at 60 Hz for $0 < s < 0.1$ with

(a) constant rated terminal pd;

(b) constant amplitude of the air-gap flux wave at the value corresponding to rated operation.

Chapter 7

Speed Control by AC Power Controller

7.1. INTRODUCTION

Introduction of impedance into the lines that supply the stator of an inducti
motor reduces the terminal pd of the motor, particularly when it is loaded.
Section 6.3.2 showed, this variation in terminal pd can be used to give
measure of speed control of the loaded motor if the rotor-circuit resistance
high. The introduction of controlled semiconductor devices into the sup
lines by a power controller also provides control of the effective terminal pd
somewhat the same way as variable impedances.

Because the Class D squirrel-cage induction motor normally used in t
kind of control system is essentially a linear device, with virtually consta
rotor circuit parameters at all speeds, its equivalent circuit may be obtain
from the normal locked-rotor and no-load test results. These motors usua
have a full-load slip of about 0.15.

Apart from providing speed control, power controllers may be used
starting large squirrel-cage motors for by this means the current drawn fr
the line can be held to a reasonably low value.

7.1.1. Common Controller Configurations

A balanced power-circuit for a power controller and motor is illustrated in F
7.1. The effective terminal pd at the motor may be controlled by alternate
turning on all thyristors for a finite number of cycles of the source and th
removing the gating signals for a further finite number of cycles. Provided th
the driven mechanical system has substantial inertia and the source ca
tolerate this intermittent load and the accompanying switching transients, th
may be an acceptable method of speed control.

A more frequently used method of speed control consists in varying t
point in the cycle of the source pd at which each thyristor, in sequence,
turned on. This method, called *phase control*, provides continuously variab
speed control, which the previously described method does not, and is also t

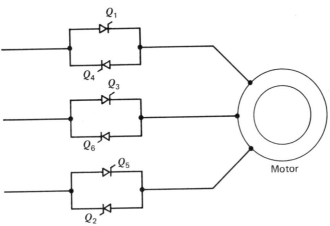

Fig. 7.1. Symmetrical AC power controller.

method that must be used to accelerate the motor from standstill with a constant frequency supply if large starting currents are to be avoided.

Certain alternatives to the symmetrical arrangement in Fig. 7.1 reduce the cost of the installation. One replaces one thyristor in each inverse-parallel connected pair by a diode. The three devices that carry positive or negative line current are changed. One adverse consequence of this arrangement is an increase in the already considerable harmonic content of the line and motor currents. A second alternative consists of removing the pair of devices from one line. The effect of unbalance is now added to that of harmonics to cause further deterioration in motor performance. To some extent the economies made in reducing the complexity of the controller are offset by the need to derate the motor even further than would be required for the six-thyristor system in Fig. 7.1.

A symmetrical arrangement that has the advantage of reducing the required current rating of the devices is shown in Fig. 7.2. This can be used only if both

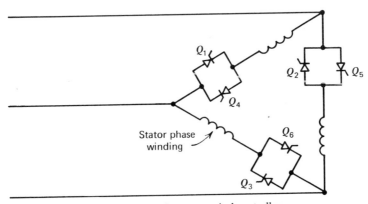

Fig. 7.2. Alternative symmetrical controller.

ends of each stator phase winding are accessible and this is not the case in standard motors.

A large economy that can be introduced for relatively low-power drives without the penalty of further deterioration in motor performance replaces each inverse-parallel connected pair of thyristors with a triac. This simplifies the control logic and reduces the controller wiring.

7.2. OPERATION OF THE SYMMETRICAL CONTROLLER

Figure 7.3 shows the symmetrical controller configuration with the addition of two pairs of devices that can be brought into operation to give reversal of the phase sequence of the motor excitation and may therefore provide braking by plugging and reverse driving. Because the rotor-circuit resistance is high, the currents during plugging may not cause serious overheating and the braking torque developed can be substantial. If the mechanical system overhauls the motor regenerative braking will take place; therefore for a particular phase-control setting of the thyristors the four-quadrant diagram in Fig. 7.4 is applicable.

The speed-torque curves illustrated in Fig. 7.4 will not necessarily correspond to those that would be obtained if the motor were driven from a three-phase source of constant pd. Indeed, they will do so only if the delay angle α is so small that the controller is inoperative. It can be shown that if α, the phase angle at which the reference thyristor is turned on, is equal to or less than the angle

$$\varphi = \tan^{-1} \frac{\omega_s L}{R} \text{ rad} \tag{7.1}$$

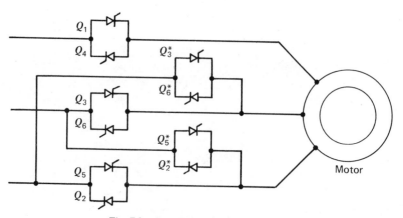

Fig. 7.3. Reversing power controller.

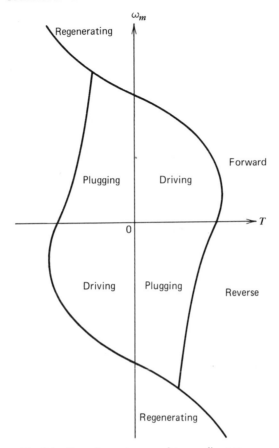

Fig. 7.4. Reversing system speed-torque diagram.

where ω_s = angular frequency of the source
     L = per-phase inductance of the motor at operating speed
     R = per-phase resistance of the motor at operating speed

the system will operate as a normal three-phase motor drive with no thyristors in the lines. The pd's at the motor terminals and the motor line current will be sinusoidal. As each line thyristor ceases to conduct current in one direction, its inverse-parallel connected partner begins to conduct current in the reverse direction. An increase in α, or in speed which causes an increase in R and a reduction in φ, disturbs this pattern of behavior and results in a gap between the turn-off of one thyristor and the turn-on of its partner.[5] Consequently the line current flows in alternating pulses, as illustrated in Fig. 7.5 for three values of delay angle α. Under these conditions the motor departs from the speed-torque characteristics obtained from the constant pd source. Because the line currents are nonsinusoidal, current harmonics are present in the motor, and unfortunately, the magnitudes of these harmonics are difficult to calculate.

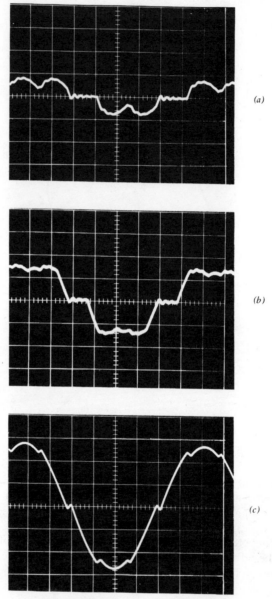

Fig. 7.5. Waveforms of line current for a motor running at a speed such that $\phi = \pi/4$: (a) $\alpha = 135°$; (b) $\alpha = 120°$; (c) $\alpha = 90°$.

7.3. PUMP OR FAN DRIVES

The ideal efficiency of an induction motor, which neglects all losses other than the resistive losses in the rotor circuit, is expressed by

$$\eta = 1 - s \text{ pu} \tag{7.2}$$

In the interests of energy conservation, therefore, speed control of an induction motor by variation of terminal pd is suitable only when a narrow range of speeds at relatively low slip is required. Drives that answer this description are those for fans and centrifugal pumps, for which, to a close approximation, the load torque at the motor coupling may be expressed by

$$T_L = k\omega_m^2 \text{ N} \cdot \text{m} \tag{7.3}$$

where k is a constant. For such a drive the variation in internal torque developed by the motor may be represented by a characteristic like that marked $T_{\text{loss}} + T_L$ in Fig. 6.7. The volume of fluid delivered by the fan or pump against a constant pressure head is proportional to the power output of the motor, that is, to the cube of the speed, and a speed range of 2:1 is sufficient to provide a delivery range of 8:1, which is as much as normally required. Consequently, although the high-slip motor has a low efficiency even at full speed, operation at half speed results in an ideal efficiency of half that at full speed, but this occurs when energy consumption is low. These drives therefore are frequently acceptable.

The torque developed by a motor excited by a power controller will have components due to the fundamental and harmonic components of both the current and flux that occur in the motor. Because these harmonics and their effects cannot be calculated easily, only approximate predictions of performance are made and, even with R_c omitted, the equivalent circuit in Fig. 6.3 may be more elaborate than justified for many purposes and can be further simplified by the omission of the magnetizing inductance branch. This yields the equivalent circuit in Fig. 7.6 in which

$$I_a = I_a' \text{ A} \tag{7.4}$$

In Chapter 6 it is shown that the power dissipated in motor friction and windage is small compared with rated output power; the further assumption is therefore made that

$$P_{FW} = 0 \text{ W} \tag{7.5}$$

Consequently

$$T = T_L \text{ N} \cdot \text{m} \tag{7.6}$$

This also means that

$$P_{\text{mech}} = P_0 \text{ W} \tag{7.7}$$

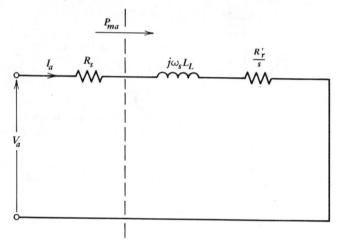

Fig. 7.6. Motor equivalent circuit for power-controller drives.

or

$$\frac{3(1-s)}{s}R'_rI_a^2 = \frac{2}{p}\omega_s(1-s)T \ \text{W} \tag{7.8}$$

from which

$$T = \frac{3p}{2}\frac{R'_rI_a^2}{s\omega_s} = k\left[\frac{2}{p}\omega_s(1-s)\right]^2 \ \text{N}\cdot\text{m} \tag{7.9}$$

From Eq. 7.9

$$I_a = (1-s)\sqrt{Ks} \ \text{A} \tag{7.10}$$

where

$$K = \frac{8\omega_s^3}{3p^3}\cdot\frac{k}{R'_r} \tag{7.11}$$

The slip at which the maximum value of I_a occurs may be obtained by setting $dI_a/ds = 0$. When this is done the result is

$$I_a = I_{a\,\text{max}} \ \text{A} \qquad s = \tfrac{1}{3} \ \text{pu} \tag{7.12}$$

The rated torque T_rated of the motor occurs at the rated slip s_rated when the motor is drawing rated current I_rated; therefore from Eq. 7.9

$$T_\text{rated} = \frac{3p}{2}\frac{R'_rI_\text{rated}^2}{\omega_s s_\text{rated}} = k\left[\frac{2}{p}\omega_s(1-s_\text{rated})\right]^2 \ \text{N}\cdot\text{m} \tag{7.13}$$

From Eqs. 7.9 and 7.13

$$\frac{T}{T_\text{rated}} = \frac{(1-s)^2}{(1-s_\text{rated})^2} \tag{7.14}$$

and

$$\left[\frac{I_a}{I_{rated}}\right]^2 = \frac{s(1-s)^2}{s_{rated}(1-s_{rated})^2} = \frac{sT}{s_{rated}T_{rated}} \tag{7.15}$$

Substitution from Eq. 7.12 of $I_a = I_{a\,max}$ and $s = 1/3$ in Eq. 7.15 yields

$$\frac{I_{a\,max}}{I_{rated}} = \frac{2}{3\sqrt{3}\,(1-s_{rated})\sqrt{s_{rated}}} \tag{7.16}$$

If, in a typical design D motor, $s_{rated} = 0.15$, then

$$I_{a\,max} = 1.17 I_{rated}\ \text{A} \tag{7.17}$$

Equation 7.17 indicates that a derating factor of 0.85 should be applied to the motor if it is anticipated that it will run continuously at $s = \frac{1}{3}$. However, when the approximations leading to this conclusion and the less effective cooling at reduced speed are considered it becomes probable that a factor of 0.75 would be nearer the mark.

For line current I_a at slip s, V_a may be calculated from

$$V_a = \left[\left(R_s + \frac{R_r'}{s}\right)^2 + X_L^2\right]^{1/2} \times I_a\ \text{V} \tag{7.18}$$

The input power to the motor is

$$P_{in} = P_{mech} + 3\left(R_s + R_r'\right)I_a^2\ \text{W} \tag{7.19}$$

If, at this stage, it is considered desirable to add a quantity to the right side of Eq. 7.19 corresponding to the nonresistive losses in the motor, it would not be unreasonable to assume that these losses were proportional to V_a^2.

If $\bar{V}_a$ is now defined as $V_a \underline{/0°}$

$$\bar{I}_a = I_a \underline{/-\varphi_r}\ \text{A} \tag{7.20}$$

$$\varphi_r = \tan^{-1}\frac{X_L}{R_s + R_r'/s} \tag{7.21}$$

The motor power factor is

$$PF = \cos\varphi_r \tag{7.22}$$

and the efficiency of the motor is

$$\eta = \frac{P_0}{P_{in}}\ \text{pu} \tag{7.23}$$

If the losses in the controller are neglected the input current to the controller and the power developed at its input will be the same as those for the motor. If the line-to-line source pd is V_s the system power factor is

$$PF_s = \frac{P_{in}}{\sqrt{3}\,V_s I_a} \tag{7.24}$$

This will necessarily be lower than the motor power factor because $V_s/\sqrt{3} > V_a$. Because the controller is assumed to be lossless, the efficiency of the system is the same as that of the motor.

Because harmonics in the system variables have been neglected, the foregoing analysis will give optimistic results that will yield lower currents and higher power factors than are met in practice.

It remains to determine an approximate range of the controller delay angle α required in this kind of drive and, because not even an approximate analysis can be readily carried out, this is best done by using experimental results.

Some experimentally determined curves of normalized rms line current versus delay angle α for an RL load circuit of four different impedance angles φ are shown in Fig. 7.7. The base current used is

$$I_{base} = \frac{V}{\sqrt{3}\,Z}\ \text{A} \tag{7.25}$$

When, from the preceding analysis, the current and power factor of the motor

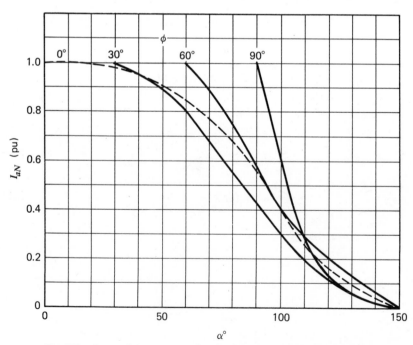

Fig. 7.7. Curve of I_{aN} versus α for the motor and converter in Fig. 7.1.

for any condition of operation have been determined an approximate corresponding value of α may be obtained by interpolation in this diagram. At the upper end of the current range the motor will be operating at or near rated terminal pd and the minimum value of α will be equal to the phase angle of the motor line current under rated conditions. At the lower end of the current range the value of α taken from the curves by interpolating the line-current magnitude and angle will be high because harmonics will raise the rms current above the value reached by calculation of the fundamental component. A range of α obtained by this method will therefore include, but be greater than, the range required in practice. This error is no greater than those introduced by other approximations in the system model because the inductance of the motor load suppresses current harmonics to a great extent.

Example 7.1

A 60-hp (44.8-kW), 460-V, 60-Hz, 1530-rpm, Class D, squirrel-cage induction motor has the following equivalent-circuit parameters:

$$R_s = 0.119\ \Omega, \qquad R'_r = 0.508\ \Omega, \qquad \omega_s L_L = 0.860\ \Omega$$

It is supplied from the 460-V, three-phase, ac source by a power controller of the form shown in Fig. 7.1. It is required to operate over a speed range of $765 < n < 1530$ rpm when driving a centrifugal pump that absorbs 60 hp at 1530 rpm.

Determine the range of α required in the controller by using the approximate equivalent circuit in Fig. 7.6.

Solution

Rated slip is

$$s = \frac{1800 - 1530}{1800} = 0.150$$

Motor impedance at full load

$$\bar{Z}_m = 0.119 + \frac{0.508}{0.150} + j0.860 = 3.610 \underline{/13.78°}\ \Omega$$

The minimum value of α is 13.78°. Slip at 765 rpm is

$$s = \frac{1800 - 765}{1800} = 0.575$$

$$Z_m = 0.119 + \frac{0.508}{0.575} + j0.860 = 1.323 \underline{/40.64°}\ \Omega$$

Motor full-load current is

$$I_{rated} = \frac{460}{3.61\sqrt{3}} = 73.57 \text{ A}$$

From Eq. 7.15 current at 765 rpm is obtained from

$$\frac{I_a^2}{73.57^2} = \frac{0.575(1 - 0.575)^2}{0.150(1 - 0.150)^2}$$

from which

$$I_a = 72.02$$

Base current at 7.65 rpm is

$$I_{base} = \frac{460}{1.321\sqrt{2}} = 201.0 \text{ A}$$

$$I_{aN} = \frac{72.02}{201.0} = 0.358 \text{ A}$$

Interpolation at $I_{aN} = 0.358$ and $\varphi = 40.64$ in Fig. 7.7 yields

$$\alpha = 98°$$

An available range of $10° < \alpha < 100°$ should be satisfactory.

Example 7.2

A 100-hp (74.6-kW), 460-V, 60-Hz, Class D, squirrel-cage induction motor develops rated power at 1026 rpm and has the following equivalent-circuit parameters:

$$R_s = 0.0591 \text{ }\Omega, \qquad R_r' = 0.311 \text{ }\Omega, \qquad \omega_s L_L = 0.588 \text{ }\Omega,$$

$$\omega_s L_{ms} = 7.79 \text{ }\Omega, \qquad R_c = 41.0 \text{ }\Omega$$

Friction and windage losses are negligible.

The motor is used in the system in Fig. 7.1 to drive a fan that absorbs 100 hp at 1026 rpm. The ac source pd is 460 V, line-to-line.

Using the equivalent circuit in Fig. 6.3, plot curves of motor current, power factor, and efficiency as well as system power factor as functions of speed in rpm over the speed range of $250 < n < 1026$ rpm.

Solution

At any speed n the following relationships apply:

$$s = \frac{1200 - n}{1200}$$

The impedance of the right branch of the circuit is

$$Z'_a = \left[\left(0.0591 + \frac{0.311}{s}\right)^2 + 0.588^2\right]^{1/2} \ \Omega$$

$$\angle Z'_a = \tan^{-1}\frac{0.588}{0.0591 + 0.311/s} \ \text{rad}$$

From Eq. 7.15, using I'_a in place of I_a,

$$I'_a = 357.8(1 - s)\sqrt{s} \ \text{A}$$

$$\bar{I}'_a = ReI'_a + jGmI'_a = 357.8(1 - s)\sqrt{s}\left(\cos\angle Z'_a - j\sin\angle Z'_a\right) \ \text{A}$$

$$V_a = Z'_a I'_a \ \text{V}$$

$$I_{ma} = \frac{V_a}{7.79} \ \text{A}$$

$$I_c = \frac{V_a}{41.03} \ \text{A}$$

$$I_a = \left[\left(ReI'_a + I_c\right)^2 + \left(GmI'_a + I_{ma}\right)^2\right]^{1/2} \ \text{A}$$

$$\angle I_a = \tan^{-1}\left(\frac{GmI'_a + I_{ma}}{ReI'_a + I_c}\right) \ \text{rad}$$

$$PF_m = \cos\angle I_a$$

$$P_{in} = 3V_a I_a PF_m \ \text{W}$$

$$P_{cu} = 3(0.0591 + 0.311)\left(I'_a\right)^2 = 1.110\left(I'_a\right)^2 \ \text{W}$$

$$P_{\bar{0}} = P_{in} - P_c - P_{cu}$$

$$\eta = \frac{P_0}{P_{in}}$$

$$PF_s = \frac{P_{in}}{460\sqrt{3} \times I_a}$$

When these relations are used with various values of n the curves shown in Fig. 7.8 are obtained. Note that, in accordance with Eq. 7.12, the maximum

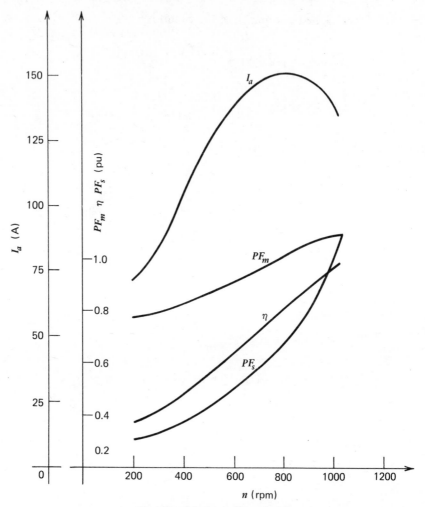

Fig. 7.8.   Solution to Example 7.2.

value of I_a occurs at $s \simeq 1/3$, that is $n = 800$ rpm. As this current is about 13% in excess of the full-load current, and the rms value would be further increased by harmonics, a derating of motors for this kind of drive of from 25% to 30% appears advisable.

7.4.   CLOSED-LOOP SYSTEM

For loads with a single invariable speed-torque characteristic the open-loop control system described in the preceding sections can work quite satisfactorily, because a given control setting can be relied on to provide a known speed and to maintain that speed once the system reaches a thermal equilibrium. Changes in ambient temperature will result in only minor divergencies from the set speed. If, however, the supply system pd were subject to variation a feedback loop might be required.

For pump or fan drives in which the nature of the pumped fluid and the pressure head can vary a closed-loop system must often be used. A typical arrangement would have an internal current loop to provide a current limit and an outer speed loop. Stability problems need not be anticipated but predictions of rapidity and accuracy of response can be made reliably only from the results of digital or analog computer simulations.

PROBLEMS

7.1. A centrifugal pump requires a driving torque of 285 N · m at 1500 rpm. It is proposed to drive it in the system in Fig. 7.1 by direct coupling to a 460-V, 75-hp (56.0-kW), Class D, squirrel-cage induction motor with the following equivalent-circuit parameters:

$$R_s = 0.0862 \ \Omega, \qquad R'_r = 0.427 \ \Omega, \qquad \omega_s L_L = 0.736 \ \Omega$$

The rated speed of the motor is 1530 rpm. Friction and windage loss is negligible. Using the equivalent circuit of Fig. 7.6,

(a) determine at what speed the system will run when α is set at the value that will yield sinusoidal terminal pd and line current;

(b) determine the line current at $s = \frac{1}{3}$ and the value of α required at that slip.

7.2. Repeat Problem 7.1, using the equivalent circuit in Fig. 6.3. The additional circuit parameters are

$$\omega_s L_{ms} = 11.3 \ \Omega, \qquad R_c = 48.2 \ \Omega$$

7.3. The converter and motor combination in Problems 7.1 and 7.2 is required to drive a load over the maximum possible speed range with a constant torque of 100 N · m. Using the equivalent circuit in Fig. 6.3, determine the permissible speed range and the corresponding range of the control variable α.

7.4. For the system in Problem 7.3 plot curves of I_a, PF_m, η, and PF_s as functions of n over the available speed range. If the current may not exceed the rated value determined in Problem 7.1 what is the permissible speed range? Is this a suitable application for this type of system? Give reasons.

7.5. A motor for the system in Figure 7.1 is required to drive a fan that presents a load torque of 175 N · m at 1500 rpm. Using the equivalent circuit in Fig. 7.6, select a suitable motor from the four specified below. The criterion is that the motor current obtained in this approximate calculation may not exceed 85% of the rated current of the chosen motor. Friction and windage losses of the motor may be neglected. The motors are all 60-Hz, 460-V, and have the following ratings and equivalent-circuit parameter values:

	Horsepower	I_{rated}	n	R_s	R'_r	R_c	X_L	X_{ms}
A	40	56	1525	0.185	0.813	100	1.29	14.8
B	50	68	1545	0.130	0.612	77.8	1.11	13.9
C	60	82	1540	0.119	0.519	62.8	0.860	11.0
D	75	102	1520	0.0862	0.440	45.3	0.73	11.3

Chapter 8

Speed Control
by Slip-Energy Recovery
(Subsynchronous Converter Cascade)

8.1. INTRODUCTION

The type of drive discussed in this chapter is, like that in Chapter 7, suitable for driving centrifugal pumps and fans but can be of very high power (20 MW). Induction-motor drives for pipeline pumps have been standard equipment for many years. There are pipelines, however, that are required to carry a variety of fluids at various rates, and if this is to be done efficiently a flexible system is essential. The operating point of a pump can be changed by partly closing a valve and changing the resistance characteristic of the pipeline or, more efficiently, by changing the speed of the pump.

Part of this system is similar to that shown in Fig. 6.6, in that a three-phase diode bridge is connected to the rotor terminals of a wound-rotor motor, but the pd's introduced into the rotor circuits to reduce the motor speed are no longer provided by the terminal pd of the single resistor R_{ex} in that diagram. Instead, the resistor is replaced by the dc side of a three-phase controlled bridge circuit operating as a naturally commutated fixed-frequency inverter. The ac side of this inverter is connected to the lines that supply the stator of the induction motor, as shown in Fig. 8.1. The pd at the dc terminals of the inverter can be varied by varying the delay angle α; thus the motor speed can be controlled. Energy is no longer wasted in a resistor but instead, with minimal losses, is fed back to the source that supplies the motor. The inductor in the dc link between the diode rectifier and the inverter smooths the rectified output pd of the rotor as it appears at the dc terminals of the inverter. At all times the value of $\bar{v}_{LK}$ in Fig. 8.1 is equal to that of $\bar{v}_0$, which is negative, apart from a small average pd due to the resistance of the inductor.

Because of losses due to current and flux harmonics, standard motors must be derated by about 15%. The ratings of the two converters must allow for the large ranges of rotor terminal pd and current that occur over the operating speed range of the motor. Rotor terminal pd will be high at low speed, at

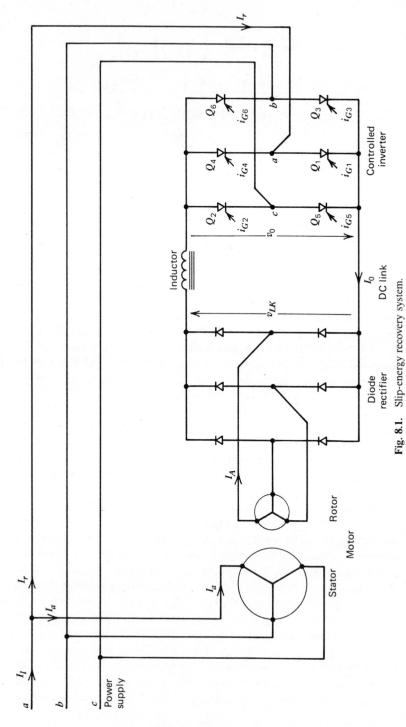

Fig. 8.1. Slip-energy recovery system.

which, for a pump drive, current will be low because torque is low. The converse will be true at high speed. Thus the effective power ratings of the converters must be well in excess of the power fed back to the supply system. This excess may be reduced by operating the control over a narrow speed range near the synchronous speed of the motor and accelerating the motor from standstill by conventional starting equipment that is switched out of circuit when the controlled-speed range is reached. A further factor that must be considered is the reliability of the supply system. Loss of the supply, or serious reduction of the source pd, may result in short-circuit through the thyristors of the inverter because, in terms of Fig. 4.3, $E_a < -\sqrt{2}\,V$.

This system lends itself readily to automatic control and, due to the low inertia of the centrifugal pump, a fast-response system is obtained with only a single-quadrant drive because the pumped fluid provides effective braking. Closed-loop speed control with an internal current-limit loop is used.

8.2. OPERATION OF THE SYSTEM

Inverter operation of the controlled inverter in Fig. 8.1, when considered as a three-phase rectifier, requires that $\bar{v}_O$, the direct terminal potential difference of the converter, shall be negative while the input current i_O remains positive. In this way the dc "output" power of the controlled converter becomes negative and inverter operation takes place.

The required phase relationships of the gating signals for the thyristors to the ac source pd's must be determined. It is assumed that the phase sequence of the source is *abc*. If the output of a three-phase controlled bridge rectifier is to increase smoothly from zero certain gating signals must be applied to the thyristors even at zero output.[5] The diagram in Fig. 8.2 shows the relationship between source pd v_{ab} and $\bar{v}_O$ which appears at the inverter dc terminals when the induction motor is stationary. The turns ratio of the induction motor must be such that under these conditions $|\bar{v}_O| < \sqrt{2}\,V$; otherwise short-circuit of the source through the thyristors will occur. If the motor turns ratio does not satisfy this requirement a transformer may be introduced between the ac source and the ac terminals of the inverter. If the motor is to start smoothly from standstill, then, at $\omega t = \eta$ in Fig. 8.2, thyristor Q_1 must be on the point of receiving a gating signal while Q_6 is on the point of losing one; that is to say, $\omega t = \eta$ defines the beginning of the gating signal i_{G1} and the end of the gating signal i_{G6}. Any advance in the starting point of i_{G1} will allow current to flow from terminal a of the source to terminal b via the diode rectifier. This current is driven by pd $v_{ab} - \bar{v}_O$, both of which are negative. The starting and end points of all the other gating signals for zero current may now be determined from the two points already defined. The resulting signals are shown in Fig. 8.2.

The delay angle α of the reference thyristor Q_1 is defined as follows; *α is the interval in electrical angular measure by which the starting point of conduction is*

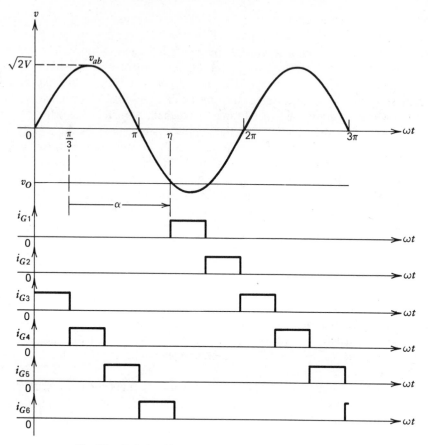

Fig. 8.2. Relationship of gating signals to v_{ab} for $\omega_m = 0$.

delayed by phase control in relation to the operation of the same circuit in which the thyristors are replaced by diodes and the dc load circuit is purely resistive. For a three-phase bridge rectifier $\alpha = 0$ at $\omega t = 60°$;[5] thus the value of α for zero speed is as shown in Fig. 8.2.

As α is reduced from the standstill value $\bar{v}_O$ becomes less negative. This means that the flow of current i_O results in three-phase rotor currents on the ac side of the diode rectifier, which cause the motor to accelerate. Acceleration results in a fall in $\bar{v}_{LK}$ and a reduction in the negative value of $\bar{v}_O$. If α is set at some value $90° < \alpha < \eta - 60°$ the motor will accelerate until the rotor currents develop the torque required to overcome rotational losses and the load torque on the rotor shaft, under which conditions the motor runs at constant speed.

The lower limit to α is $90°$ because below that value $\bar{v}_O$ goes positive and the diode rectifier acts as a short circuit on the dc terminals of the inverter. It is thus not possible for the rectifier to supply power to the rotor of the motor to cause it to run at more than synchronous speed. If converter losses are neglected and it is assumed that the dc link inductor makes i_O effectively constant at value I_O the relationships of the ac terminal variables of the rectifier/inverter with $\alpha = 90°$ are as shown in Fig. 8.3. Because under these conditions the ac-line current i_r is in quadrature with v_a, power developed at the ac terminals of the rectifier/inverter is zero. An increase in α permits i_r to fall back in phase in relation to v_a, and the resulting phase angle of more than 90° shows that inversion is taking place and energy is being delivered to the ac power source. Because the motor line current i_a will lag v_a by a substantial phase angle, the fundamental component of i_l formed from the fundamental components of i_a and i_r will lag v_a by a still greater angle. This indicates that the system as a whole will operate at a lower power factor than that of the motor.

It may be noted that regenerative braking at supersynchronous speed is not possible in this system because the polarity of $\bar{v}_{LK}$ does not change when the phase sequence of the rotor emf's reverses. A loaded induction motor controlled by slip-energy recovery can be decelerated more rapidly than a conventionally controlled motor. When α is increased to give a speed reduction rotor current momentarily falls to zero and zero driving torque is developed. When, in conventional control, the rotor-circuit resistance is increased to give a speed reduction rotor current is merely reduced and a reduced driving torque acts during deceleration.

The principal disadvantage of speed control by variation of motor terminal pd was seen in Chapter 7 to be the waste of energy in the rotor-circuit resistance when the motor was running at high slip. Moreover, the rotor-circuit

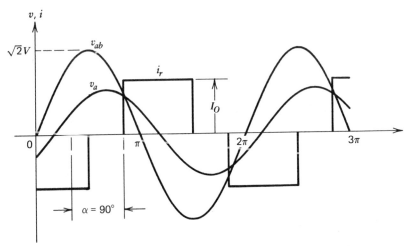

Fig. 8.3. Phase relationships of controlled-inverter terminal variables.

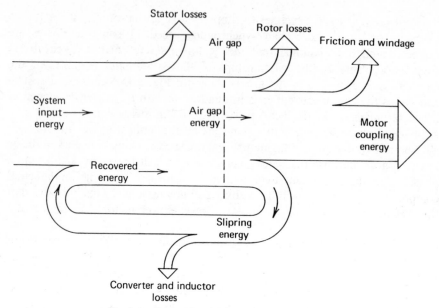

Fig. 8.4. Energy flow in the System of Fig. 8.1.

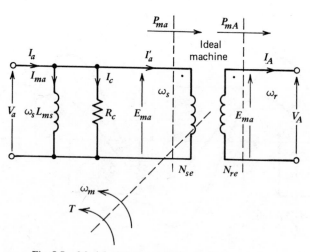

Fig. 8.5. Model of the wound-rotor induction motor.

resistance was made high to give the necessary motor speed-torque characteristic. This consideration does not apply in nearly the same degree to the slip-energy recovery system because the rotor-circuit resistance is as low as design will permit and nearly all of the energy crossing the air gap is converted to mechanical form or returned to the supply system thus the ideal efficiency equation (7.2) does not apply. The energy flow in the system is illustrated in Fig. 8.4.

To determine the details of performance of the system at any point in the speed-torque characteristic of a given load it is necessary to derive some basic relationships for the slip-energy recovery system.

8.2.1. Basic Relationships

To reduce the complication of the necessary calculations while still making acceptable performance predictions the approximate motor equivalent circuit shown in Fig. 8.5 is used. Winding resistances are small and leakage reactances much less than that of the dc-link inductor. Therefore they may be neglected. The parameters L_{ms} and R_c are considered constant because the motor terminal pd is constant. For this equivalent circuit

$$s = \frac{\omega_r}{\omega_s} \tag{8.1}$$

$$\frac{V_A}{V_a} = s\frac{N_{re}}{N_{se}} \tag{8.2}$$

$$\frac{I_A}{I_a'} = \frac{N_{se}}{N_{re}} \tag{8.3}$$

$$\frac{P_{mA}}{P_{ma}} = s \tag{8.4}$$

$$P_{mech} = 3(P_{ma} - P_{mA}) = 3(1-s)P_{ma} \text{ W} \tag{8.5}$$

In Eq. 8.5 P_{mech} is the power converted to mechanical form. If the source pd's are defined as

$$v_{ab} = \sqrt{2}\,V\sin\omega_s t$$

$$v_{bc} = \sqrt{2}\,V\sin\left(\omega_s t - \frac{2\pi}{3}\right) \text{ V} \tag{8.6}$$

$$v_{ca} = \sqrt{2}\,V\sin\left(\omega_s t - \frac{4\pi}{3}\right)$$

then for the inverter the average pd appearing at the dc terminals is

$$\bar{v}_O = \frac{3\sqrt{2}\,V}{\pi}\cos\alpha \text{ V} \tag{8.7}$$

In Fig. 8.5

$$V_a = \frac{V}{\sqrt{3}} \text{ V} \tag{8.8}$$

For the diode rectifier in the rotor circuit $\alpha = 0$ and from Eq. 8.7 the average link-circuit pd is

$$\bar{v}_{LK} = \frac{3\sqrt{2}}{\pi} \times \sqrt{3}\,V_A \text{ V} \tag{8.9}$$

At slip s

$$V_A = s\frac{N_{re}}{N_{se}}V_a = s\frac{N_{re}}{N_{se}}\frac{V}{\sqrt{3}} \text{ V} \tag{8.10}$$

and

$$\bar{v}_{LK} = \frac{3\sqrt{2}}{\pi}s\frac{N_{re}}{N_{se}}V = -\bar{v}_O = -\frac{3\sqrt{2}\,V}{\pi}\cos\alpha \text{ V} \tag{8.11}$$

From which

$$s = -\frac{N_{se}}{N_{re}}\cos\alpha = \frac{\omega_s - (p/2)\omega_m}{\omega_s} \tag{8.12}$$

and this yields

$$\omega_m = \frac{2}{p}\omega_s\left(1 + \frac{N_{se}}{N_{re}}\cos\alpha\right) \text{ rad/s} \tag{8.13}$$

Thus speed appears to be a function of α alone and is independent of torque. In practice, some speed regulation appears when load is applied, due to the neglected equivalent-circuit parameters and the fact that the converters are not lossless. The regulation between no load and full load will be approximately equal to the difference between the synchronous speed and the rated speed of the motor and will be the same for any value of α. In practice, this yields curves that resemble the subsynchronous characteristics of Fig. 6.8.

From Eqs. 8.4 and 8.5

$$P_{\text{mech}} = 3\left(\frac{P_{mA}}{s} - P_{mA}\right) = 3\frac{(1-s)}{s}P_{mA} \text{ W} \tag{8.14}$$

and in this system

$$3P_{mA} = \bar{v}_{LK}I_O \text{ W} \tag{8.15}$$

Thus

$$P_{mech} = \frac{(1-s)}{s}\bar{v}_{LK}I_O \text{ W} \tag{8.16}$$

Substitution for $\bar{v}_{LK}$ from Eq. 8.11 then yields

$$P_{mech} = \frac{3\sqrt{2}}{\pi}(1-s)\frac{N_{re}}{N_{se}}VI_O \text{ W} \tag{8.17}$$

Also

$$P_{mech} = T\omega_m = \frac{2}{p}(1-s)\omega_s T \text{ W} \tag{8.18}$$

where T is the air-gap torque developed by the motor. Equating the two expressions for P_{mech} in Eqs. 8.17 and 8.18 then yields

$$I_O = 0.740 \times \frac{2}{p}\omega_s \cdot \frac{N_{se}}{N_{re}} \cdot \frac{T}{V} \text{ A} \tag{8.19}$$

This relationship shows that I_O is dependent only on T and is independent of motor speed.

8.2.2. Limit to Ratio N_{re}/N_{se}

The inductor in the dc link is introduced for the purpose of making I_O as nearly constant as possible and this means that the link current will be continuous. It can be shown[5] that if the direct current from a three-phase rectifier is continuous α may not exceed $\pi - \omega t_{off} - \mu$ rad, where t_{off} is the turn-off time of the thyristors and μ is the overlap angle. Typically, t_{off} is of the order of 50 μs and at 60 Hz ωt_{off} is approximately 1.08°, whereas μ may be three or four degrees. A safe upper limit for α may therefore be taken as 170°.
From Eq. 8.11

$$s\frac{N_{re}}{N_{se}} = -\cos\alpha \tag{8.20}$$

Substitution of $\alpha = 170°$ and $s = s_{max}$ in Eq. 8.20 yields

$$\frac{N_{re}}{N_{se}} = \frac{0.985}{s_{max}} \tag{8.21}$$

and this equation establishes a maximum permissible value for the effective turns ratio of the motor. If a motor with a turns ratio exceeding this value must be used a transformer must be introduced between the ac source and the controlled inverter in Fig. 8.1. In these circumstances Eq. 8.11 becomes

$$\bar{v}_{LK} = \frac{3\sqrt{2}}{\pi} \cdot s \cdot \frac{N_{re}}{N_{se}} V = -\bar{v}_O = \frac{-3\sqrt{2}}{\pi} \cdot \frac{N_p}{N_s} \cdot V\cos\alpha \qquad (8.22)$$

where N_s = the transformer turns on the source side; N_p = the transformer turns on the inverter side.

In other words, if the pd at the rotor terminals is too high, then that at the inverter ac terminals must be raised. Induction motors, however, are usually manufactured with turns ratio N_{re}/N_{se} less, and often substantially less, than unity; therefore the practical situation will be that a transformer is necessary to *lower* the pd at the ac terminals of the inverter.

From Eq. 8.22

$$s\frac{N_{re}}{N_{se}} = -\frac{N_p}{N_s}\cos\alpha \qquad (8.23)$$

and at the lower speed limit of operation

$$\frac{N_{re}}{N_{se}} \cdot \frac{N_s}{N_p} = \frac{0.985}{s_{max}} \qquad (8.24)$$

At the upper end of the speed range, when s approaches zero, Eq. 8.23 shows that α must approach 90°. Thus the required control range is

$$90° < \alpha < \cos^{-1}\left(-s_{max}\frac{N_{re}}{N_{se}} \cdot \frac{N_s}{N_p}\right) \text{ deg} \qquad (8.25)$$

For a system that must operate down to zero speed and in which N_{re}/N_{se} does not exceed the limiting value and no transformer is fitted the control range required is

$$90° < \alpha < \cos^{-1}\left(-\frac{N_{re}}{N_{se}}\right) \text{ deg} \qquad (8.26)$$

8.3. PERFORMANCE PREDICTION

In the motor equivalent circuit of Fig. 8.5 V_a is sinusoidal; therefore E_{ma} is assumed to be sinusoidal. If the normal assumption of sinusoidally distributed machine windings is made the rotating flux wave in the air gap will have a sinusoidal space distribution and will rotate at constant speed $(2/p)\omega_s$ rad/s. The sinusoidal flux wave will interact to produce torque only with the fundamental component of rotor current. If this rotor current is constant, no matter what its wave shape, a constant air-gap torque will be developed.

If the inductor in the dc link is considered to eliminate all harmonics from i_O the inverter ac line currents as well as the rotor currents will have the rectangular waveform shown in Fig. 8.3.[5] The amplitude of this wave will be I_O.

Once again, as in Chapter 7, performance prediction may start from consideration of a specific point on the speed-torque characteristic of the load, and although pump and fan loads have been especially mentioned in the foregoing the analysis that follows is applicable to any type of load characteristic.

Consider a point $[T_L, \omega_m]$ on the load characteristic. The slip at this speed is

$$s = \frac{\omega_s - (p/2)\omega_m}{\omega_s} \tag{8.27}$$

and from Eq. 8.12

$$\alpha = \cos^{-1}\left(-s\frac{N_{re}}{N_{se}}\right) \text{ rad} \tag{8.28}$$

From Eq. 8.11

$$\bar{v}_{LK} = -\frac{3\sqrt{2}\, V}{\pi}\cos\alpha \text{ V} \tag{8.29}$$

The power output of the motor is

$$P_o = T_L \cdot \omega_m \text{ W} \tag{8.30}$$

The friction and windage power P_{FW} may be obtained from the tests described in Chapter 6. The mechanical power developed by the motor is then

$$P_{\text{mech}} = P_o + P_{FW} \text{ W} \tag{8.31}$$

From Eq. 8.16

$$I_O = \frac{s}{1-s} \cdot \frac{P_{\text{mech}}}{\bar{v}_{LK}} \text{ A} \tag{8.32}$$

Because the waveform of I_A is known, its rms value may be calculated:

$$I_{AR} = \sqrt{\tfrac{2}{3}}\, I_O = 0.8165 I_O \text{ A} \tag{8.33}$$

The rms value of the fundamental component of I_A is

$$I_{A1} = \frac{4I_O}{\sqrt{2}\,\pi}\cos\frac{\pi}{6} = 0.7797I_O \text{ A} \tag{8.34}$$

and the rms value of the harmonics in I_A is

$$I_{Ah} = \left[I_{AR}^2 - I_{A1}^2\right]^{1/2} = 0.2424I_O \text{ A} \tag{8.35}$$

In the magnetizing and coreloss branches of the equivalent circuit

$$I_{ma} = \frac{V}{\sqrt{3}\,\omega_s L_{ms}} \text{ A} \tag{8.36}$$

$$I_c = \frac{V}{\sqrt{3}\,R_c} \text{ A} \tag{8.37}$$

both of which are invariable, fundamental-frequency currents. Thus the fundamental motor input current is

$$\bar{I}_{a1} = I_{a1}\!\diagdown\!-\varphi_{a1} \text{ A} \tag{8.38}$$

where

$$I_{a1} = \left[\left(\frac{N_{re}}{N_{se}}I_{A1} + I_c\right)^2 + I_{ma}^2\right]^{1/2} \text{ A} \tag{8.39}$$

and

$$\varphi_{a1} = \tan^{-1}\left[\frac{I_{ma}}{(N_{re}/N_{se})I_{A1} + I_c}\right] \text{ rad} \tag{8.40}$$

The rms motor input current is then

$$I_{aR} = \left[I_{a1}^2 + \left(\frac{N_{re}}{N_{se}}I_{Ah}\right)^2\right]^{1/2} \text{ A} \tag{8.41}$$

Because the waveform of I_r is also rectangular and of amplitude I_O, the rms value of its fundamental component is the same as that of I_A; that is,

$$I_{r1} = 0.7797I_O \text{ A} \tag{8.42}$$

and the rms value of I_r is

$$I_{rR} = 0.8165I_O \text{ A} \tag{8.43}$$

Figure 8.3 shows that the fundamental component I_{r1} lags V_a by the delay angle α and

$$\bar{I}_{r1} = I_{r1}\underline{/-\alpha} \text{ A} \tag{8.44}$$

The fundamental component of source current is thus

$$\bar{I}_{l1} = \bar{I}_{a1} + \bar{I}_{r1} = I_{l1}\underline{/-\varphi_{l1}} \text{ A} \tag{8.45}$$

If filters at the input of the system virtually eliminate harmonics in the power supply lines the source power factor is

$$PF_l = \cos\varphi_{l1} \tag{8.46}$$

In calculating the efficiency of the system, the motor winding resistances, which have been neglected in the foregoing, must be taken into account. Thus the power at the motor terminals is

$$P_m = P_{\text{mech}} + 3\left(R_c I_c^2 + R_s I_{aR}^2 + R_r I_{AR}^2\right) + \bar{v}_{LK}I_O \text{ W} \tag{8.47}$$

The power developed by the source is equal to the power at the motor terminals, less that fed back via the inverter. Thus

$$P_l = P_m - \bar{v}_{LK}I_O \text{ W} \tag{8.48}$$

and the efficiency of the system is

$$\eta = \frac{P_o}{P_l} \tag{8.49}$$

Example 8.1

A centrifugal pump presents a load torque of 485 N · m at 110 rpm and is to be driven by a slip-energy recovery system incorporating a 460-V, 100-hp (74.6-kW), 1180-rpm wound-rotor motor for which the equivalent-circuit parameters are

$$R_s = 0.0591 \ \Omega, \qquad \omega_s L_{ms} = 7.79 \ \Omega,$$

$$R_r = 0.0604 \ \Omega, \qquad N_{re}/N_{se} = 0.810,$$

$$R_c = 57.2 \ \Omega$$

It may be assumed that friction and windage losses in the motor are negligible and that the supply pd is maintained constant at 460 V. The motor is to accelerate from standstill to the minimum operating speed by means of the converter system and the required operating speed range is $550 < n < 1100$ rpm.

Draw curves of motor speed n, motor line current I_{aR}, power output P_o, delay angle α, dc-link pd $\bar{v}_{LK}$, link current I_O, system fundamental line current I_{l1}, system power factor PF_l and system efficiency η as functions of load torque T_L.

Solution

The required values are calculated in the following for a specified value of T_L by the procedure described in Section 8.3. For this load

$$T_L = k\omega^2$$

At 1100 rpm or 115.2 rad/s $T_L = 485$ N · m thus

$$k = \frac{485}{115.2^2} = \frac{1}{27.36}$$

The minimum load torque occurs at 550 rpm or 57.60 rad/s and is

$$T_{L\,min} = \frac{57.60^2}{27.36} = 121.3 \text{ N} \cdot \text{m}$$

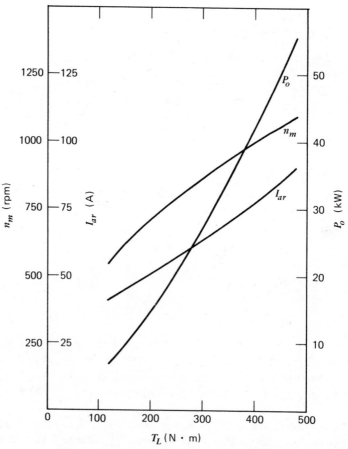

Fig. 8.6. Solution to Example 8.1. Motor Variables.

The operating range of load torque is therefore

$$485 \geq T_L \geq 121.3 \text{ N} \cdot \text{m}$$

For the specified point on the curve of T_L vs n the choice was $T_L = 300$ N $\cdot$ m.
Then

$$\omega_m = [300 \times 27.36]^{1/2} = 90.60 \text{ rad/s}$$

and

$$n = 865.1 \text{ rpm}$$

$$s = \frac{1200 - 865.1}{1200} = 0.2790$$

From Eq. 8.28

$$\alpha = \cos^{-1}(-0.2790 \times 0.81) = 103.1°$$

$$\bar{v}_{LK} = \frac{-3\sqrt{2} \times 460}{\pi} \cos 103.1° = 140.4 \text{ V}$$

$$P_o = 300 \times 90.60 = 27180 \text{ W}$$

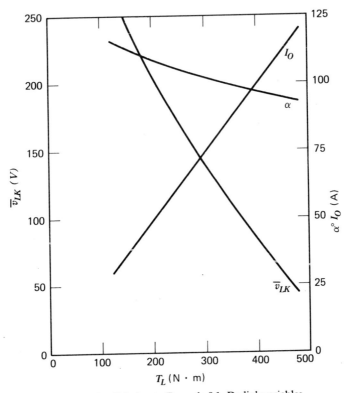

Fig. 8.7. Solution to Example 8.1. Dc-link variables.

and because friction and windage are to be neglected this is also P_{mech}. From Eq. 8.32

$$I_O = \frac{0.2790}{1 - 0.2790} \times \frac{27180}{140.4} = 74.91 \text{ A}$$

$$I_{AR} = 0.8165 \times 74.91 = 61.17 \text{ A}$$

$$I_{A1} = 0.7797 \times 74.91 = 58.41 \text{ A}$$

$$I_{Ah} = (61.17^2 - 58.41^2)^{1/2} = 18.17 \text{ A}$$

$$I_{ma} = \frac{460}{7.79\sqrt{3}} = 34.09 \text{ A}$$

$$I_c = \frac{460}{57.2\sqrt{3}} = 4.643 \text{ A}$$

$$I_{a1} = \left[(0.81 \times 58.41 + 4.643)^2 + 34.09^2\right]^{1/2} = 62.14 \text{ A}$$

$$\varphi_{a1} = \tan^{-1}\frac{34.09}{0.81 \times 58.41 + 4.643} = 33.27°$$

$$\bar{I}_{a1} = 62.14\underline{/-33.270} \text{ A}$$

$$I_{aR} = \left[62.14^2 + (0.81 \times 18.17)^2\right]^{1/2} = 63.86 \text{ A}$$

$$I_{r1} = I_{A1} = 58.41 \text{ A}$$

$$I_{rR} = I_{AR} = 61.17 \text{ A}$$

$$\bar{I}_{r1} = 58.41\underline{/-103.1°} \text{ A}$$

$$I_{l1} = 62.14\underline{/-33.27°} + 58.41\underline{/-103.1°} = 98.87\underline{/-66.95°} \text{ A}$$

$$PF_l = \cos 66.95 = 0.3915$$

$$P_l = P_m - \bar{v}_{LK}I_O = 27180 + 3(57.2 \times 4.643^3 + 0.0591 \times 63.86^2$$

$$+ 0.0604 \times 61.17^2) = 32280 \text{ W}$$

$$\eta = \frac{27180}{32280} = 0.8420$$

Similar calculations for a series of values of T_L yielded the curves shown in Figs. 8.6 to 8.8.

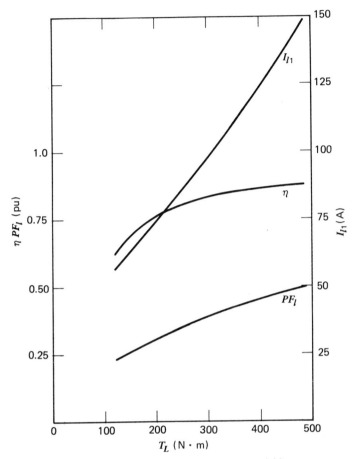

Fig. 8.8. Solution to Example 8.1. System variables.

Example 8.2

A transformer of turns ratio $N_p/N_s = 0.5$ is fitted between the ac source and the inverter in the system in Example 8.1. The operating speed range is unchanged but the motor is to be run up to 550 rpm by conventional starting equipment and then switched over to converter control. The transformer may be considered ideal.

Draw curves of delay angle α, system fundamental line current I_{l1}, and system power factor PF_l as functions of load torque T_L.

Solution

As in Example 8.1, the required quantities are calculated for $T_L = 300$ N · m. Many will be unchanged from Example 8.1 because the addition of the transformer does not affect the motor or link variables.

From Eq. 8.23

$$\alpha = \cos^{-1}(-0.2790 \times 0.81 \times 2) = 116.9°$$

and from Eq. 8.22

$$\bar{v}_{LK} = \frac{-3\sqrt{2}}{\pi} \times \frac{460}{2}\cos 116.9° = 140.4$$

that is, the same value as for Example 8.1. Now, however,

$$\bar{I}_{r1} = \frac{58.41}{2}\underline{/-116.9°} = 29.20\underline{/-116.9°} \text{ A}$$

$$I_{l1} = 62.14\underline{/-33.27°} + 29.20\underline{/-116.9°} = 71.53\underline{/-57.21°} \text{ A}$$

$$PF_l = \cos 57.21° = 0.5416$$

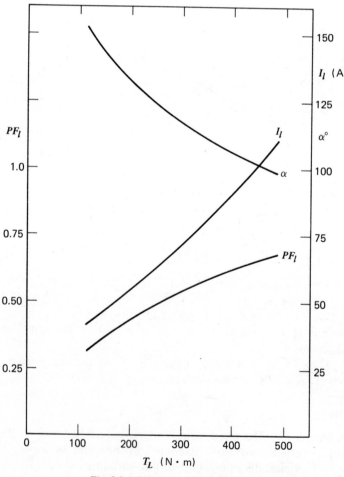

Fig. 8.9. Solution to Example 8.2.

Similar calculations for a series of values of T_L yielded the curves shown in Fig. 8.9.

8.3.1. Discussion of System Performance

When the curves in Fig. 8.9 are compared with those in Fig. 8.8 the improvement in performance due to the introduction of the transformer becomes immediately obvious. The system with the transformer operates at a substantially higher power factor; consequently the line current is much reduced. Furthermore, although the rms value of the inverter ac current is unchanged, the applied ac terminal pd is halved so that the rating of the inverter thyristors is halved.

It may also be noted that a transformer of even greater turns ratio could have been used because α at the lower controlled speed limit is still far from 170°. However, although a transformer of the chosen ratio could be a standard design available from stock, a special ratio to suit the system even better might require a special transformer design. The choice of a transformer turns ratio, or even the question of fitting a transformer at all, is a complicated economic problem in which the decreased operating costs and the cost of the inverter must be weighed against that of the transformer.

If the curves in Figs. 8.6 and 8.9 are compared with those in Fig. 7.8 the superior performance of the slip-energy recovery system is clear. Efficiency is higher over the entire speed range, there is no disconcerting peak of motor current as speed and torque are reduced, and motor current falls to a low value at low speed. Although the system power factor for the slip-energy recovery system is lower at high speed, it need not be markedly so.

Thus, even though the slip-energy recovery system would be more costly to install than the power controller, it would be cheaper to run. It also has the advantage of an available increase in top speed, which may approach the rated speed of a conventionally driven wound-rotor motor, whereas that of the Class D squirrel-cage motor is unavoidably a good deal lower.

It should be noted that in the foregoing example motor losses other than the resistive losses have been neglected. Stray-load and friction and windage losses give rise to an additional power component of the motor input current and both increase that current and the power factor of the system as a whole. In choosing a motor for a particular system these additional losses should be taken into consideration; otherwise the motor chosen may be overloaded.

As stated in Section 8.1, closed-loop speed control could also be applied to the slip-energy recovery system.

PROBLEMS

8.1. A fan absorbs 25 hp at its maximum speed of 1750 rpm. It is proposed to drive it by a slip-energy recovery system with a 460-V, 30-hp (22.4-kW), 37.3-A, 1765-rpm motor with the following equivalent-circuit parameters:

$$\omega_s L_{ms} = 20.6 \ \Omega, \qquad R_c = 224 \ \Omega, \qquad N_{re}/N_{se} = 0.53$$

Friction and windage losses may be neglected. On the assumption that, to allow for losses neglected in the calculation, the input current determined for the motor is only 0.85 of that which would arise in practice, show that this motor is big enough for the application.

8.2. For the drive in Problem 8.1 the required speed range is $1150 \geq n \geq 1750$ rpm. Determine the following:

(a) the minimum turns ratio N_p/N_s that may be used in a transformer between the ac source and the inverter;

(b) round *up* the turns ratio obtained in (a) to two digits and calculate the volt-ampere rating of the transformer and of the inverter in this system if the motor is to be run up to 1150 rpm by conventional starting equipment;

(c) express the transformer or inverter rating as a percentage of the motor volt-ampere rating.

8.3. For the modified system in Problem 8.2 determine the system power factor and efficiency at maximum and minimum speed of operation. Additional equivalent-circuit parameters required are

$$R_s = 0.245, \qquad R'_r = 0.143$$

8.4. For the modified system in Problem 8.2 determine the motor line current, system power factor, and system efficiency at maximum speed of operation, taking into consideration losses that have been neglected in Problem 8.3. From test results on the motor these are

$$\text{friction and windage loss, } P_{FW} = 100 \ \text{W}$$

$$\text{stray load loss, } P_{SL} = 1245 \ \text{W}$$

The stray load losses should be considered to be dissipated in an equivalent-circuit resistive element in parallel with R_c because they are almost entirely additional core losses. (Note that this calculation *still* neglects losses in the motor due to additional flux harmonics caused by the converters and the losses in the converters themselves.)

8.5. The converters, transformer, and motor in Example 8.2 are required to drive a load that presents a constant torque of 485 N · m at all speeds. The operating speed range and starting arrangements are those of

Example 8.2. For the minimum speed determine motor line current I_{aR}, system fundamental line current I_{l1}, system power factor PF_l, and system efficiency η. Compare the values obtained with those in Figs. 8.7 (I_{aR}), 8.8 (η), and 8.9 (I_{l1}, PF_l).

8.6. For the system in Problem 8.5 determine the VA rating of the inverter and transformer as a percentage of that of the motor. The motor rated line current is 119 A.

Chapter 9

Induction Motors with Voltage-Source Inverters

9.1. INTRODUCTION

A voltage-source inverter is supplied from a direct voltage source. Ideally, this is a source of zero internal impedance that will deliver unlimited current at constant, controllable, terminal pd. The inverter may be used to excite a standard, three-phase, squirrel-cage induction motor at controllable frequency and potential difference. A number of possible converter combinations will drive the motor or motors and one of the advantages of the voltage-source inverter is that it can drive a group of similar motors connected in parallel.

Usually the source of power is a three-phase ac system and the basic converter combination consists of a rectifier and inverter connected by a dc link. This combination may be referred to as an "ac/ac converter with dc link," but this terminology is not used here because it may lead to confusion when alternative combinations are discussed.

9.1.1. Converter Combinations

If, as explained in Section 6.3.3, the speed of an induction motor is to be controlled by variation in the source frequency, variation in the source pd is also essential. Any converter combination therefore must meet this requirement. The simplest voltage-source inverter circuits have a fixed ratio of dc-input-terminal pd to ac-output-terminal pd. With this inverter control of dc input pd is necessary and may be obtained by the combination shown in Fig. 9.1a, in which the controlled rectifier varies the dc input pd to the inverter at the same time as the inverter output frequency is varied. The rectifier is line-commutated and the inverter is forced-commutated. The dc link may include a series inductance, but the important component is the capacitor which smooths the dc input pd to the inverter to an effectively constant value V_{LK}. This system is not able to regenerate, because a reversal of i_O would be required. If regeneration is necessary it may be obtained by replacing the phase-controlled rectifier with a dual converter.

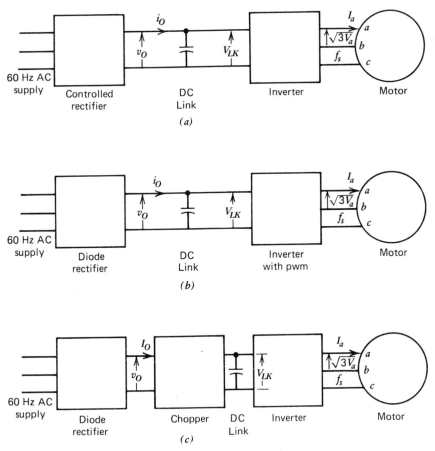

Fig. 9.1. Dc-voltage-source inverter drive systems.

A system in which the dc link pd is constant is shown in Fig. 9.1*b*. The control of ac output terminal pd is carried out in the inverter by pulse-width modulation (PWM). Regeneration is not possible in this system as it stands; however, if the fixed pd dc source to the inverter is a dc distribution system that can accept regenerated energy, as in a streetcar or rapid transit system, a number of motors in different states of driving and regenerative braking could operate from the single dc source.

A third possibility is illustrated in Fig. 9.1*c*, in which the variation of pd is obtained by the chopper. This is a combination that is used when a high-frequency output is required; and PWM in the inverter is therefore not possible. In addition, a high input power factor is obtained from the diode rectifier. This arrangement may also be used with dc distribution for a transportation system because the chopper will exclude from the distribution system the wide range of harmonics that would otherwise be produced in it by the inverter. These harmonics may interfere with signaling or communication systems in which the known harmonic frequencies produced by the chopper can be suppressed. A Class C chopper would permit regenerative braking.

The losses in the converters considered hitherto have been low, and even in the chopper in which forced commutation is used it has been possible to consider them lossless. In the systems in Fig. 9.1 the inverters are also forced-commutated and with PWM there are many such commutations per cycle. In any calculations of performance it must be borne in mind that the losses are greater than in the other drives discussed so far; in fact, their effect limits the ratings of these drives to the use of standard motors of not more than 500 hp (373 kW).

The basic principles of operation of controlled rectifiers and choppers were dealt with in Chapters 4 and 5, respectively. Before considering the systems in Fig. 9.1 in any detail some discussion of the operation of voltage-source inverters is necessary.

9.2. THREE-PHASE VOLTAGE-SOURCE INVERTER

Figure 9.2a shows the power circuit of a three-phase inverter supplied by a dc link from a voltage source. As in Chapter 5, the thyristor symbol surrounded by a circle indicates a thyristor that can be turned off by forced commutation. The thyristors in this circuit are numbered in the sequence in which the gating signals are applied and these signals are shown as waveforms of i_{G1} to i_{G6} in Fig. 9.2b. In the arrangement illustrated the duration of the gating signals is such that three thyristors are turned on at any time. Each thyristor is forced-commutated after an interval of one-half cycle of the output pd (in fact, slightly less, to allow time for turn-off in order that V_{LK} may not be shorted through two thyristors in series).

When any thyristor is turned on that thyristor and the diode connected in antiparallel with it constitute a short circuit. When, for example, thyristor Q_1 is turned on output terminal a is brought to the potential of the positive dc terminal. If, at the same time, thyristor Q_6 is turned on output terminal b is brought to the potential of the negative dc terminal and $v_{ab} = V_{LK}$. In this way the pattern of gating signals shown in Fig. 9.2b results in the waveforms of line-to-line output terminal pd, also shown.

It is possible to operate the inverter circuit in Fig. 9.2a with gating signals of duration $2\pi/3$ rad so that only two thyristors are turned on at any instant. Although this has the practical advantage of providing ample time for turn-off, the duration of the gating signals has little effect on the behavior of a motor driven by the inverter, and because the waveforms of line-to-line pd are no longer defined difficulties in analysis arise. For this reason only the case in which three thyristors are turned on at any instant is considered here.

From the foregoing discussion it is clear that the amplitude of the ac line-to-line, terminal pd's will be equal to V_{LK}; therefore the amplitude of these pd's can be varied by varying V_{LK}. This is the method of control of the systems in Figs. 9.1a and c.

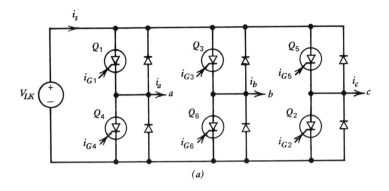

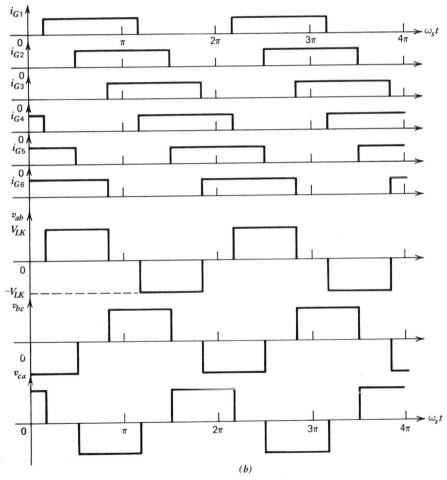

Fig. 9.2. Three-phase bridge inverter.

223

9.2.1. Pulse-Width Modulation

In the system in Fig. 9.1b V_{LK} is constant and the line-to-line pd's applied to the motor are varied by PWM in the inverter. One method by which this may be done is illustrated in Fig. 9.3. Each half-wave of line-to-line terminal pd now consists of two separate pulses and there are intervals during the cycle in which all three of the line-to-line pd's are zero. This condition is achieved by turning on thyristors Q_1, Q_3, and Q_5, or alternatively, Q_2, Q_4, and Q_6, simultaneously, thus bringing terminals a, b, and c in Fig. 9.2a to a common potential. To utilize all thyristors uniformly these two combinations of three thyristors are used alternately throughout the cycle. The gating signals that achieve this alternation, also shown in Fig. 9.3, reveal that each thyristor must now be commutated three times per cycle instead of once.

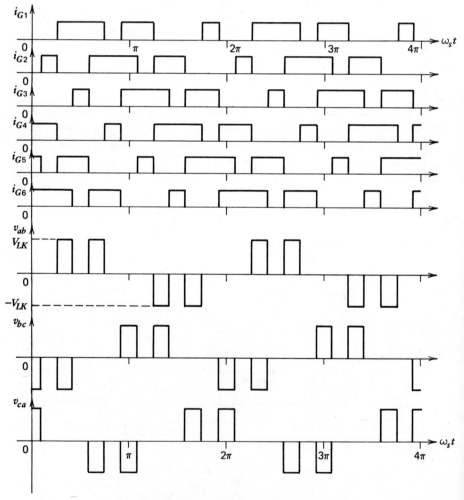

Fig. 9.3. Pulse-width modulation in a three-phase inverter.

In practice, many more than two pulses per half-cycle are used, and the pulses are not arranged symmetrically in each half-wave; that is to say, the pulse frequency is not made an integral multiple of the output frequency ω_s because this would generate undesirable harmonics of relatively low frequency. There is, however, a practical limit to the number of pulses per half-cycle, and this for two reasons. In the first place the commutation of a thyristor takes a definite time which limits the pulse frequency. In the second place each forced commutation of a thyristor is accompanied by some energy loss and a high pulse rate lowers the efficiency of the inverter.

As far as the motor is concerned, the pulse rate can be made high enough to avoid any effect on motor performance. The output waveform may, in fact, be considered to be that shown in Fig. 9.2 and to have an amplitude equal to the average value of the pulses taken over one-third of a cycle.

The components of the pd waveforms shown in Fig. 9.2, that give rise to the desired torque in the motor are, of course, the fundamentals. Torque components are also produced by the harmonics of this waveform and the resulting harmonic currents in the motor, but the motor is a highly inductive device and harmonic fluxes are small. Therefore the resulting torques have a negligible effect on motor performance.

One disadvantage, however, to the simple waveform in Fig. 9.2 and the equivalent produced by PWM of the type described in the foregoing appears at low speed, therefore at low values of ω_s. The sinusoidal waveforms of terminal pd applied by a normal, three-phase, ac source to the stator of an induction motor produce sinusoidally varying currents in the machine windings and a sinusoidal space wave of flux that rotates at constant speed in the air gap. Waveforms of terminal pd illustrated in Fig. 9.2 tend to produce a flux wave that moves around the air gap in steps. This phenomenon can cause the motor to move in jerks when starting and can produce torsional oscillations in shafts when it is running. These disadvantages can be eliminated, if necessary, by a more elaborate form of PWM.

9.2.2. Sinusoidal Pulse-Width Modulation

If the pulse width is made a sinusoidal function of $\omega_s t$ a marked reduction in the harmonic content of the line-to-line pd's is obtained, the rectangular waveforms are replaced by effective sinusoids, and the "stepping" tendency of the rotating field in the motor is eliminated.

The waveforms of the potential at inverter terminals a and b, relative to a neutral point, that result from this type of PWM, are illustrated in Fig. 9.4b. The method of determining the positions and widths of the pulses is shown in Fig. 9.4a, in which each intersection of one of the reference sinusoids with the sawtooth wave results in the turn-on or commutation of a thyristor (accompanied, of course, by the commutation or turn-on of the series thyristor in one of the three branches of the circuit in Fig. 9.2a). In fact, the diagram in Fig. 9.4a illustrates the basis of an electronic technique that may be used to control the required gating signals in the inverter.

The waveform of v_{ab} that results from those of v_a and v_b is shown in Fig. 9.4c, as is also its fundamental component. Inclusion of a reference waveform $v_{c\,\text{REF}}$ in a and the addition of a corresponding waveform of v_c to b would permit derivation of the waveform of v_{bc} and v_{ca} that with v_{ab} form the three-phase motor excitation. A motor driven by this system may be considered to be supplied simply by the fundamental components of the three line-to-line pd's.

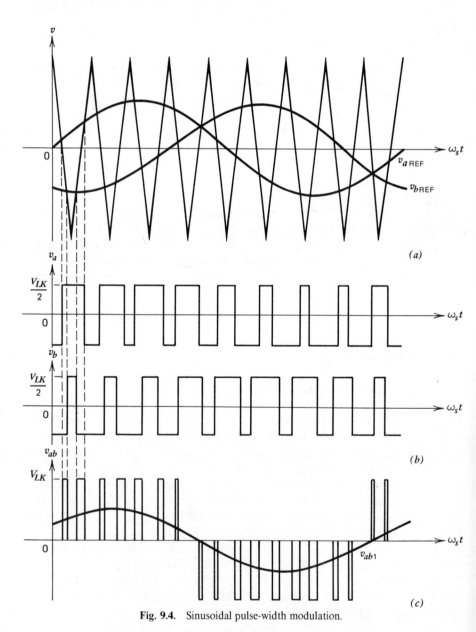

Fig. 9.4. Sinusoidal pulse-width modulation.

9.2.3.   Relative Merits of the Systems in Fig. 9.1

The great attraction of all three systems in Fig. 9.1 is, of course, that they can drive simple, cheap, and reliable squirrel-cage motors over a wide speed range because the upper limit of output frequency attainable is well above the rated value. One voltage-source inverter may also be used to drive a group of induction motors. They will not necessarily run at exactly the same speeds if the motors are driving different loads, but if they are coupled by electric shafts or mechanically by the driving wheels and rails of a multimotor rail-guided vehicle they will do so.

The speed of these drives can be controlled accurately, and by the addition of current control maximum permissible motor torque can be developed at any speed. The method of control can also be modified to suit the load characteristic.

Each of the drives illustrated in Fig. 9.1 has its advantages and disadvantages. At low speed the input power factor of the controlled rectifier in system *a* will be low. That of the other two systems will be virtually unity at all speeds. Although sinusoidal PWM can be installed in system *b*, the size of the motor that can be driven will be limited by the long turn-off time required by large thyristors and the inverter losses will be increased by the large number of commutations per cycle. In systems *a* and *c* the variation in V_{LK} with speed necessitates a separate dc source for the inverter commutation circuits. System *c* introduces a third forced-commutated converter; therefore system losses are increased.

As already explained in Section 9.1.1, additional equipment is required in all three systems if regenerative braking is to be provided. Dynamic braking could be provided by connecting a chopper-controlled resistor across the dc terminals of any of the inverters.

9.2.4.   Basic Relationships and Methods of Control

Figure 9.5*a* shows the connections between the ac output terminals of the inverter in Fig. 9.2*a* and the stator windings of a wye-connected induction motor. Figure 9.5*b* repeats the line-to-line pd waveforms of Fig. 9.2*b* and, in addition, lists the thyristors that are turned on in each of the six modes of operation of an inverter without PWM.

The line-to-neutral pd's of the three motor phases have the waveforms shown in Fig. 9.5*c*[5] and can be described by a Fourier series. Thus by the method of discontinuities of Appendix A

$$v_a = \frac{8}{3\pi} V_{LK} [0.7500 \sin \omega t + 0.1500 \sin 5\omega t + 0.1071 \sin 7\omega t + \cdots] \text{ V}$$

$$(9.1)$$

If v_a is applied to the per-phase equivalent circuit in Fig. 6.3 the motor input

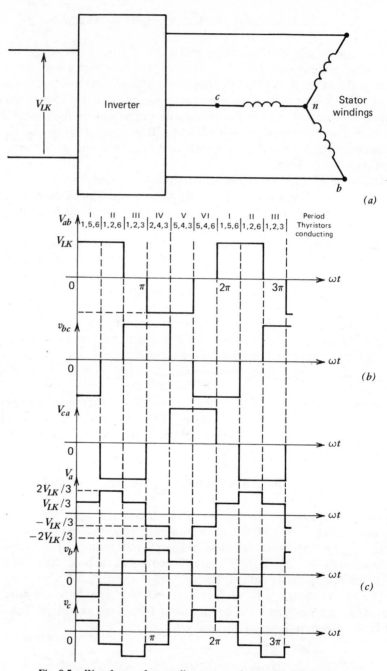

Fig. 9.5. Waveforms of motor line-to-neutral potential differences.

current will be

$$i_a = i_{ma} + i_c + i'_a \text{ A} \qquad (9.2)$$

Because of the high inductance of the magnetizing branch, the harmonic components of i_{ma}, and, consequently, of air-gap flux, will be small. Thus, although i'_a may have appreciable harmonic components at low speeds, the harmonic torques that may be developed will be small and can be neglected in making predictions of system performance. Even the harmonic components of i'_a are so small that their effect on the magnitude of the motor line current is negligible.

From the waveform of v_a in Fig. 9.5 the rms value may be determined as

$$V_a = 0.4714 V_{LK} \text{ V} \qquad (9.3)$$

and from Eq. 9.1 the rms value of the fundamental component of v_a is

$$V_{a1} = \frac{8}{3\pi} V_{LK} \times \frac{0.7500}{\sqrt{2}} = 0.4502 V_{LK} \text{ V} \qquad (9.4)$$

9.3. CONSTANT AMPLITUDE OF AIR-GAP FLUX WAVE

By using the approximate equivalent circuit in Fig. 6.3 the behavior of a motor with constant air-gap flux was discussed in Section 6.3.3. This called for a constant ratio of V_a/ω_s, but it was pointed out that this ratio would yield inaccurate results at low speeds and low values of ω_s. If the air-gap flux is really to remain constant what is required is a constant ratio of E_{ma}/ω_s (Fig. 6.2).

The following equations may be written for the equivalent circuit in Fig. 6.2, in which $R_c \rightarrow \infty$:

$$\frac{E_{ma}}{\omega_s} = k \text{ V} \cdot \text{s/rad} \qquad (9.5)$$

$$s = \frac{\omega_s - (p/2)\omega_m}{\omega_s} \text{ pu} \qquad (9.6)$$

$$\overline{Z}'_A = \frac{R'_r}{s} + j\omega_s l'_{lr} \text{ } \Omega \qquad (9.7)$$

$$I'_a = \frac{E_{ma}}{Z'_A} \text{ A} \qquad (9.8)$$

and if friction and windage losses of the motor are neglected the power

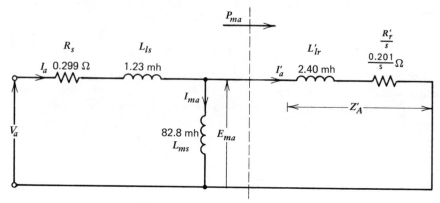

Fig. 9.6. Diagram I for Example 9.1.

output is

$$\omega_m T_L = \frac{3(1-s)}{s} R_r' (I_a')^2 \text{ W} \tag{9.9}$$

From these five equations a relation between T_L and ω_m may be obtained for any given value of ω_s. Thus

$$I_a' = \frac{k\omega_s}{Z_A'} \text{ A} \tag{9.10}$$

$$\omega_m T_L = \frac{3(1-s)}{s} R_r' \left(\frac{k\omega_s}{Z_A'} \right)^2 \text{ W} \tag{9.11}$$

from which

$$T_L = \frac{3R_r' k^2 [\omega_s - (p/2)\omega_m]}{(R_r')^2 + \{[\omega_s - (p/2)\omega_m] L_{lr}'\}^2} \text{ N} \cdot \text{m} \tag{9.12}$$

For any value of ω_s this relationship will yield a curve similar to those in Fig. 6.8.

The equivalent circuit for a 460-V, 25-hp, 60-Hz, 3515 rpm, three-phase, squirrel-cage induction motor is shown in Fig. 9.6; a family of speed-torque curves for this motor obtained by Eq. 9.12 is shown in Fig. 9.7. The ratio of E_{ma}/ω_s used was that for the rated operating condition of the motor.

Although, under transient conditions, the motor operating point might move over much of the plane of the diagram in Fig. 9.7, continuous operation would be restricted to conditions under which the line current would not overheat the motor. This limitation of line current might be imposed by a current-limit loop in the control system. Therefore it is of interest to determine

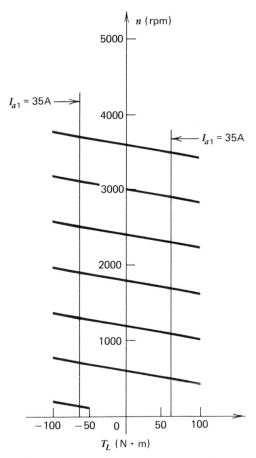

Fig. 9.7. Diagram II for Example 9.1. Speed-torque characteristics for a motor with ratio E_{ma}/ω_s constant.

the boundaries within which this limit might confine the motor operating point.

Regenerative braking occurs in the second quadrant of Fig. 9.7. This operation at low speed has a theoretical boundary formed by the speed-torque curve for $\omega_s = 0$ which passes through the origin of the diagram. In the upper part of both quadrants speed will be limited by maximum pd that may be applied at the motor terminals. These boundaries are illustrated by a numerical example.

Example 9.1

For the 25-hp (18.6-kW), 460-V, 60-Hz, 3515 rpm, three-phase, squirrel-cage induction motor whose full-load equivalent circuit is shown in Fig. 9.6 draw lines on Fig. 9.7 to show the permissible limits of driving and braking torque subject to the following constraints:

(a) The motor terminal pd may not exceed 460-V, line-to-line.
(b) The motor line current may not exceed 35 A.
(c) The ratio of E_{mal}/ω_s is maintained at the ratio of E_{ma}/ω_s for rated operating conditions.
(d) The lower speed limit for regenerative braking is arbitrarily taken to be 500 rpm.

Also plot curves of V_{al}, ω_s and s as functions of speed n for motoring operation. Friction and windage losses as well as core losses may be neglected, as may the effect of all current harmonics.

Solution

Ratio E_{ma}/ω_s must be determined for rated operation:

$$s = \frac{3600 - 3515}{3600} = 0.02361$$

From Eq. 6.10

$$25 \times 746 = \frac{3(1 - 0.02361)}{0.02361} \times 0.201\left(I_a'\right)^2 \text{ W}$$

from which

$$I_a' = 27.35 \text{ A}$$

From Fig. 9.6

$$\overline{Z}_A' = \frac{0.201}{0.02361} + j120\pi \times 2.4 \times 10^{-3} = 8.561 \underline{/6.07°} \ \Omega$$

$$E_{ma} = 8.561 \times 27.35 = 234.1 \text{ V}$$

$$\frac{E_{ma}}{\omega_s} = \frac{234.1}{120\pi} = 0.6210 \text{ V} \cdot \text{s/rad (Tesla)}$$

Torque T_L is now required for a series of values of speed n subject to the constraints

$$\frac{E_{mal}}{\omega_s} = 0.6210 \text{ V} \cdot \text{s/rad}$$

$$I_{al} = 35 \text{ A}$$

$$V_{al} \ngtr \frac{460}{\sqrt{3}} \text{ V}$$

Under all conditions

$$I_{ma1} = \frac{E_{ma1}}{0.0828\omega_s} = \frac{0.6210}{0.0828} = 7.500 \text{ A}$$

For a chosen value of speed n assume a value of slip s. Then

$$\omega_m = \frac{n\pi}{30} \text{ rad/s}$$

$$\omega_s = \frac{p}{2} \cdot \frac{\omega_m}{1-s} \text{ rad/s}$$

$$E_{ma1} = 0.6210\omega_s$$

$$\overline{Z}_A' = \frac{0.201}{s} + j0.0024\omega_s \ \Omega$$

$$\overline{I}_{a1}' = \frac{\overline{E}_{ma1}}{\overline{Z}_A'} \text{ A}$$

Let

$$\overline{E}_{ma1} = E_{ma1}\big/\underline{0} \text{ V}$$

Then

$$\overline{I}_{ma1} = -j7.500 \text{ A}$$

$$\overline{I}_{a1} = \overline{I}_{a1}' + \overline{I}_{ma1} \text{ A}$$

If

$$I_{a1} \neq 35$$

modify the value of s until it is. Then

$$\overline{Z}_s = 0.299 + j0.00123\omega_s$$

$$\overline{V}_{a1} = \overline{E}_{ma1} + \overline{Z}_s\overline{I}_{a1} \text{ V}$$

If

$$V_{a1} > 265.6 \text{ V}$$

modify the value of n and start again. When $I_{a1} = 35A$ and $V_{a1} \leq 265.6V$

$$P_o = P_{\text{mech}} = \frac{3(1-s)}{s} \times 0.201\left(I_{a1}'\right)^2 = \frac{0.603(1-s)}{s}\left(I_{a1}'\right)^2 \text{ W}$$

$$T_L = \frac{P_{\text{mech}}}{\omega_m} \text{ N} \cdot \text{m}$$

The lines in Figs. 9.7 and the curves in Fig. 9.8 were obtained by the foregoing procedure.

As expected with a constant line current, the torque at the motor coupling is virtually constant throughout the speed range for motoring and regenerating. The curves in Fig. 9.8 show that for this line current (which exceeds rated current) the permissible terminal pd and rated frequency do not occur simultaneously and the nameplate speed of the motor may be exceeded without overstressing the insulation.

With the motor drawing the specified load current at standstill, the equivalent-circuit model still yields an undiminished value for the developed torque with both V_{a1} and ω_s very low. It is questionable, however, just how the system would behave at such a low frequency. Certainly, because of the inverter output waveform, the rotating flux wave in the air gap would tend to move in steps rather than at constant angular velocity. Thus control to extremely low speeds may not be satisfactory.

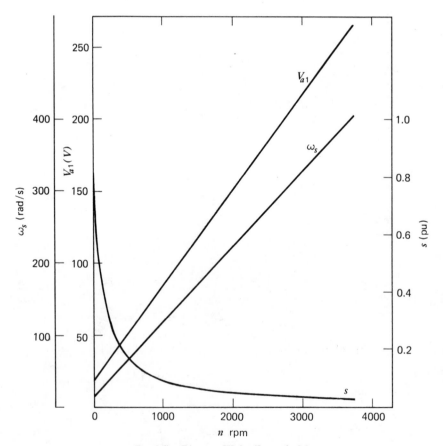

Fig. 9.8. Diagram III for Example 9.1.

If the drive were required to operate from a low speed it might be possible to start it with the inverter. For this method a limit on motor line current would have to be imposed to protect the thyristors.

Example 9.2

The minimum output frequency of the inverter in the system in Example 9.1 is 5 Hz. If the motor is to be started from standstill at this frequency and the line-current limit of 35 A is still to apply determine the permissible value of fundamental motor terminal pd V_{a1} and the starting torque developed.

At standstill

$$\overline{Z}'_A = 0.201 + j10\pi \times 2.40 \times 10^{-3} = 0.201 + j0.07540 = 0.2147\underline{/20.56°}\ \Omega$$

$$\overline{Z}_{ms} = j10\pi \times 0.0828 = 2.601\underline{/90°}\ \Omega$$

$$\overline{Z}_s = 0.299 + j10\pi \times 1.23 \times 10^{-3} = 0.299 + j0.03864\ \Omega$$

The motor impedance is

$$\overline{Z}_m = \overline{Z}_s + \frac{\overline{Z}'_A \overline{Z}_{ms}}{\overline{Z}'_A + \overline{Z}_{ms}} = 0.299 + j0.03864 + \frac{0.2147\underline{/20.56°} \times 2.601\underline{/90°}}{2.684\underline{/85.71°}}$$

$$= 0.5038\underline{/14.49°}\ \Omega$$

$$V_{a1} = 0.5038 \times 35 = 17.63\ V$$

$$I'_{a1} = \left|\frac{\overline{Z}_{ms}}{\overline{Z}'_A + \overline{Z}_{ms}}\right| I_{a1} = \frac{2.601}{2.684} \times 35 = 33.92\ A$$

$$3P_{ma} = 3 \times 0.201 \times 33.92^2 = 693.7\ W$$

and for this two-pole motor

$$T_L = \frac{693.7}{10\pi} = 22.08\ N \cdot m$$

9.3.1. Approximate Speed-Torque Characteristics

If it is assumed that the characteristics up to base frequency ω_b in Fig. 6.8 or those in Fig. 9.7 are straight lines that pass through the vertical intercept $(2/p)(\omega_s/\omega_b)$ a simple method of determining required source frequency at a given speed and load torque is possible. This method, however, should not be used for load torques far outside the range $-T_{rated} < T_L < T_{rated}$ nor yet at low motor speeds.

The assumed characteristics have the form shown in Fig. 9.9 (possibly extended somewhat beyond the boundaries $T_L = \pm T_{rated}$), and because

$$\omega_r = \omega_s - \frac{p}{2}\omega_m \text{ rad/s} \tag{9.13}$$

then

$$\frac{2}{p}\frac{\omega_r}{\omega_b} = \frac{2}{p}\frac{\omega_s}{\omega_b} - \frac{\omega_m}{\omega_b} \tag{9.14}$$

If the rated angular speed of the motor is ω_{rated} rad/s it follows that the intercept on the vertical line $T = T_{rated}$ between a horizontal line through the point $(2/p)(\omega_s/\omega_b)$ on the vertical axis and the approximate characteristic through that same point is

$$\frac{2}{p}\frac{\omega_r}{\omega_b} = \frac{2}{p}\frac{\omega_s}{\omega_b} - \frac{\omega_{rated}}{\omega_b} \tag{9.15}$$

At base frequency, when $\omega_s = (p/2)\omega_b$, this intercept may be calculated and given the symbol K. Thus

$$\frac{2}{p}\frac{\omega_r}{\omega_b} = 1 - \frac{\omega_{rated}}{\omega_b} = K \tag{9.16}$$

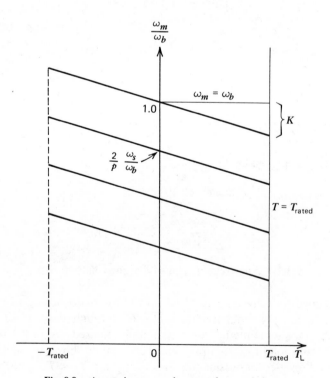

Fig. 9.9.   Approximate speed-torque characteristics.

Thus when rated torque is developed from Eqs. 9.14 and 9.16

$$K = \frac{2}{p}\frac{\omega_s}{\omega_b} - \frac{\omega_m}{\omega_b} \tag{9.17}$$

and for some other torque $T_L \neq T_{rated}$

$$\frac{T_L}{T_{rated}}K = \frac{2}{p}\frac{\omega_s}{\omega_b} - \frac{\omega_m}{\omega_b} \tag{9.18}$$

Given any two of the values T_L, ω_s, and ω_m, the third may be calculated from Eq. 9.18. All the remaining system variables may then be obtained without resort to numerical solutions.

Example 9.3

A 460-V, 60-Hz, 50-hp (37.3-kW), 1180 rpm, three-phase, squirrel-cage, induction motor is to drive a load that demands a constant torque of 275 N · m over a speed range of $150 \leq n \leq 1150$ rpm. The motor equivalent-circuit parameters at 60 Hz are

$$R_s = 0.191\ \Omega \qquad \omega_s L_{ls} = 0.753\ \Omega$$

$$R_r' = 0.0707\ \Omega \qquad \omega_s L_{lr}' = 0.377\ \Omega$$

$$R_c \to \infty \qquad \omega_s L_{ms} = 16.9\ \Omega$$

The motor is to be driven from an inverter which is supplied in turn by a dc link from a dc source of controllable pd.

Plot curves of inverter input pd V_{LK}, inverter input current i_o, motor fundamental input current I_{a1}, motor slip s, motor power factor PF, and motor efficiency η as functions of speed n.

In determining power factor and efficiency, the actual waveform of the motor terminal pd and the fifth harmonic of motor current should be taken into consideration. Friction and windage losses of the motor and the torques produced by current harmonics other than the fundamental may be neglected.

The approximation of Fig. 9.9 may be used.

Solution

The required quantities are calculated for a speed of 650 rpm.

$$\omega_b = 1200 \times \frac{\pi}{30} = 40\pi\ rad/s$$

From Eq. 9.16

$$K = 1 - \frac{1180}{1200} = 0.01667$$

For this motor

$$T_{\text{rated}} = \frac{50 \times 746 \times 30}{1180\pi} = 301.9 \text{ N} \cdot \text{m}$$

From Eq. 9.18

$$\frac{275}{301.9} \times 0.01667 = \frac{2}{b} \times \frac{\omega_s}{40\pi} - \frac{\omega_m}{40\pi}$$

from which

$$\omega_s = 5.724 + 3\omega_m \text{ rad/s}$$

$$\omega_m = 650 \times \frac{\pi}{30} = 68.07 \text{ rad/s}$$

$$\omega_s = 209.9 \text{ rad/s}$$

$$s = \frac{5.724}{209.9} = 0.02727$$

$$P_{\text{mech}} = 275 \times 68.07 = \frac{3(1 - 0.02727)}{0.02727} \times 0.0707(I'_{a1})^2$$

from which $I'_{a1} = 49.74$ A;

$$\bar{Z}'_{A1} = \frac{0.0707}{0.02727} + j0.377 \times \frac{209.9}{120\pi} = 2.593 + j0.2099 = 2.601\big/4.63° \; \Omega$$

$$E_{ma1} = 2.601 \times 49.74 = 129.4 \text{ V}$$

Let

$$\bar{E}_{ma1} = 129.4\big/0 \text{ V}$$

$$\bar{Z}_{ms1} = j16.9 \times \frac{209.9}{120\pi} = 9.410\big/90° \; \Omega$$

$$\bar{I}_{ma1} = -j\frac{129.4}{9.410} = 13.75\big/-90° \text{ A}$$

$$\bar{I}_{a1} = 49.74\big/-4.63 + 13.75\big/-90° = 49.57 - j17.77$$

$$= 52.66\big/-19.72° \text{ A}$$

$$\bar{Z}_{s1} = 0.191 + j0.753 \times \frac{209.9}{120\pi} = 0.191 + j0.4192 = 0.4607\big/65.50° \; \Omega$$

$$\bar{V}_{a1} = 129.7\big/0 + 0.4607\big/65.50° \times 52.67\big/-19.76°$$

$$= 146.6 + j17.38 = 147.6\big/6.76° \text{ V}$$

From Eq. 9.4

$$V_{LK} = \frac{147.6}{0.4502} = 327.9 \text{ V}$$

To determine motor power factor, motor efficiency, and inverter input current to the specified degree of accuracy it is now necessary to calculate the fifth harmonic components of the motor currents. First obtain the motor impedance to the fifth harmonic current:

$$\overline{Z}'_{A5} = 2.593 + j5 \times 0.2099 = 2.593 + j1.050 = 2.797 \underline{/22.04°} \ \Omega$$

$$\overline{Z}_{ms5} = 5 \times 9.410 \underline{/90°} = 47.05 \underline{/90°} \ \Omega$$

$$\overline{Z}_{s5} = 0.191 + j5 \times 0.4192 = 0.191 + j2.096 = 2.105 \underline{/84.79°} \ \Omega$$

The impedance of the motor is given by

$$\overline{Z}_{m5} = \overline{Z}_{s5} + \frac{\overline{Z}'_{A5} \times \overline{Z}_{ma5}}{\overline{Z}'_{A5} + \overline{Z}_{ma5}} = \overline{Z}_{s5} + \overline{Z}_5 \ \Omega$$

$$\overline{Z}'_{A5} + \overline{Z}_{ms5} = 2.593 + j48.10 = 48.17 \underline{/86.91°} \ \Omega$$

$$\overline{Z}_5 = \frac{2.797 \underline{/22.04°} \times 47.05 \underline{/90°}}{48.17 \underline{/86.91°}} = 2.732 \underline{/25.13°} = 2.473 + j1.160 \ \Omega$$

$$\overline{Z}_{m5} = 2.664 + j3.256 = 4.207 \underline{/50.71°} \ \Omega$$

From Eq. 9.1 the rms value of the fifth harmonic of V_a is

$$V_{a5} = \frac{1}{\sqrt{2}} \times \frac{8}{3\pi} 0.15 V_{LK} = 29.52 \text{ V}$$

$$I_{a5} = \frac{29.52}{4.207} = 7.017 \text{ A}$$

$$I'_{a5} = \left| \frac{\overline{Z}_{ms5}}{\overline{Z}_{ms5} + \overline{Z}'_{A5}} \right| I_{a5} = \frac{47.05}{48.17} \times 7.017 = 6.854 \text{ A}$$

Motor power input is

$$P_{in} = 275 \times 68.07 + 3[0.191(52.66^2 + 7.017^2) + 0.0707(49.74^2 + 6.854^2)]$$
$$= 20870 \text{ W}$$

$$\eta = \frac{275 \times 68.07}{20870} = 0.897$$

From Eq. 9.3

$$V_a = 0.4714 \times 327.9 = 154.6 \text{ V}$$

$$I_a = (52.66^2 + 7.017^2)^{1/2} = 53.12 \text{ A}$$

$$PF = \frac{20870}{3 \times 154.6 \times 53.12} = 0.847$$

$$\bar{i}_O = \frac{20870}{327.9} = 63.6 \text{ A}$$

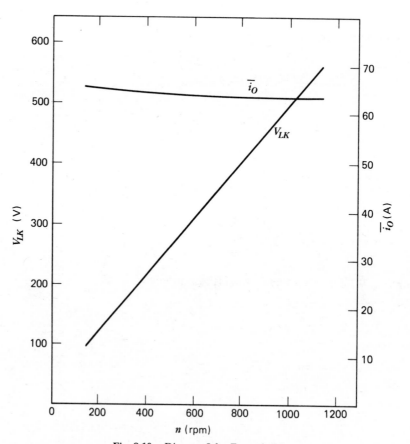

Fig. 9.10. Diagram I for Example 9.3.

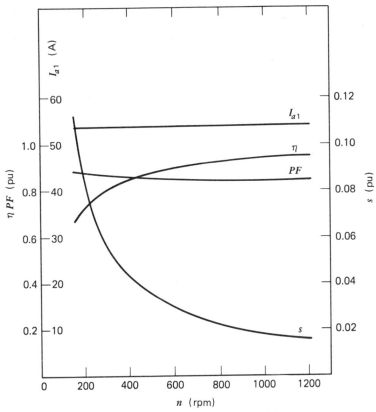

Fig. 9.11. Diagram II for Example 9.3.

Repetition of the foregoing calculation for a series of values of n yielded the curves shown in Figs. 9.10 and 9.11.

It may be noted that the constant load torque resulted in a constant motor line current. The decreasing motor efficiency at low speed, due to increasing slip, resulted in an increase in inverter input current at low speed. Motor power factor is high and virtually constant. The high efficiency values at high speed are optimistic largely because of the neglect of core loss, particularly that due to harmonics in the applied terminal pd.

9.3.2. Control System for Constant Air-Gap Flux Density

If a constant ratio of E_{ma1}/ω_s is to be maintained a feedback loop is required. Figure 9.12 is intended to illustrate the basic principles of a control system for this purpose rather than to show an actual system in which the blocks correspond to specific pieces of hardware.

The emf E_{ma} is not directly measurable. Conceivably, the air-gap flux density might be measured and a feedback signal of its value used, but it is easiest in practice to simulate the value of E_{ma} and to use that simulated value as a feedback signal. This could be done by an analogue of the equivalent circuit to which V_a, I_a, ω_s, and s were applied. The required function generator or *observer* in Fig. 9.12 produces a signal E_{mais}, the existing emf of the motor. Thus, while the speed command determines the inverter output frequency, the emf error determines the inverter output pd.

As far as speed is concerned, the system in Fig. 9.12 is open-loop. A regulated speed control would require a further feedback signal of n, which, after comparison with the speed command, would provide an error input to the ω_s logic. A current limit would require a further feedback loop. This would act to reduce the torque available for acceleration of the system, because it would be so designed that the current limit would not be reached during steady-state operation. Thus the limit would reduce the rate of increase of ω_s. Excessive current in any steady state would stall the motor and could be used for protection.

The diode rectifier in Fig. 9.12 would result in a high system power factor, but the PWM inverter would have high commutation losses and the overall system efficiency would be substantially lower than that of the motor. If the controlled rectifier and an inverter without PWM were used commutation losses in the inverter would be much reduced but the system power factor at the rectifier input would be low at low speed.

The system in Fig. 9.12 will not, as it stands, provide regenerative braking. If this were needed, the diode rectifier could be replaced by a dual converter that would exercise no control over V_{LK}. The thyristors of one of the controlled rectifiers would simply be turned off as those of the other were turned full on (with an interval allowed for turn-off time of the thyristors). Thus, in effect, a

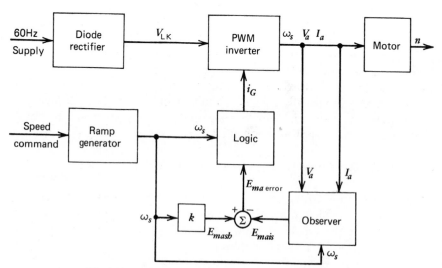

Fig. 9.12. Control system for constant air-gap flux density.

diode rectifier would be obtained for the transfer of energy in the positive direction and a line-commutated inverter for the transfer of regenerated energy back to the 60-Hz source. If the rectifiers were replaced by a fixed pd, dc supply system regeneration would require a Class C chopper and PWM would not be necessary.

9.4. OPERATION WITH FIELD WEAKENING

In many drive systems the inverter frequency may be increased further after the motor terminal pd has reached and remained fixed at its rated value. Operation under these conditions yields a family of speed-torque characteristics like those above the base characteristic in Fig. 6.8. This range of operation is used typically in transportation drives, where the developed torque of the motor is mainly taken up in accelerating the mass of the vehicle rather than in matching some steady-state, speed-torque characteristic of the load. The response of transportation systems to changes in speed command is so slow that at any speed they may be considered to be operating in a quasi steady-state.

Once the rated terminal pd is reached the constant ratio of E_{ma1}/ω_s is abandoned and ω_s is further increased while V_{a1} remains fixed. The consequence is a fall in magnetizing current I_{ma} and a reduction in the amplitude of the air-gap flux wave, which, by analogy with the operation of dc machines, may be called *field weakening*. The current limit is still applied, but as a consequence of the weakened field the developed torque per ampere falls with increase in ω_s. This is shown in Fig. 6.8 by the reduction in breakdown torque above the base characteristic. Because the condition in Eq. 9.5 no longer applies, it is not possible to derive a speed-torque relationship similar to that in Eq. 9.12 and simple numerical methods must be used to predict the operation of the system. A numerical example illustrates this point.

Example 9.4

The system in Example 9.1 is to be operated up to a speed of 5000 rpm by increasing ω_s while V_{a1} is held constant at the value of the rated line-to-neutral terminal pd of the motor. Line current is also to be held constant at the value of 35 A obtaining in Example 9.1.

Using the assumptions in Example 9.1 and the equivalent circuit in Fig. 9.6, draw curves to show the permissible limits of driving and braking torque under these conditions.

Solution

Proceed as follows for a chosen value of n:

$$\omega_m = \frac{n}{9.549} \text{ rad/s}$$

Assume a value of slip s; then

$$\omega_s = \frac{\omega_m}{1 - s} \text{ rad/s}$$

The rotor branch impedance in Fig. 9.6 is

$$\overline{Z}_A' = \frac{0.201}{s} + j0.0024\omega_s \ \Omega$$

The magnetizing branch impedance is

$$\overline{Z}_{ms} = j0.0828\omega_s \ \Omega$$

The stator impedance is

$$\overline{Z}_s = 0.299 + j0.00123\omega_s \ \Omega$$

The motor impedance is

$$\overline{Z}_m = \overline{Z}_s + \frac{\overline{Z}_{ms}\overline{Z}_A'}{\overline{Z}_{ms} + \overline{Z}_A'} = \overline{Z}_s + \overline{Z} = Z_m \underline{/Z_m} \ \Omega$$

The calculated value of the first harmonic terminal pd is

$$V_{a1C} = 35.0 Z_m \ \text{V}$$

If

$$V_{a1C} \neq 265.6 \ \text{V}$$

modify the chosen value of s and recalculate. When $V_{a1C} = 265.6$ V

$$I_{a1}' = \left| \frac{\overline{Z}_{ms}}{\overline{Z}_{ms} + \overline{Z}_A'} \right| \times 35.0 \ \text{A}$$

$$P_{\text{mech}} = 3 \times 0.201 \frac{(1 - s)}{s} (I_{a1}')^2 \ \text{W}$$

$$T_L = \frac{P_{\text{mech}}}{\omega_m} \ \text{N} \cdot \text{m}$$

The curves obtained by the foregoing procedure are shown in Fig. 9.13 joined to short sections of the vertical lines from Fig. 9.7. Figures 9.7 and 9.13 combined show the area of the $n - T_L$ plain that may be used if the line current does not exceed 35 A and the speed does not exceed 5000 rpm.

There is, however, a limit beyond which operation with field weakening at constant line current cannot be pursued. As field is weakened, the breakdown torque of the motor decreases, and the operating point of the motor on the speed-torque curve approaches the breakdown point as speed increases. When the two points coincide line current, and consequently developed torque, must be decreased if the motor is not to be stalled. The curved sections in Fig. 9.13 must therefore be terminated at a limiting curve, which may be thought of as the envelope of the speed-torque characteristics above the base characteristic in Fig. 6.8.

As an approximate guide to the limit to which operation under field weakening can be pursued it may be assumed that, with the line current at the rated value, the ratio of the maximum permissible speed to the rated speed is equal to the ratio of the breakdown torque to rated torque at rated terminal pd and frequency. At lower currents, of course, a higher speed is permissible. In traction applications ratios of the order of four to one are not uncommon because the torque required at constant top speed is much less than that required in the initial stage of acceleration.

9.4.1. Control System for Field Weakening

When, in the system of Fig. 9.12, the fundamental component of the motor terminal pd V_{a1} reaches the rated value of V_a the system must be modified to

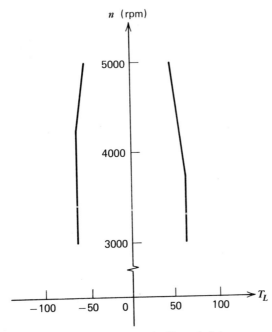

Fig. 9.13. Diagram for Example 9.4.

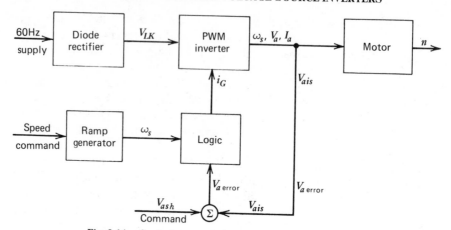

Fig. 9.14. Control system for operating with field weakening.

operate with V_a fixed. A possible system is shown in Fig. 9.14, which may be obtained by switching from the system in Fig. 9.12; the switching operation is initiated by V_a. In this operation there is the danger of sudden oscillation caused by the application of two new signals to the summer that supplies the input signal to the PWM logic. If, however, a ramp-function generator is included at this point this oscillation could be avoided.

Once again, neither a speed loop nor a current-limit loop is included in the system. Excessive current in the steady state would not necessarily stall the motor. If the excess were not too great it might simply move the operating point down the curved part of the motoring characteristic shown in Fig. 9.13.

9.5. CONSTANT RATIO OF TERMINAL PD TO FREQUENCY

The control system in Fig. 9.12 is relatively complicated because of the need to simulate the magnitude of E_{ma} in the motor; moreover, a very accurate speed transducer is required to provide a sufficiently accurate value of slip for the simulation. If the maintenance of a constant ratio of V_a/ω_s, as opposed to E_{ma}/ω_s, is accepted the control system is simplified and might be reduced to that in Fig. 9.15 or some equivalent arrangement of converters. In that system the speed command causes the inverter logic to generate an inverter output frequency ω_s, which, multiplied by a constant k, yields a signal V_{ash}, the terminal pd that should be applied to the motor. This signal is compared with V_{ais}, the terminal pd actually appearing at the motor, and the error is applied to the controlled rectifier to modify the link pd V_{LK} as required.

The main disadvantage of the system in Fig. 9.15 has already been pointed out in Chapter 6. It is that, at low speed, field weakening takes place because of the loss of potential in the stator resistance and as a consequence torque per motor ampere is reduced. Typically, this effect becomes significant at about one-third of rated motor speed, and at standstill it may reduce the developed

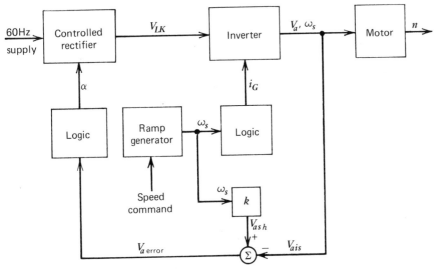

Fig. 9.15. Control system for fan or pump-type loads.

torque to about half the rated value when the motor is drawing rated current. This system, therefore, is suitable for drives with low starting torque in which a narrow controlled speed range below the rated value is required. Fans or pumps may be driven this way.

The system in Fig. 9.15 is efficient because commutation losses in the inverter are low and in the controlled rectifier, nonexistent. Low power factor at the rectifier ac terminals and low efficiency of the motor at low speed are not important because the drive would not operate continuously at anything less than about one-half rated speed. The system is not satisfactory for applications that demand rapid speed change because response of the controlled rectifier is slow and, in any event, a dual converter would be required for regenerative braking. If rapid speed change were, in fact, necessary a diode rectifier and an inverter with PWM could be used. Commutation losses would then be increased but the system power factor would be high at all speeds.

Once again, this is an open-loop system as far as speed is concerned and accurate speed control would call for a speed feedback loop. If the system were to be started from standstill by the inverter a ramp generator to determine the rate of increase in the speed command might be required.

Because numerical calculation with Fig. 6.2 is scarcely more complicated than with Fig. 6.3, it seems scarcely worthwhile to incur the additional approximation that results from the use of the latter model. The equivalent circuit in Fig. 6.2, as shown in Fig. 9.6, is therefore used in the following numerical example.

Example 9.5

The system (motor and converter/s) in Example 9.1 is operated with the ratio V_{a1}/ω_s held constant at the ratio V_a/ω_s for rated operating conditions and the line current limited to 35 A. Determine the developed torque of the motor under these conditions at 3000, 500, and 1 rpm. The approximations used in Example 9.1 apply.

Solution

For this motor

$$\frac{V_a}{\omega_s} = \frac{460}{\sqrt{3} \times 120\pi} = 0.7045$$

$$I_{a1} = 35 \text{ A}$$

Torque T_L is required for the given speeds subject to these constraints. For a chosen value of speed n assume a value of slip s. Then

$$\omega_m = \frac{n\pi}{30} \text{ rad/s}$$

$$\omega_s = \frac{p}{2} \cdot \frac{\omega_m}{1-s} \text{ rad/s}$$

Determine the impedance of the machine Z_m at this set of values of s and ω_s from

$$\overline{Z}_m = \overline{Z}_s + \frac{\overline{Z}_{ms}\overline{Z}_A'}{\overline{Z}_{ms} + \overline{Z}_A'} \ \Omega$$

If

$$35 Z_m \neq 0.7045\omega_s \text{ V}$$

modify the value of s and recalculate, after which

$$I_{a1}' = \left| \frac{\overline{Z}_{ms}}{\overline{Z}_{ms} + \overline{Z}_A'} \right| \times 35 \text{ A}$$

$$P_{\text{mech}} = 0.603 \frac{(1-s)}{s} (I_{a1}')^2 \text{ W}$$

$$T_L = \frac{P_{\text{mech}}}{\omega_m} \text{ N} \cdot \text{m}$$

The resulting values are

n	3000	500	1	rpm
T_L	65.0	53.2	27.8	N · m

These figures show the loss of torque due to reduced field at low speed.

9.6.   MOTOR AND INVERTER RATINGS

For the purposes of this discussion a transportation drive is considered, although the principles involved will apply to other applications.

The rating of an inverter may be expressed as a product of the maximum terminal pd that must be provided and the maximum line current that may be drawn from it; that is, the rating

$$S_I = 3V_{a\,max}I_{a\,max}\ \text{VA} \qquad (9.19)$$

The rating of the motor is given by the nameplate output power and, if necessary, a volt-amphere rating may be deduced from this power, the typical efficiency, and the typical operating power factor of the particular class of machine.

A transportation drive is accelerated by increasing simultaneously the motor terminal pd and frequency, as already discussed in Section 9.3. This acceleration takes place at a current that, for simplicity, will be taken to be the rated current of the motor. Once the maximum terminal pd of the motor or the pd limit of the supply is reached at this rated current the pd is increased no further. The inverter frequency, however, continues to be increased and the motor accelerates further with field weakening, as described in Section 9.4. The acceleration with field weakening must normally take place at constant power because the capacity of the supply system is limited. The question to be decided is how the inverter and motor ratings should be related to one another to provide the optimal combination from the point of view of space required on the vehicle and total cost of the drive. Some approximation is unavoidable in a general discussion, and for this reason the stator impedance of the motor is neglected and the equivalent circuit is assumed to be that in Fig. 9.16.

From the equivalent circuit in Fig. 9.16 it can be shown by the methods in Chapter 6 that the motor developed torque T, which here is assumed to be

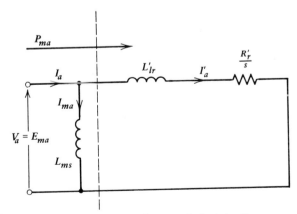

Fig. 9.16.   Approximate equivalent circuit.

equal to the shaft torque, is given by

$$T = \frac{3}{\omega_s} \cdot \frac{p}{2} \cdot \frac{R'_r}{s} \cdot \frac{V_a^2}{\left(R'_r/s\right)^2 + \left(\omega_s L'_{lr}\right)^2} \ \text{N} \cdot \text{m} \qquad (9.20)$$

If this expression for torque is differentiated with respect to s and the derivative equated to zero the slip for maximum torque is

$$s = \pm \frac{R'_r}{\omega_s L'_{lr}} \qquad (9.21)$$

The positive value applies to motoring, and if it is substituted for s in Eq. 9.20 the breakdown torque is

$$T_{\max} = \frac{3p V_a^2}{4\omega_s^2 L'_{lr}} \ \text{N} \cdot \text{m} \qquad (9.22)$$

Only a small error is introduced if it is assumed that

$$\omega_s = \frac{p}{2}\omega_m \ \text{rad/s} \qquad (9.23)$$

and substitution for ω_s in Eq. 9.22 then yields

$$T_{\max} = \frac{3 V_a^2}{p L'_{lr} \omega_m^2} \ \text{N} \cdot \text{m} \qquad (9.24)$$

Thus to a reasonable approximation

$$T_{\max} \propto \frac{1}{\omega_m^2} \ \text{N} \cdot \text{m} \qquad (9.25)$$

and ω_m is, of course, directly proportional to vehicle speed. If, at the end of the acceleration with increasing terminal pd, the vehicle drive is to draw constant power from the supply system, it is necessary that

$$T \propto \frac{1}{\omega_m} \ \text{N} \cdot \text{m} \qquad (9.26)$$

The effect of the relationships in Eqs. 9.25 and 9.26 is illustrated in Fig. 9.17a, where the motor-frame size is such that its motor operates at rated current and base pd at the commencement of field weakenings when $\omega_m = \omega_b$, the rated speed. Acceleration with field weakening and increase in inverter frequency then follows up to three times the base speed of the motor. The speed-torque curve for constant-power acceleration is marked $T\omega_m = k_1$ in Fig. 9.17a. The torque that the motor is capable of delivering without break-down is shown by the curve marked $T_{max}\omega_m^2 = k_2$. Both k_1 and k_2, of course, are constants. The motor can deliver constant power at base terminal pd and rated current only up to the speed at which the two curves intersect. The shaded area between the two curves shows a range in which the drive system is unable to deliver the required acceleration.

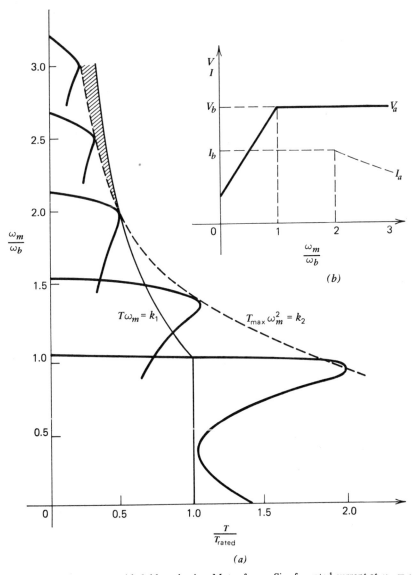

Fig. 9.17. Induction motor with field weakening. Motor frame. Size for rated current at $\omega_m = \omega_b$.

The variation of motor terminal pd and line current over the whole speed range for this unsatisfactory system is shown in Fig. 9.17b. At the high-speed end of this range the breakdown torque of the motor is less than the torque required for constant-power operation and current must be reduced. This example therefore shows that it is not satisfactory simply to select a motor with a rating equal to that of the inverter because the specified system acceleration is not thereby achieved. A squirrel-cage motor in which breakdown torque is twice rated torque can be operated only at constant power to twice its base or rated speed ω_b.

As shown in Fig. 9.17a, the required torque would be achieved if the intersection of the curves $T\omega_m = k_1$ and $T_{max}\omega_m^2 = k_2$ were to take place at the maximum speed ω_{max}; that is to say,

$$\frac{k_1}{\omega_{max}} = \frac{k_2}{\omega_{max}^2} \ \text{N} \cdot \text{m} \tag{9.27}$$

If the torque required by the load at speed ω_b is given the symbol T_b

$$k_1 = T_b\omega_b \ \text{W} \tag{9.28}$$

and from Eqs. 9.27 and 9.28

$$k_2 = T_b\omega_b\omega_{max} \tag{9.29}$$

Thus at $\omega_m = \omega_b$, where the motor can develop its full breakdown torque T_{max},

$$T_{max} = \frac{T_b\omega_b\omega_{max}}{\omega_b^2} \ \text{N} \cdot \text{m} \tag{9.30}$$

and

$$\frac{T_{max}}{T_b} = \frac{\omega_{max}}{\omega_b} = r \tag{9.31}$$

This conclusion might have been reached by considering the proportions of Fig. 9.17a.

The motor speed-torque curve shown in Fig. 9.17a is that for a typical Class B squirrel-cage induction motor for which breakdown torque is equal to twice rated torque (the ratio for a Class C motor is slightly less). Thus, if for the case illustrated, in which $r = 3$, Eq. 9.31 is to be satisfied, a motor with a frame size such that it can develop a breakdown torque $T_{max} = 3T_b$ at speed ω_b must be used. The curve of I_a in Fig. 9.17b would then be a horizontal line but motor rating would be much greater than inverter rating.

Motors in rapid-transit systems are limited in size because they must be mounted on the truck beneath the vehicle where space is limited. There is, however, an alternative to a motor of large frame size and that is a motor capable of withstanding a higher terminal pd than required for base operation and increasing the inverter output pd at speeds above that at which the intersection of the curves in Fig. 9.17a occurs. The question is, how much increase in pd is necessary?

From Eq. 9.22 at any speed ω_{m1} and the corresponding terminal pd V_{a1} the breakdown torque of the motor is

$$T_{max1} = \frac{3pV_{a1}^2}{4\omega_{m1}^2 L_{lr}'} \text{ N} \cdot \text{m} \quad (9.32)$$

Similarly, at speed ω_{m2} and pd V_{a2}

$$T_{max2} = \frac{3pV_{a2}^2}{4\omega_{m2}^2 L_{lr}'} \text{ N} \cdot \text{m} \quad (9.33)$$

From Eqs. 9.32 and 9.33

$$\frac{V_{a1}}{V_{a2}} = \sqrt{\frac{\omega_{m1}}{\omega_{m2}}} \quad (9.34)$$

If ω_{m1} is the speed at which intersection of the curves in Fig. 9.17a takes place when $V_{a1} = V_b$, the base terminal pd of the motor, then at any higher speed ω_{m2} the corresponding terminal pd should be

$$V_{a2} = V_b \sqrt{\frac{\omega_{m2}}{\omega_{m1}}} \text{ V} \quad (9.35)$$

Because constant power is to be drawn from the supply system during this phase of acceleration, it follows that the corresponding current will be

$$I_{a2} = I_b \sqrt{\frac{\omega_{m1}}{\omega_{m2}}} \text{ A} \quad (6.36)$$

Variations of V_a and I_a for this method of control are shown in Fig. 9.18. The maximum value of terminal pd that the motor is required to withstand is given by

$$V_{a\,max} = V_b \sqrt{\frac{\omega_{max}}{\omega_{m1}}} \text{ V} \quad (9.37)$$

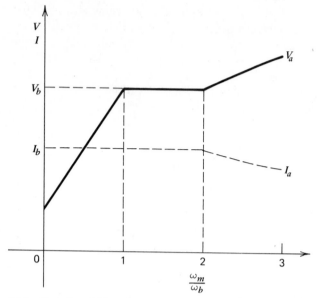

Fig. 9.18. Variation of V_a and I_a with ω_m. Motor frame size for $\omega_m = 2\omega_b$.

With this arrangement the required acceleration at constant power is achieved with a motor of small frame size. The inverter power, however, defined by Eq. 9.19, has been increased because the fact that $V_{a\,\text{max}}$ and $I_{a\,\text{max}}$ do not occur simultaneously does not reduce the size of the thyristors which must withstand the one and deliver the other.

9.6.1. Usable Inverter Power

Usable inverter power, expressed as a proportion of inverter rating, depends essentially on the switching frequency of the thyristors. The higher the switching frequency, the smaller the usable proportion of the zero-frequency power rating. The cause of the reduction is chiefly the commutating losses that occur in the thyristors and affect their heat balance. This means that if a high switching frequency is to be used the converter must be oversized. Also, at high frequencies the output pd of the inverter falls because of the increasing proportion of the cycle taken up by the dead time that must elapse to permit turn-off of one thyristor before another can be turned on.

Switching frequency of the inverter can be kept low if the ac output terminal pd V_a is controlled by variation of the dc input terminal pd V_{LK}; but such control demands a further converter, either a chopper or a controlled rectifier, and involves a large increase in the bulk, weight, and cost of the on-board equipment.

If the output terminal pd of the inverter is controlled by PWM the commutating frequency is at least doubled, as illustrated by the waveforms of Fig. 9.3. If it is desirable to reduce the amplitude of lower frequency harmonics in the system a greater number of pulses than shown in Fig. 9.3 must be used at low speeds.

Figure 9.19 illustrates the proportion of the inverter rating that can be obtained as usable power for a range of commutating frequency from 0 to 1000 Hz; for example, at the highest speed shown in Fig. 9.17 the required fundamental frequency exceeds 180 Hz. If waveforms like those in Fig. 9.3 were used the commutation frequency would be 360 Hz and, from Fig. 9.19, little more than half the inverter rating would be available as usable power. At the top speed of any system, however, it would no doubt be satisfactory to use the waveforms in Figs. 9.2 and 9.5 and, from Fig. 9.19, some 70% of the inverter low-frequency rating would be available as output power. At lower speeds PWM could be used, with the frequency of commutations increased at lower speeds, if necessary in several steps. For starting the motor from standstill a commutation rate unrelated to the fundamental frequency could be selected and could be of the same order as that at maximum speed.

In the foregoing brief discussion only the principal factors that affect the relation between the motor and converter ratings have been introduced, but this no doubt has been sufficient to show that a complicated problem of optimization is involved. Further considerations might be the efficiency of the gears between the motor and the driving wheels and the adhesion of those wheels to the track in rail-guided vehicles.

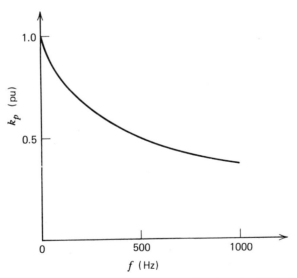

Fig. 9.19. Usable inverter power $k_p V_{max} I_{max}$ as a function of switching frequency.

PROBLEMS

9.1. The 460-V, 60-Hz, 25-hp (18.6-kW), 2515-rpm motor in Example 9.1 is supplied by a voltage-source inverter and drives a mechanical system whose load speed-torque characteristic may be represented by a straight line passing through the points $[0.85T_{rated}, 3500]$ and $[0.75T_{rated}, 0]$. The ratio E_{ma1}/ω_s is to be maintained constant over the entire speed range of $0 < n < 3500$ rpm at the value of E_{ma}/ω_s for rated operating conditions. Plot curves of rms line-to-neutral motor pd V_a, rms fundamental line current I_{a1R}, inverter apparent power output $3(V_a I_{a1R})$, motor slip s, motor power factor PF, and motor efficiency η. Friction and windage losses and core losses may be neglected, as also may the effect of current harmonics other than the fundamental.

9.2. A belt conveyer is to be driven at variable speed by the system in Fig. 9.12. The speed-torque characteristic of the loaded conveyer referred to the motor shaft may be described by $T_L = 425 - 0.225\omega_m$ N · m. A 250-hp (186-kW), 460-V, 60-Hz, 3550-rpm, three-phase, squirrel-cage motor is to drive the conveyer. The motor parameters for the equivalent circuit in Fig. 6.2 are:

$$R_s = 0.0203\ \Omega \qquad \omega_s L_{ls} = 0.0890\ \text{mH}$$

$$R'_r = 0.0127\ \Omega \qquad \omega_s L'_{lr} = 0.166\ \text{mH}$$

$$R_c \to \infty \qquad \omega_s L_{ms} = 5.70\ \text{mH}$$

The ratio of E_{ma1}/ω_s is to be held constant at the ratio of E_{ma}/ω_s for rated operation. Windage losses and friction of the motor may be neglected. Motor current harmonics other than the fundamental may be ignored. Determine fundamental inverter output pd V_{a1}, frequency ω_s, and current I_{a1} when the motor is running at (a) 3500 rpm and (b) 1500 rpm.

9.3. A 50-hp, (37.3-kW), 460-V, 60-Hz, 1770-rpm, three-phase, squirrel-cage induction motor has the following parameters for the equivalent circuit in Fig. 6.2:

$$R_s = 0.130\ \Omega \qquad L_{ls} = 1.03\ \text{mH}$$

$$R'_r = 0.0764\ \Omega \qquad L'_{lr} = 1.91\ \text{mH}$$

$$R_c \to \infty \qquad L_{ms} = 36.9\ \text{mH}$$

The motor is to be driven at variable speed by the system in Fig. 9.1*a*. The ratio E_{ma1}/ω_s is to be maintained constant at the value of the ratio of E_{ma}/ω_s under rated operating conditions. The converters may be assumed to be ideal. Only the fundamental component of any currents should be considered and the inverter input pd V_{LK} may be assumed to be perfectly smooth.

(a) If the maximum speed required is 1725 rpm and at that speed the load torque T_L reaches its maximum of 85% of motor rated torque determine the minimum required line-to-line pd of the ac system that supplies the controlled rectifier.

(b) If the pd determined in (a) is rounded up to the nearest 50 V (400, 450, 500, etc.) and the motor runs at 900 rpm driving a load torque equal to 60% of the rated motor torque determine the fundamental power factor PF_1 at the ac terminals of the controlled rectifier.

9.4. A 30-hp (22.4-kW), 460-V, 60-Hz, 1770-rpm, squirrel-cage induction motor is to be driven by an inverter supplied by a Class A chopper from a 600-V, dc supply system. The parameters of the motor for the equivalent circuit of Fig. 6.2 are

$$R_s = 0.185 \ \Omega \qquad L_{ls} = 1.37 \ \text{mH}$$

$$R'_r = 0.103 \ \Omega \qquad L'_{lr} = 2.05 \ \text{mH}$$

$$R_c \rightarrow \infty \qquad L_{ms} = 39.3 \ \text{mH}$$

The motor is to operate over a speed range $0 < n < 1750$ rpm and the ratio E_{ma1}/ω_s is to be held constant at the value of the ratio E_{ma}/ω_s for rated operation. The load torque over the speed range is 100 N · m. Friction and windage losses of the motor and the effect of current harmonics other than the fundamental may be neglected. Draw a curve of motor speed n versus chopper ratio t_{ON}/T_p for the specified speed range.

9.5. For the system in Problem 9.4 use the same conditions and approximations and draw a curve of t_{ON}/T_p versus T_L at 1000 rpm for a load-torque range $0 < T_L < 200$ N · m.

9.6. A 460-V, 200-hp (149-kW), 1780 rpm, three-phase, squirrel-cage induction motor is one of several motors that will drive a rapid-transit train from a 600-V, dc distribution system. The inverter input-terminal pd V_{LK} is supplied from a Class C chopper and the ratio E_{ma1}/ω_s in the motor is maintained constant at the value of E_{ma}/ω_s for rated operation. Components of motor input current other than the fundamental may be neglected, as also may motor friction and windage losses. The converters may be assumed to be ideal and the inverter dc terminal pd and current may be assumed to be perfectly smooth. The approximate motor characteristics of Fig. 9.9 may be used. The equivalent-circuit parameters of the motor are

$$R_s = 0.0188 \ \Omega \qquad L_{ms} = 0.232 \ \text{mH}$$

$$R_r' = 0.0143 \ \Omega \qquad L_{lr}' = 0.349 \ \text{mH}$$

$$R_c \to \infty \qquad L_{ms} = 12.36 \ \text{mH}$$

(a) Determine the value of chopper ratio t_{ON}/T_p and the average current drawn from the dc supply system when the motor is driving at 1500 rpm and developing rated torque.

(b) If, at the speed in (a), the inverter frequency is changed to call for a regenerative braking torque of 400 N · m at the motor coupling determine the required chopper ratio t_{ON}/T_p and the average current delivered to the dc supply system.

9.7. The motor in the system in Problem 9.6 is driving, with field weakening, at 3000 rpm. The fundamental motor line current is limited to 220 A. The fundamental motor terminal pd is held at $460/\sqrt{3}$ V. On the basis of the assumptions and approximations in Problem 9.6, determine the motor torque, the inverter frequency, and the current drawn from the dc supply system.

9.8. A 460-V, 60-Hz, 100-hp (74.6-kW), 1180-rpm, three-phase, squirrel-cage induction motor is used to drive a fan that presents a load characteristic described by the equation

$$T_L = \frac{\omega_m^2}{30} \ \text{N} \cdot \text{m}$$

where ω_m is the angular speed of the fan and motor in rad/s. The parameters of the motor for the equivalent circuit of Fig. 6.2 are:

$$R_s = 0.0591 \ \Omega \qquad L_{ls} = 0.624 \ \text{mH}$$

$$R_r' = 0.0396 \ \Omega \qquad L_{lr}' = 0.936 \ \text{mH}$$

$$R_c \to \infty \qquad L_{ms} = 20.7 \ \text{mH}$$

The motor is supplied from a three-phase, 480-V, 60-Hz system by the arrangement of converters shown in Fig. 9.1b. The ratio of V_{a1}/ω_s for the motor is kept constant at the value of V_a/ω_s for rated operation. Components of motor input current other than the fundamental may be neglected in calculating motor torque and the link current i_O, as also may motor friction and windage losses. The converters may be assumed to be ideal and the inverter dc terminal pd V_{LK} and current i_O may be assumed to be perfectly smooth.

(a) Determine the fundamental motor line current and the rms line current at the rectifier input terminals when the fan is being driven at 1000 rpm.
(b) What is the effective power factor at the input terminals of the rectifier under these conditions?

Chapter 10

Induction Motor
with Current-Source Inverter

10.1. INTRODUCTION

A current-source inverter is supplied from a direct-current source. Ideally, it is, a source of infinite internal impedance that will provide unlimited terminal pd at constant controllable output current. An inverter supplied in this way will excite a standard three-phase squirrel-cage induction motor at controllable frequency and line current. Normally only a single motor is driven or a number of similar motors mechanically coupled as in a rapid-transit system.

10.1.1. Converter Combinations

When an ac power distribution system of constant pd is available provision of a direct voltage source is a simple matter, as shown in the converter combinations in Fig. 9.1. When a constant direct-current source must be obtained from a constant pd ac-power distribution system the situation is more complicated; it calls for ac/dc conversion with a feedback loop to maintain the desired value of current. Two alternative converter combinations are shown in Fig. 10.1. The phase-controlled rectifier in (a) has the familiar disadvantage that at low load the power factor at the rectifier ac terminals is very low. It has the advantage of simplicity in that forced commutation is not needed. Input current to the inverter is kept constant by a feedback loop that changes delay angle α in the rectifier as required. The dynamic response of this rectifier is relatively slow but so is that of the entire system, partly because of the large inductance in the dc link that is needed to smooth the rectifier output current and partly because of the limited dynamic response of the inverter itself; commutation problems appear if a too rapid change in input current is demanded.

The system shown in Fig. 10.1b has the advantage of high power factor at the rectifier ac terminals at all loads. Forced commutation, however, is required in the chopper. Input current to the inverter is kept constant by a feedback loop that changes conduction time t_{ON} in the chopper as required. The

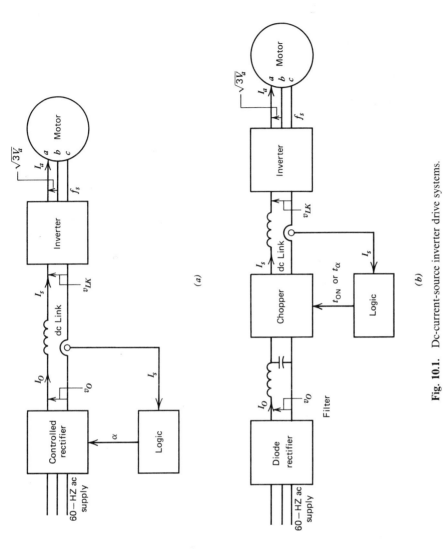

Fig. 10.1. Dc-current-source inverter drive systems.

chopper has the disadvantage of requiring fast-response, therefore more expensive, thyristors. This system, without the diode rectifier, can be used in situations in which a dc distribution network is available.

Typical applications for the drives in Fig. 10.1 are

(a) pumps and fans;
(b) conveyors;
(c) cranes;
(d) transportation drives.

It will be noted that none of these applications calls for a drive in which rapid dynamic response is required. The systems in Fig. 10.1 involve relatively inexpensive converters and, if necessary, can provide a high starting torque.

In general, converter losses in these systems are low because forced commutation is required only in the chopper. The basic principles of operation of controlled rectifiers and choppers were dealt with in Chapters 4 and 5, respectively. Before considering the systems in Fig. 10.1 in any detail some discussion of the operation of current-source inverters is necessary.

10.2. THREE-PHASE CURRENT-SOURCE INVERTER

Figure 10.2 shows the power circuit of a three-phase inverter that is supplied via a dc link from a direct current source. The thyristors in this circuit are numbered in the sequence in which the gating signals are applied for positive-sequence currents at load terminals A, B, C. The six identical commutating capacitors are connected in delta across the three phases of the circuit. Because one thyristor is commutated by the application of a gating signal to another, the converter may be considered to be line-commutated. On the other hand, if the capacitors are regarded as part of the three-phase load the converter may be considered to be load-commutated.

The gating signals are shown in Fig. 10.3, as also are the ideal waveforms of the resulting currents. It will be noted that only two thyristors conduct at any instant. The commutation process can be understood by considering that switch SW in Fig. 10.2 is opened immediately after thyristor Q_2 is turned on. This causes a pulse of current to flow through the capacitors (its rate of rise is limited by di/dt inductors in series with the thyristors but not shown in Fig. 10.2) and this pulse charges C_1 so that v_{ab} is positive. Meantime, current has been growing in the RL load circuit. When the capacitors are fully charged and the system has reached a steady state the path of the load current is that shown in heavy line in Fig. 10.4a. When thyristor Q_3 is turned on and gating signal i_{G1} is simultaneously removed from Q_1 capacitor C_1 begins to discharge, and immediately turns off Q_1. The path of the load current is then that shown in Fig. 10.4b. When the capacitors are again fully charged, in particular with C_3 charged ready to commutate Q_3, the path of the load current is that shown in

Fig. 10.4c. A similar series of events causes turn-on of thyristor Q_4 to commutate Q_2.

As described in the preceding paragraph, the commutation process appears to be simple; in practice, it may not be quite so simple, although basically unchanged. Much depends on the load parameters and the frequency at which the inverter is started up. If the load at starting is low, so that the required source current is low, then precharging of the commutation capacitors may be needed, which implies that the current source is always applied when one

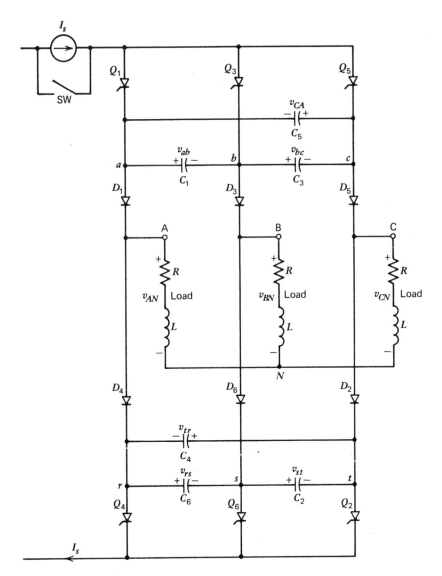

Fig. 10.2. Three-phase, current-source inverter.

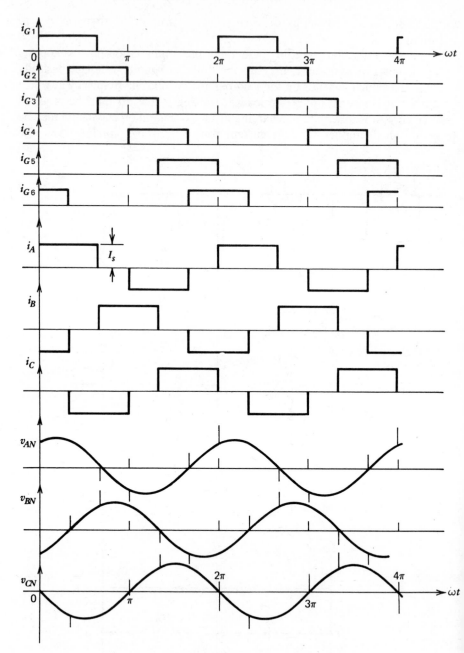

Fig. 10.3. Waveforms of the circuit variables in Fig. 10.2.

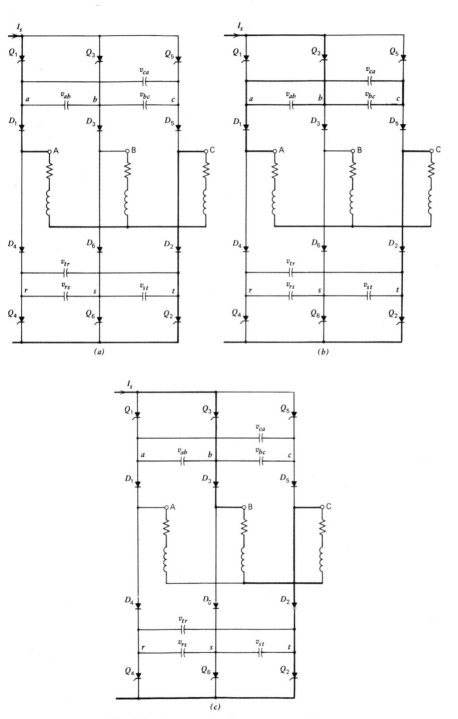

Fig. 10.4. Current-source inverter commutation.

particular pair of thyristors is already turned on. Furthermore, there may be oscillations in the parallel circuit formed by the RL load and the commutating capacitors. Also the starting frequency may be so high that no steady state is reached before a commutation takes place. In fact, this is normal when an induction motor is driven from a current-source inverter. Compared with the duration of a half-cycle of inverter output current, however, the time taken to transfer current from one branch of the load circuit to the next is usually short and only a small approximation is involved in representing the current pulses by the rectangular half-waves in Fig. 10.3.

Reversal of the phase sequence of the inverter output currents is obtained by reversal of the sequence of the gating signals applied to the thyristors.

10.3. OPERATION OF AN INDUCTION MOTOR ON A CURRENT SOURCE OF VARIABLE FREQUENCY

In Section 6.2.2 the behavior of an induction motor operated on a current source of rated frequency was analyzed and the results were shown in Fig. 6.4, in which they could be compared with those for the same motor operating on a voltage source of rated frequency. Comparison showed that the rated operating point of the motor lay on the unstable part of the speed-torque curve for current-source operation, so that the motor could not be operated on open loop from such a source. Furthermore, it was found that the terminal pd of the motor would rise to excessively high values if an attempt was made to operate the motor on the stable part of the speed-torque curve. These high values of terminal pd would, in practice, result in saturation of the magnetic circuit of the machine and the actual breakdown torque achieved would be much less than that calculated from the linear equivalent circuit (Fig. 6.4). However, there are definite advantages to operating an induction motor from a variable-frequency, controllable-current source, and it is therefore important to determine how this may be done without unduly saturating the motor.

As discussed in Chapter 9, in variable frequency drives magnetic saturation may be avoided by keeping the ratio E_{ma}/ω_s constant because this has the effect of holding the magnetizing current I_{ma} constant at some predetermined magnitude. As a model for analyzing the behavior of the motor under these conditions, the equivalent circuit of Fig. 6.2 with element R_c omitted is used, as shown in Fig. 10.5. From that circuit

$$I_{ma} = \left| \frac{(R_r'/s + j\omega_s L_{lr}')}{R_r'/s + j\omega_s (L_{ms} + L_{lr}')} \right| I_a \text{ A} \tag{10.1}$$

and since $\omega_r = s\omega_s$, this may be modified to

$$I_{ma} = \left[\frac{(R_r')^2 + (\omega_r L_{lr}')^2}{(R_r')^2 + \omega_r^2 (L_{ms} + L_{lr}')^2} \right]^{1/2} \times I_a \text{ A} \tag{10.2}$$

With a current source I_a is constant; thus Eq. 10.2 shows that if ω_r, the rotor or slip frequency, is held constant so also is I_{ma}. If the required value of I_{ma} is known the value of ω_r for any source current I_a can be determined from Eq. 10.2. If, however, I_{ma} is to be held constant at varying values of I_a, ω_r also must vary and I_a will, of course, vary with the load on the motor.

The consequence of the relation in Eq. 10.2 may be illustrated by a numerical example.

Example 10.1

A 460-V, 50-hp (37.3-kW), 1180 rpm, three-phase squirrel-cage induction motor has the following equivalent-circuit parameters:

$$R_s = 0.191\ \Omega \qquad L_{ls} = 1.20\ \text{mH} \qquad L_{ms} = 44.8\ \text{mH}$$

$$R_r' = 0.0707\ \Omega \qquad L_{lr}' = 1.79\ \text{mH}$$

Friction and windage losses are negligible:

(a) If I_{ma} is to be held constant at the value for rated operation and the line current varies from no-load to 1.5 times the full-load value determine the required range in ω_r.

(b) If ω_r is held constant at the value for rated operation and the line current varies over the range in (a) determine the resulting range of I_{ma}.

Solution

For rated operation

$$s = \frac{1200 - 1180}{1200} = 0.01667$$

$$\omega_r = 120\pi \times 0.01667 = 6.283\ \text{rad/s}$$

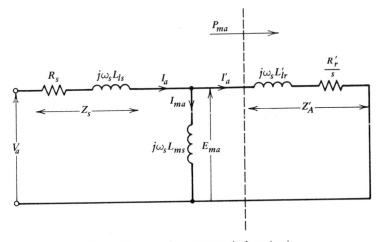

Fig. 10.5.   Induction-motor equivalent circuit.

The motor output power is

$$50 \times 746 = \frac{3(1 - 0.01667)}{0.01667} \times 0.0707(I_a')^2 \text{ W}$$

from which

$$I_a' = 54.60 \text{ A}$$

$$\overline{Z}_A' = \frac{0.0707}{0.01667} + j120\pi \times 1.79 \times 10^{-3} = 4.294\underline{/9.04°} \; \Omega$$

$$E_{ma} = 4.294 \times 54.60 = 234.5 \text{ V}$$

$$I_{ma} = \frac{234.5}{120\pi \times 44.8 \times 10^{-3}} = 13.88 \text{ A}$$

Let

$$\overline{E}_{ma} = 234.5\underline{/0°} \text{ V}$$

then

$$\overline{I}_{ma} = 13.88\underline{/-90°} \text{ A}$$

$$\overline{I}_a' = 54.60\underline{/-9.04°} \text{ A}$$

$$\overline{I}_a = 13.88\underline{/-90°} + 54.60\underline{/-9.04°} = 58.41\underline{/-22.61°} \text{ A}$$

This is the full-load current. The range in I_a is therefore

$$13.88 < I_a < 87.62 \text{ A}$$

(a) At $I_a = 13.88$, from Eq. 10.2

$$1 = \frac{0.0707^2 + \left(\omega_r \times 1.79 \times 10^{-3}\right)^2}{0.0707^2 + \omega_r^2(1.79 + 44.8)^2 \times 10^{-6}}$$

from which, as would be expected from physical reasoning

$$\omega_r = 0$$

At $I_a = 87.62$

$$\frac{13.88}{87.62} = \left[\frac{4.998 \times 10^{-3} + 3.204 \times 10^{-6}\omega_r^2}{4.998 \times 10^{-3} + 2171 \times 10^{-6}\omega_r^2}\right]^{1/2}$$

from which

$$\omega_r = 9.751 \text{ rad/s}$$

The range of ω_r is therefore

$$0 < \omega_r < 9.751 \text{ rad/s}$$

(b) $\omega_r = 6.283$. At $I_a = 13.88$

$$I_{ma} = \left[\frac{0.0707^2 + (6.283 \times 1.79 \times 10^{-3})^2}{0.0707^2 + 6.283^2 (1.79 + 44.8)^2 \times 10^{-6}} \right]^{1/2} \times 13.88$$

$$= \left[\frac{5.124}{90.69} \right]^{1/2} \times 13.88 = 3.299 \text{ A}$$

At $I_a = 87.62$

$$I_{ma} = \left[\frac{5.124}{90.69} \right]^{1/2} \times 87.62 = 20.83 \text{ A}$$

Thus the range of I_{ma} is

$$3.299 < I_{ma} < 20.83 \text{ A}$$

The results of part (a) in Example 10.1 show that if I_{ma} is to be held constant at all loads and speeds not only must ω_r be controlled but it must also be made a function of I_a. This complication in the control system is undesirable. It is much simpler to hold ω_r constant, in which case the results of part (b) in the example become relevant.

The results in part (b) show that if ω_r is held constant at the value for rated operation the motor will operate with field weakening at currents below the full load value and will saturate if, for short periods, the motor draws currents above the full-load value. It is therefore probable that in practice ω_r should be chosen for a line current somewhat in excess of the rated value, but this excess would be a matter of judgment by the system designer, based on a knowledge of the saturation curve of the motor and the anticipated work cycle. In the following the value of ω_r is chosen for the rated full-load current of the motor, and it must, as usual, be borne in mind that the torque predicted from the linear model for greater line currents will be optimistic.

Perhaps surprisingly, the per-phase pd's of a motor supplied from a rectangular-waveform current source vary approximately sinusoidally and are therefore represented by sinusoidal waveforms in Fig. 10.3. This may be explained from the motor model of Fig. 10.5. The line current, with its rectangular waveform, passes through the stator impedance and is then divided between the magnetizing branch and the rotor branch of the equivalent circuit. The much higher inductance of the magnetizing branch blocks the harmonic components of the line current and consequently I_{ma} is virtually a sinsoid of fundamental frequency. The result is that the rotating field produced in the air gap has a sinusoidal distribution virtually without space harmonics; therefore the induced emf E_{ma} is sinusoidal. Thus, apart from the slight distortion produced by Z_s, terminal pd V_a is sinusoidal. Essentially all of the current harmonics and part of the fundamental current must therefore be considered to flow in the rotor-circuit impedance Z_A'.

One feature disturbs the approximately sinusoidal pd waveforms and it is due to the high emf's induced in the motor by the rapid changes of current at the beginning and end of each rectangular (or rather trapezoidal) pulse of line current. These high emf's are matched by high peaks of terminal pd at the inverter input terminals (thyristors and diodes are protected against these peaks by snubbers not shown in Fig. 10.2). Commutation "spikes" are therefore indicated in the pd waveforms of Fig. 10.3.

The angle by which the motor phase pd's lead the fundamental components of line currents depends on the angle of the motor impedance, which in turn depends on the rotor frequency, which is determined by the speed at which the motor is running and the frequency at which it is excited. When regeneration takes place the waveforms of pd in Fig. 10.3 advance in phase to lead the fundamental components of the current waveforms by more than 90°. Because the direction of source current I_s is unchanged when this takes place, the input pd of the inverter becomes negative.

A unidirectional current at positive or negative pd can be supplied by the single controlled rectifier in the system in Fig. 10.1a. This system can therefore provide regeneration which, in conjunction with reversal of the sequence of the inverter gating signals, will give a four-quadrant drive. In the system in Fig. 10.1b, regeneration would require a Class D chopper and the diode rectifier would have to be replaced by a controlled rectifier in which the gating signals were switched from $\alpha = 0$ to $\alpha = (\pi - \omega t_{off} - \mu)$ when the input pd of the chopper was required to go negative. If a dc distribution system capable of accepting regenerated energy were available the controlled rectifier would not be needed.

10.3.1. Basic Relationships

From Eq. 6.24, for a machine operating at constant line current I_a,

$$T = \frac{3p}{2\omega_s} \cdot \frac{R_r'}{s} \cdot \frac{(\omega_s L_{ms})^2 I_a^2}{(R_r'/s)^2 + \omega_s^2 (L_{ms} + L_{lr}')^2} \ \text{N} \cdot \text{m} \qquad (10.3)$$

and because $\omega_r = s\omega_s$ substitution in Eq. 10.3 yields

$$T = \frac{3p}{2} \cdot \frac{R_r' \omega_r (L_{ms} I_a)^2}{(R_r')^2 + \omega_r^2 (L_{ms} + L_{lr}')^2} \ \text{N} \cdot \text{m} \qquad (10.4)$$

Thus if ω_r is held constant the developed torque is proportional to the square of the line current and independent of motor speed.

In a motor driven from the current source inverter I_a in Eqs. 10.3 and 10.4 must be replaced by I_{a1}, the rms value of the fundamental component of the line current. From the current waveforms in Fig. 10.3 the rms value of the line current is

$$I_a = \sqrt{\tfrac{2}{3}}\,I_s = 0.8165 I_s \text{ A} \tag{10.5}$$

and by using the methods in Appendix A the rms value of the fundamental component of line current is

$$I_{a1} = 0.7797 I_s \text{ A} \tag{10.6}$$

The rms value of all current harmonics other than the fundamental is then

$$I_{ah} = \left(I_a^2 - I_{a1}^2 \right)^{1/2} = 0.2424 I_s \text{ A} \tag{10.7}$$

In the equivalent circuit in Fig. 10.5 the fundamental component of the line current is divided into I_{ma1} and I'_{a1}, where

$$I_{ma1} = \frac{|R'_r/s + j\omega_s L'_{lr}|I_{a1}}{|R'_r/s + j\omega_s (L_{ms} + L'_{lr})|} \text{ A} \tag{10.8}$$

$$I'_{a1} = \frac{\omega_s L_{ms} I_{a1}}{|R'_r/s + j\omega_s (L_{ms} + L'_{lr})|} \text{ A} \tag{10.9}$$

The mechanical power developed by the motor is

$$P_{mech} = T\omega_m = 3\left(I'_{a1} \right)^2 R'_r \frac{(1-s)}{s} \text{ W} \tag{10.10}$$

and substitution from Eq. 6.2 yields

$$T\omega_m = 3\left(I'_{a1} \right)^2 R'_r \frac{(\omega_s - \omega_r)}{\omega_r} \text{ W} \tag{10.11}$$

The resistive losses in the motor are

$$P_R = 3\left[R_s I_a^2 + R'_r \left(I'_{a1} \right)^2 + R'_r I_{ah}^2 \right] \text{ W} \tag{10.12}$$

The motor input power is

$$P_{in} = P_{mech} + P_R \text{ W} \tag{10.13}$$

and the motor efficiency is

$$\eta = \frac{P_{\text{mech}}}{P_{\text{in}}} \text{ pu} \qquad (10.14)$$

If the inverter is assumed to be ideal

$$\bar{v}_{LK} I_s = P_{\text{in}} \text{ W} \qquad (10.15)$$

from which $\bar{v}_{LK}$, the average value of the inverter input pd, can be determined. If the inductance in the dc link is assumed to have negligible resistance the average output pd of the converter that supplies the inverter is equal to $\bar{v}_{LK}$.

It is important to be able to calculate the motor terminal pd or, what amounts to nearly the same thing, the rms magnitude of the fundamental component of that pd because this may be limited by the source that supplies the inverter and also must not become great enough to endanger the motor insulation. If, by definition,

$$\bar{E}_{ma1} = E_{ma1} \underline{/0} \text{ V} \qquad (10.16)$$

then

$$\bar{I}_{ma1} = I_{ma1} \underline{/-90°} \text{ A} \qquad (10.17)$$

From Eq. 10.8, substituting $\omega_r = s\omega_s$,

$$I_{ma1} \underline{/-90°} = \frac{(R_r' + j\omega_r L_{lr}')\bar{I}_{a1}}{R_r' + j\omega_r (L_{ms} + L_{lr}')} \text{ A} \qquad (10.18)$$

and because the magnitudes of I_{ma1}, I_{a1}, and ω_r are known the phase angle of $\bar{I}_{a1}$ may be calculated. At any frequency

$$\bar{E}_{ma1} = \omega_s L_{ms} I_{ma1} \underline{/0} \text{ V} \qquad (10.19)$$

The corresponding fundamental terminal pd will then be

$$\bar{V}_{a1} = \omega_s L_{ms} I_{ma1} \underline{/0} + (R_s + j\omega_s L_{ls})\bar{I}_{a1} \text{ V} \qquad (10.20)$$

The fundamental power factor at which the motor is operating is

$$PF_1 = \cos\left[\underline{/V_{a1}} - \underline{/I_{a1}}\right] \qquad (10.21)$$

Because of the effect of current and flux harmonics in increasing heating, integral horsepower motors must be derated by about 10%. When rated torque is required below 30% of rated speed and the cooling fan becomes ineffective further derating or a separately driven fan becomes necessary.

Because the foregoing discussion assumed that ω_r was held constant, it is desirable at this stage to determine how that may be done.

10.3.2.   Control of Rotor Frequency

Figure 10.6 is a block diagram of one possible drive system in which rotor frequency is controlled. The two command signals are Ω_r, the selected rotor frequency, and Ω_m, the required motor speed. The transfer function of the polarity sensor may be defined as follows:

$$k_T(\Omega_m - \omega_m) \geq 0 \qquad \text{output} = +1$$

$$k_T(\Omega_m - \omega_m) < 0 \qquad \text{output} = -1 \qquad (10.22)$$

where k_T is the transfer function of the tachometer.

The current setpoint generator delivers an output signal $k_{TR}I_{REF}$, where k_{TR} is the transfer function of the current transducer that measures inverter input current. This output signal has a minimum value for zero input and a positive value for positive or negative input.

Consider that the system is at rest when power is switched on and signal Ω_r is applied but signal Ω_m remains set to zero. The output of the polarity sensor is +1 and multiplier M1 transmits a positive signal $k_T\Omega_r$ to the frequency summer. This applies $k_T\Omega_r$ to the inverter logic, which generates gating signals at frequency $\omega_s = \Omega_r$ for the inverter. The input to the current setpoint generator is zero so that its output signal corresponds to the current drawn by the stalled motor at frequency $\omega_s = \Omega_r$. The output of the current summer is $k_{TR}(I_{REF} - I_s)$ and multiplier M2 applies it with a positive sign to the rectifier logic. This reduces the delay angle α from 90° and the consequent small output terminal pd of the rectifier produces inverter input current I_s which corresponds to the line current of the stalled motor.

Now let the speed command be set at some finite value Ω_m. The ramp generator applies to the speed summer a signal that increases at a controlled rate from zero. The output of the polarity sensor remains at +1. The output from the current setpoint generator increases and delay angle α decreases further from 90° so that the rectifier output pd increases. Consequently, motor current increases and the motor accelerates and eventually reaches speed $\omega_m = \Omega_m$. The system then runs in a steady state.

If Ω_m is reduced the ramp generator output decreases at a controlled rate, the input to the current setpoint generator moves through zero to become negative, and signal $k_{TR}I_{REF}$ decreases through the minimum value and increases again. As the speed error signal $k_T(\Omega_m - \omega_m)$ moves through zero the polarity sensor output changes to -1 and α increases through 90°, reversing the output terminal pd of the rectifier. At the same time the input to

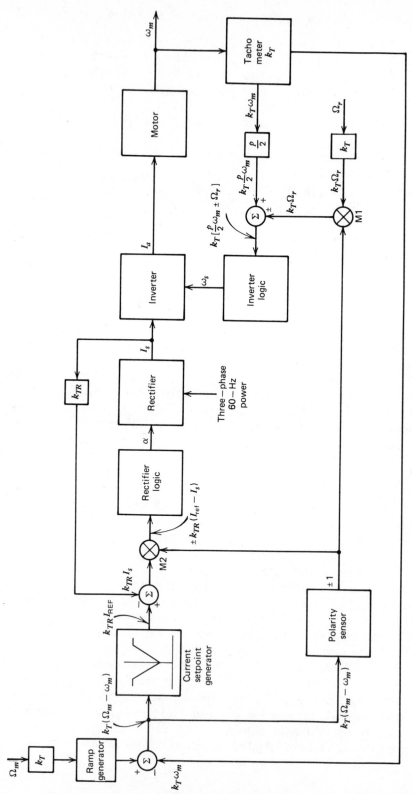

Fig. 10.6. Induction-motor drive with rotor-frequency control.

the inverter logic changes to $k_T[(p/2)\omega_m - \Omega_r]$; therefore ω_s decreases. The motor then regenerates and decelerates. This process continues until ω_m passes down through the new command value Ω_m and steady-state driving is resumed.

Example 10.2

A 460-V, 60-Hz, 25-hp (18.6-kW), 1180-rpm, three-phase, squirrel-cage induction motor has the following parameters for the equivalent circuit in Fig. 10.5:

$$R_s = 0.455 \ \Omega \qquad L_{ls} = 1.59 \text{ mH} \qquad L_{ms} = 65.3 \text{ mH}$$

$$R'_r = 0.149 \ \Omega \qquad L'_{lr} = 2.39 \text{ mH}$$

The motor is to be driven by the system in Fig. 10.6. The available power supply is three-phase, 440 V, 60 Hz. Friction, windage, and core losses in the motor may be neglected.

(a) Determine the rotor frequency, per-phase magnetizing current, and line current for rated operation of the motor.
(b) If the motor is developing 0.75 of rated torque at 1000 rpm with the rotor frequency controlled at the value obtained in (a), determine
   (1) fundamental motor line current;
   (2) percentage of field weakening compared with the field strength for rated operation;
   (3) Inverter frequency.
(c) For the conditions of operation in (b) determine the magnitude of the fundamental component of the motor terminal pd and the rms value of the motor line current.
(d) For the same conditions of operation determine the inverter input current, the average rectifier output pd and the fundamental power factor at the ac terminals of the rectifier.

Solution

(a) For rated operation

$$s = \frac{1200 - 1180}{1200} = \frac{1}{60}$$

$$\omega_r = s\omega_s = \frac{1}{60} \times 120\pi = 2\pi \text{ rad/s}$$

$$P_{mech} = 3(I'_a)^2 R'_r \frac{(1-s)}{s} = 25 \times 746$$

from which, after substitution of the values of R'_r and s

$$I'_a = 26.59 \text{ A}$$

$$\overline{Z}'_A = 0.149 \times 60 + j120\pi \times 2.39 \times 10^{-3} = 8.985\underline{/5.76°} \ \Omega$$

$$E_{ma} = 8.985 \times 26.59 = 238.9 \text{ V}$$

$$\omega_s L_{ms} = 120\pi \times 65.3 \times 10^{-3} = 23.62 \ \Omega$$

$$I_{ma} = \frac{238.9}{24.62} = 9.704 \text{ A}$$

Let

$$\overline{E}_{ma} = E_{ma}\underline{/0} \text{ V}$$

Then

$$\overline{I}_a = 9.704\underline{/-90°} + 26.59\underline{/-5.76°} = 29.21\underline{/-25.06°} \text{ A}$$

(b)

$$0.75T_{\text{rated}} = \frac{0.75 \times 25 \times 746 \times 30}{1180\pi} = 113.2 \text{ N} \cdot \text{m}$$

From Eq. 10.4

$$113.2 = \frac{3 \times 6}{2} \times \frac{0.149}{2\pi} \times \frac{(2\pi \times 65.3 \times 10^{-3})^2 I_{a1}^2}{0.149^2 + (2\pi)^2 (65.3 + 2.39)^2 \times 10^{-6}}$$

from which

$$I_{a1} = 25.30 \text{ A}$$

From Eq. 10.8, substituting ω_r for $s\omega_s$,

$$I_{ma1} = \frac{|0.149 + j2\pi \times 2.39 \times 10^{-3}|}{|0.149 + j2\pi(65.3 + 2.39)10^{-3}|} \times 25.30 = 8.406 \text{ A}$$

As a percentage of the rated full-load value

$$I_{ma1} = \frac{8.406}{9.704} \times 100\% = 86.63\%$$

Percentage of field weakening = 13.37%

$$\omega_s = \frac{p}{2}\omega_m + \omega_r = \frac{6}{2} \times \frac{1000\pi}{30} + 2\pi = 102\pi \text{ rad/s}$$

(c) From Eq. 10.18

$$8.406 / -90° = \frac{(0.149 + j2\pi \times 2.39 \times 10^{-3})25.30 / x°}{0.149 + j2\pi(65.3 + 2.39)10^{-3}}$$

from which

$$x = -25.07°$$

and

$$\bar{I}_{a1} = 25.30 / -25.07° \text{ A}$$

$$\bar{V}_{a1} = 102\pi \times 65.3 \times 10^{-3} \times 8.406 +$$

$$(0.455 + j102\pi \times 1.59 \times 10^{-3}) \times 25.30 / -25.07°$$

$$= 191.9 / 2.03° \text{ V}$$

The line-to-line fundamental terminal pd is thus 332.4 V. The rms value of V_a will be slightly greater. From Eqs. 10.5 and 10.6 the rms line current is

$$\bar{I}_a = \sqrt{\frac{2}{3}} \times \frac{25.30}{0.7797} = 26.49 \text{ A}$$

(d)

$$I_s = \frac{25.30}{0.7797} = 32.45 \text{ A}$$

$$I_{ah} = 0.2424 \times 32.45 = 7.865 \text{ A}$$

$$P_R = 3[0.455 \times 26.49^2 + 0.149(23.03^2 + 7.865^2)] = 1223 \text{ W}$$

$$P_{mech} = 113.2 \times \frac{1000\pi}{30} = 11850 \text{ W}$$

$$P_{in} = 11850 + 1223 = 13070 \text{ W}$$

$$\bar{v}_O = \frac{13070}{32.45} = 402.9 \text{ V}$$

$$402.9 = \frac{3\sqrt{2} \times 440}{\pi} \cos \alpha$$

from which

$$\cos \alpha = 0.6780$$

$$PF_1 = 0.6780$$

10.4. OPERATION WITH FIELD WEAKENING AT HIGH SPEED

At some point, as the motor speed is increased, the average inverter input pd $\bar{v}_{LK}$ reaches a limit which may be determined by the fixed pd of the ac or dc power source or by the terminal pd that the insulation of the motor can withstand. In the latter case a lower limit of delay angle α in the controlled rectifier of the system in Fig. 10.1a or an upper limit of conduction period t_{ON} in the chopper of the system in Fig. 10.1b would have to be imposed. If for a controlled value of motor current I_a speed ω_m is to be increased above that at which this pd limit is reached inverter frequency ω_s must continue to increase, whereas $\bar{v}_{LK}$ and I_s will be constant. This means that an approximately constant-power range of operation is entered. In this system also speed at constant motor terminal pd and constant line current reaches a boundary formed by the locus of motor breakdown torque (see Fig. 9.17). At this boundary current must be reduced if the motor is not to stall.

In the constant-power or field-weakening range, neglecting motor rotational losses and inverter losses,

$$\bar{v}_{LK}I_s = T\omega_m + P_R \text{ W} \tag{10.23}$$

Because at constant motor line current resistive losses P_R are nearly constant

$$T\omega_m \simeq \text{const W} \tag{10.24}$$

If, in Eq. 10.4, it is assumed that

$$\omega_r^2\left(L_{ms} + L'_{lr}\right)^2 \gg \left(R'_r\right)^2 \ \Omega \tag{10.25}$$

then

$$T = \frac{3p}{2} \cdot \frac{R'_r}{\omega_r} \cdot \frac{L_{ms}^2 I_{a1}^2}{\left(L_{ms} + L'_{lr}\right)^2} \ \text{N} \cdot \text{m} \tag{10.26}$$

At constant current therefore

$$T\omega_r \simeq \text{const W} \tag{10.27}$$

so that approximately

$$\omega_r \propto \omega_m \ \text{rad/s} \tag{10.28}$$

Thus increase in speed above that at which $\bar{v}_{LK}$ reaches its limit must be obtained by increasing ω_r and a relation between ω_r and ω_m is required.

If the approximation in Eq. 10.24 is accepted, then, from Eq. 10.11, for the field-weakening range

$$3\left(I_{a1}'\right)^2 R_r' \frac{\left(\omega_s - \omega_r\right)}{\omega_r} = P_o = \text{const W} \qquad (10.29)$$

Substitution for ω_s from Eq. 6.1 yields

$$3\left(I_{a1}'\right)^2 R_r' \cdot \frac{p}{2} \cdot \frac{\omega_m}{\omega_r} = P_o = \text{const W} \qquad (10.30)$$

From Eq. 10.9

$$I_{a1}' = \frac{\omega_r L_{ms} I_{a1}}{\left|R_r' + j\omega_r\left(L_{ms} + L_{lr}'\right)\right|} \text{ A} \qquad (10.31)$$

and from Eqs. 10.30 and 10.31

$$\frac{3\left(\omega_s L_{ms} I_{a1}\right)^2 R_r'}{\left(R_r'\right)^2 + \omega_r^2\left(L_{ms} + L_{lr}'\right)^2} \times \frac{p}{2} \frac{\omega_m}{\omega_r} = P_o = \text{const W} \qquad (10.32)$$

But I_{a1} is constant; under steady-state conditions $\omega_m = \Omega_m$ and it is intended to control ω_r from the command signal Ω_m. It therefore follows from Eq. 10.32 that

$$\omega_r^2 - \frac{3pR_r'\Omega_m\left(L_{ms}I_{a1}\right)^2}{2P_o\left(L_{ms} + L_{lr}'\right)^2} \cdot \omega_r + \frac{\left(R_r'\right)^2}{\left(L_{ms} + L_{lr}'\right)^2} = 0 \qquad (10.33)$$

where I_{a1} is the line current for output power P_o at base speed. For any speed command Ω_m Eq. 10.33 yields two values of ω_r, one of which is obviously trivial.

Thus to introduce rotor-frequency control for field weakening operation into the system in Fig. 10.6 it is necessary to replace the element k_T to which Ω_r is applied by an element to which Ω_m is applied and which has a transfer function dependent on Ω_m.

Figure 10.7 shows a curve of ω_r as a function of Ω_m obtained from Eq. 10.33 for the motor in Example 10.2 with a field-weakening range that extends from rated speed up to 3000 rpm. It will be observed that the increase in ω_r is virtually a linear function of Ω_m. Thus it is sufficient to obtain the intercept a and slope b of the straight line that connects the two end points of the sloping line in Fig. 10.7 and to assume that with field weakening in the steady state

$$\omega_r = a + b\Omega_m \text{ rad/s} \qquad (10.34)$$

The transfer function of the element to replace element k_T with input Ω_r in

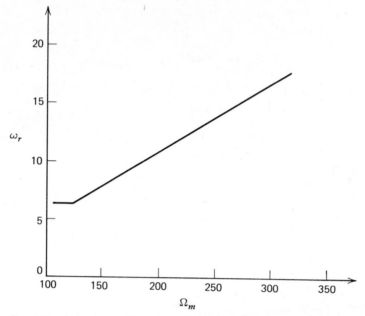

Fig. 10.7. Curve obtained from Equation 10.33 for the motor in Example 10.2.

Fig. 10.6 is

$$f(\Omega_m) = k_T \Omega_r \qquad 0 < \Omega_m \le \omega_{\text{rated}} \text{ rad/s}$$
$$f(\Omega_m) = k_T(a + b\Omega_m) \qquad \omega_{\text{rated}} < \Omega_m < \omega_{\text{max}} \text{ rad/s} \qquad (10.35)$$

where Ω_r is the fixed rotor frequency used for operation without field weakening, and ω_{max} is the top speed of operation with field weakening at constant current. The input to this new element would be taken from the output of the ramp generator in Fig. 10.6.

Example 10.3

For the system in Example 10.2 plot speed n as a function of torque T over the speed range $0 < n < 3000$ rpm and plot fundamental motor terminal pd V_{a1} as a function of speed over the same speed range. The fundamental component of the line current is to be maintained at the magnitude of the rated full-load current and field weakening is to commence at rated speed.

Solution

Constant-field range.
   From Eq. 10.4

$$T = \frac{3 \times 6}{2} \times \frac{0.149 \times 6.283 \times 0.0653^2 \times 29.21^2}{0.149^2 + 6.283^2(0.0653 + 0.00239)^2} = 150.9 \text{ N} \cdot \text{m}$$

and this is shown in Fig. 10.8. Let

$$\bar{E}_{ma1} = E_{ma1}\underline{/0} \text{ V}$$

Then from Eq. 10.18

$$I_{ma1}\underline{/-90°} = \frac{(0.149 + j6.283 \times 0.00239) \times 29.21\underline{/x°}}{0.149 + j6.283(0.0653 + 0.00239)}$$

from which $I_{ma1} = 9.711$ A and $x = -25.07°$ so that

$$\bar{I}_{ma1} = 9.711\underline{/-90°} \text{ A}$$

$$\bar{I}_{a1} = 29.21\underline{/-25.07°} \text{ A}$$

$$\omega_s = \frac{p}{2}\omega_m + \omega_r = 3\omega_m + 6.283 \text{ rad/s}$$

$$\bar{V}_{a1} = 0.0653 \times 9.711\omega_s + (0.455 + j\omega_s \times 0.00159) \times 29.21\underline{/-25.07°} \text{ V}$$

For the range $0 < \Omega_m < 123.6$ rad/s V_{a1} may now be calculated as a function of n. The result is shown in Fig. 10.9.

Field-weakening range.
From Example 10.2, at the lower limit of this range, motor speed is 1180 rpm or 123.6 rad/s and $\Omega_r = 6.283$ rad/s.
At $n = 3000$ rpm or 100π rad/s, from Eq. 10.33, $\omega_r = 17.66$ rad/s. Thus in Eq. 10.34

$$b = \frac{17.66 - 6.283}{100\pi - 123.6} = 0.05970$$

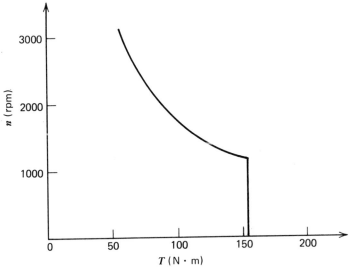

Fig. 10.8. Diagram I for Example 10.3.

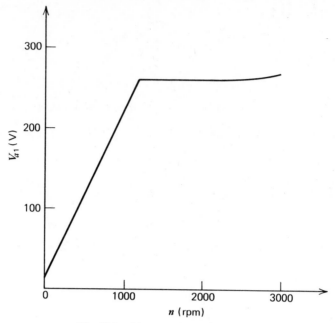

Fig. 10.9. Diagram II for Example 10.3.

At rated speed

$$6.283 = a + 0.05970 \times 123.6$$

$$a = -1.096$$

so that

$$\omega_r = 0.05970\Omega_m - 1.096 \text{ rad/s}$$

From Eq. 10.4

$$T = \frac{4.879\omega_r}{0.02220 + 0.004582\omega_r^2} \text{ N} \cdot \text{m}$$

From Eq. 10.18

$$I_{ma}\angle -90° = \frac{(0.149 + j0.00239\omega_r) \times 29.21\angle x^0}{0.149 + j\omega_r(0.0653 + 0.00239)} \text{ A}$$

from which

$$I_{ma1} = \left[\frac{4.352^2 + (0.06981\omega_r)^2}{0.149^2 + (0.06769\omega_r)^2}\right]^{1/2} \text{ A}$$

$$x = -90° - \tan^{-1}\frac{\omega_r}{62.34} + \tan^{-1}\frac{\omega_r}{2.201} \text{ deg}$$

$$\omega_s = \omega_r + \frac{p}{2}\Omega_m = (0.0597\Omega_m - 1.096) + 3\Omega_m$$

$$= 3.0597\Omega_m - 1.096 \text{ rad/s}$$

$$\overline{V}_{a1} = \overline{E}_{ma1} + \overline{Z}_s \overline{I}_{a1}$$

$$= 0.0653\omega_s I_{ma1} + (0.455 + j0.00159\omega_s) \times 29.21 \underline{/x°} \ \text{V}$$

$$\overline{Z}_s \cdot \overline{I}_{a1} = (176.6 + 0.002157\omega_s^2)^{1/2} \underline{/\tan^{-1}\frac{\omega_s}{286.2} + x°} \ \text{V}$$

Calculation from the foregoing relationships yields the curves shown in Figs. 10.8 and 10.9 for the field-weakening range.

PROBLEMS

10.1. In the system in Example 10.2 the motor is running at 850 rpm and is braking the load with a torque of 100 N · m.

(a) Determine the motor per-phase magnetizing current as a percentage of that for rated operating conditions.
(b) Determine the inverter frequency, input direct current, and average input terminal pd.
(c) Determine the value of α in the controlled rectifier.

10.2. The system in Example 10.2 is used to drive a fan that presents a load torque that may be described by the equation

$$T = \frac{\omega_m^2}{85} \ \text{N} \cdot \text{m}$$

If the line-to-line fundamental motor terminal pd may not exceed 460 V and the rotor frequency is held constant at the value for rated operation draw curves of per-unit torque, field strength, rms line current, and fundamental terminal pd versus per unit speed over the speed range of

$$500 < n < \text{permitted maximum rpm}$$

Rated values are to be used as the base quantities. Is this method of fixed maximum permitted speed acceptable? If not, what would be a better alternative? Explain.

10.3. Repeat Problem 10.2 but with a constant load torque of 120 N · m. Compare the results with those of Problem 10.2.

10.4. A 460-V, 100-hp (74.6-kW), 1775-rpm, three-phase, squirrel cage induction motor has the following equivalent-circuit parameters:

$$R_s = 0.060 \qquad L_{ls} = 0.638 \ \text{mH} \qquad L_{ms} = 23.3 \ \text{mH}$$

$$R_r' = 0.0302 \qquad L_{lr}' = 0.957 \ \text{mH}$$

The motor is to be driven from a current-source inverter with the rotor frequency controlled at the rated value. Maximum output power is to be limited to 80% of the rated value. Motor friction, windage, and core losses may be neglected. The load is to consist of a pump presenting a load characteristic described by the equation

$$T = \frac{\omega_m^2}{110} \text{ N} \cdot \text{m}$$

Determine the maximum values of motor speed, inverter frequency, rms motor line current, and fundamental line-to-line motor terminal pd at maximum power output.

10.5. A 460-V, 60-Hz, 50-hp (37.3-kW), 1770 rpm, three-phase, squirrel-cage induction motor has the following equivalent circuit parameters:

$$R_s = 0.130 \qquad L_{ls} = 1.18 \text{ mH} \qquad L_{ms} = 36.9 \text{ mH}$$

$$R_r' = 0.0764 \qquad L_{lr}' = 1.77 \text{ mH}$$

This motor is to be driven by a current-source inverter with field weakening at speeds above 1770 rpm. Rotor frequency is to be maintained at the value for rated operation up to this speed. Friction and windage losses as well as core losses in the motor are to be neglected. Draw curves of I_a and V_{a1} at 1770 rpm as functions of load torque from zero up to 150% full-load torque.

10.6. A 20-hp, (14.9-kW), 1760 rpm, 60-Hz, three-phase, squirrel-cage induction motor has the following equivalent-circuit parameters:

$$R_s = 0.420 \ \Omega \qquad L_{ls} = 1.74 \text{ mH} \qquad L_{ms} = 58.1 \text{ mH}$$

$$R_r' = 0.235 \ \Omega \qquad L_{lr}' = 2.61 \text{ mH}$$

The motor is to be driven from a current-source inverter over a speed range $0 < n < 5000$ rpm. The rms line current is to be maintained at the base value over the entire speed range. Up to 1760 rpm the rotor frequency is to be maintained at the base value; above that speed it is to be increased to maintain the motor terminal pd virtually constant by field weakening. Friction, windage, and core losses in the motor may be neglected and it may be assumed that motor resistive losses are constant at all speeds. Base rotor frequency and base line current are to be taken as the values occurring when the motor is delivering 20 hp at 1760 rpm when it is driven from a 460-V sinusoidal voltage source. For the entire speed range plot curves of
(a) rotor frequency, ω_r;
(b) developed torque, T;
(c) per-phase fundamental magnetizing current, I_{ma1};
(d) mechanical power developed, P_{mech};

(e) motor efficiency, η;

(f) fundamental motor terminal line-to-neutral pd, V_{a1};

(g) fundamental motor power factor, PF_1.

10.7. A 460-V, 100-hp (74.6-kW), 1180-rpm, three-phase squirrel-cage induction motor has the following equivalent-circuit parameters:

$$R_s = 0.0591 \ \Omega \qquad L_{ls} = 0.624 \ \text{mH} \qquad L_{ms} = 20.7 \ \text{mH}$$

$$R'_r = 0.0396 \ \Omega \qquad L'_{lr} = 0.936 \ \text{mH}$$

The motor is supplied from a 500-V, dc source by a Class D chopper and a current-source inverter. The periodic time of the chopper gating signals is $T_p = 2$ ms. The rotor frequency below 1180 rpm is held at the base value and above that speed is increased to maintain motor fundamental terminal pd approximately constant up to 2500 rpm. Motor core, friction, and windage losses may be neglected and the converters considered ideal. Resistive losses in the motor may be considered to remain constant over the entire speed range. If the rms motor line current is held at 100 A, draw curves of speed n versus available braking torque T and chopper delay time t_α versus speed n over the range $0 < n < 2500$ rpm.

10.8. A 460-V, 10-hp (7.46-kW), 3475-rpm, three-phase, squirrel-cage induction motor has the following equivalent-circuit parameters:

$$R_s = 1.02 \ \Omega \qquad L_{ls} = 3.66 \ \text{mH} \qquad L_{ms} = 158 \ \text{mH}$$

$$R'_r = 0.706 \ \Omega \qquad L'_{lr} = 5.49 \ \text{mH}$$

It is to drive a load for which the steady-state driving torque referred to the motor coupling can be expressed by

$$T_L = 2.5 + \frac{n}{560} \ \text{N} \cdot \text{m}$$

where n is the motor speed in rpm. The motor is to be driven by the system in Fig. 10.1a supplied from a three-phase, 480-V, 60-Hz, ac system. The motor line current is to be limited to 12.5 A with rotor frequency controlled up to 3475 rpm at the value it would have for rated operation on a 460-V, 60-Hz system. Above 3475 rpm rotor frequency is to be increased to hold the motor terminal pd virtually constant up to 7500 rpm. Motor core, friction, and windage losses may be neglected and the converters considered ideal. Resistance losses in the motor may be assumed constant over the entire speed range of operation. Determine: (a) the maximum speed at which the motor can drive the load, and (b) the fundamental power factor at the ac terminals of the controlled rectifier at the speed determined in (a).

Chapter 11

Synchronous Motor Drives

11.1. INTRODUCTION

Accurate speed control may be obtained by using synchronous motors to which power is provided by converters in the combinations illustrated in Figs. 9.1 and 10.1. Wound-field, permanent-magnet, or reluctance motors may be used.

Wound-field synchronous machines may provide drives of very high power for such applications as pumps, fans, compressors, conveyers, and extruders. Direct current may be supplied to the field winding in a number of alternative ways. A static source of field current that consists of a controlled rectifier or a diode rectifier and chopper may be connected to the field windings by slip rings. For large machines the long-established method of mounting the armature of a dc generator on the motor shaft with control of the field current of the synchronous motor by varying that of the dc exciter generator may be used. Both of the foregoing methods involve sliding contacts. One method of avoiding sliding contacts is illustrated in Fig. 11.1, where the rotor of the shaft-mounted exciter generator carries a three-phase winding and is driven against the revolving field of the three-phase stator, which is excited by the main power supply system. The rotor winding supplies a three-phase diode rectifier mounted on the motor shaft. The output of this rectifier is connected directly to the field winding of the motor. The motor field current is varied by a three-phase ac power controller that feeds the excitor stator. This system has two disadvantages when used with variable speed drives. The first is that the effect of motor speed on the emf induced in the exciter generator must be counteracted by the power controller. The second is that if the synchronous motor is reversed so also must be the phase sequence of the supply to the stator of the exciter generator. Both disadvantages are eliminated by the use of a rotating transformer, of which the secondary winding is a round coil mounted on the motor shaft in the plane perpendicular to the axis of that shaft and enclosed in a half core of ferromagnetic laminations open at the periphery. The primary winding, concentric and coplanar with the secondary and enclosed in a matching half-core, is supplied with a single-phase ac. This arrangement forms a transformer with an air gap in the magnetic circuit but the transforma-

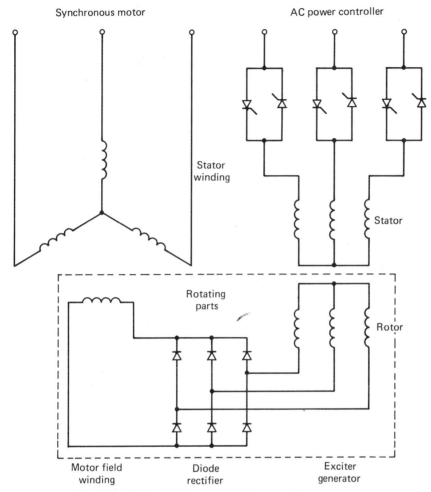

Synchronous motor   AC power controller

Stator winding

Stator

Rotating parts

Rotor

Motor field   Diode   Exciter
winding   rectifier   generator

Fig. 11.1. Field-excitation circuit of a large synchronous motor.

tion ratio remains constant as speed is varied and direction reversed. The primary winding is supplied by a single-phase ac power controller. The output of the secondary goes to a rotating single-phase rectifier and from there to the motor field winding.

Modern permanent-magnet synchronous motors are at present of smaller rating than wound-field machines. They may operate near unity power factor and have a large pull-out torque for a given frame size. In some circumstances several such motors may be driven from a single voltage-source inverter to provide, for example, roller drives for a run-out table.

The great simplicity of construction of reluctance motors is an advantage if a relatively low lagging power factor can be accepted. If a large number of low-power drives are required to rotate in synchronism, as in textile machinery, reluctance motors are often used.

As in the case of induction-motor drives, current-source inverters can usually supply only a single motor or a number of similar motors that are mechanically coupled. Wound-field or permanent-magnet machines may be operated at leading power factor because the motor then provides load commutation for the inverter.

In the following, voltage-source inverter drives are discussed first, but a necessary preliminary is the development of equivalent-circuit models of the motors. Operation of the inverters has been discussed in the preceding two chapters.

11.2. SYNCHRONOUS MOTOR WITH WOUND FIELD

11.2.1. Equivalent Circuits

The arrangement of the windings in a cylindrical-rotor, three-phase, two-pole synchronous machine is illustrated in Fig. 11.2. Each pair of conductors, aa', bb', cc', shown on the stator, represents the center of a belt of conductors distributed to produce an effectively sinusoidal distribution of mmf around the stator side of the air gap. The single pair of conductors ff' on the rotor represents the center of the rotor winding. Each of the stator conductor belts or phase windings has N_{se} effective turns, whereas the single rotor winding has N_{re} effective turns.

Although synchronous motors driven by power-semiconductor converters are usually salient-pole machines, the cylindrical-rotor machine provides a sufficiently accurate and simple model for the purposes of this chapter. For a p-pole machine the angular position of the rotor is expressed in electrical

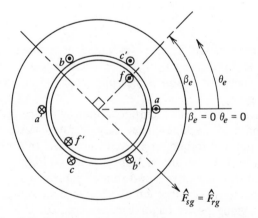

Fig. 11.2. Cylindrical-rotor, two-pole, three-phase, synchronous machine.

radians, where

$$\vartheta_e = \frac{p}{2}\vartheta \ \text{rad} \tag{11.1}$$

in which ϑ = angle in radians
ϑ_e = angle in electrical radians

For a synchronous machine the angular speed of rotation is

$$\omega_m = \frac{2}{p}\omega_s \ \text{rad/s} \tag{11.2}$$

in which

ω_s = frequency of stator currents.

Thus, for a p-pole machine the angular position of the rotor at any instant is expressed in electrical radians by

$$\beta_e = \omega_s t + \beta_{oe} \ \text{rad} \tag{11.3}$$

where β_{oe} is the angular position of the rotor at $t = 0$ with reference to some datum position.

Consider a set of balanced currents at frequency ω_s in the stator windings, where I_a is the rms current in phase a. These currents will produce an mmf wave around the air gap with a peak magnitude of

$$\hat{F}_{sg} = \frac{3N_{se}}{\sqrt{2}\,p}I_a \ \text{A} \tag{11.4}$$

and rotating at electrical angular velocity ω_s. A field current i_f will produce an mmf wave around the air gap of peak magnitude

$$\hat{F}_{rg} = \frac{N_{re}}{p}i_f \ \text{A} \tag{11.5}$$

If the rotor rotates at speed ω_m, the mmf wave will also rotate at electrical angular velocity ω_s. Then, the effect of the field can be modeled as a current source of frequency ω_s and rms magnitude $n'i_f$ where

$$n' = \frac{\sqrt{2}}{3}\frac{N_{re}}{N_{se}} \tag{11.6}$$

The angle of this current source is determined by the rotor position angle β_{oe}. The datum reference for this angle is chosen to make the stator emf have an angle of zero when the machine is open-circuited.

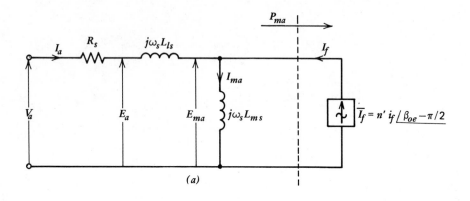

(a)

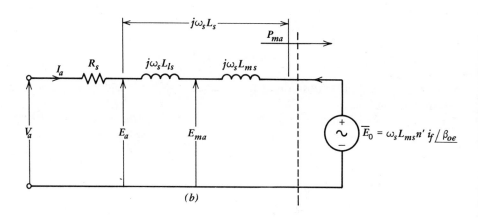

(b)

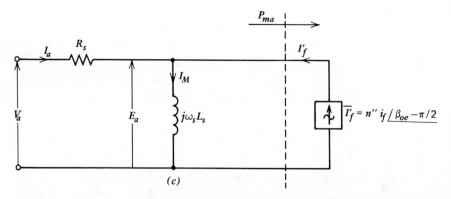

(c)

Fig. 11.3. Steady-state Equivalent Circuits of a Cylindrical-rotor Synchronous Machine.

The equivalent circuit for the synchronous machine is shown in Fig. 11.3a. In this circuit R_s is the stator resistance, L_{ls}, the stator leakage inductance, and L_{ms} the magnetizing inductance, as in an induction machine. The effect of the field is represented by the current source $\bar{I}_f$. The total emf induced in the stator winding is E_a, whereas the emf induced in the stator winding by the air-gap flux alone is E_{ma}.

Two alternative forms of equivalent circuit are shown in Fig. 11.3b and 11.3c. In the former the synchronous machine is modeled as an emf source E_o, where

$$\bar{E}_o = \omega_s L_{ms} n' i_f \big/ \beta_{oe} \text{ V} \tag{11.7}$$

The sum of the stator leakage inductance and the magnetizing inductance is known as the synchronous inductance L_s, where

$$L_s = L_{ls} + L_{ms} \text{ H} \tag{11.8}$$

The other useful form of equivalent circuit shown in Fig. 11.3c is a simplification of that in Fig. 11.3a in which the current source is

$$\bar{I}_f' = \frac{L_{ms}}{L_s} n' i_f \big/ \beta_{oe} - \pi/2 = n'' i_f \big/ \beta_{oe} - \pi/2 \text{ A} \tag{11.9}$$

where

$$n'' = \frac{L_{ms}}{L_{ls} + L_{ms}} \frac{\sqrt{2}}{3} \frac{N_{re}}{N_{se}} \tag{11.10}$$

The parameters of the equivalent circuits in Fig. 11.3 may be determined by the usual method of open and short circuit tests.[1] When magnetic saturation is significant the magnetizing inductance should be the value appropriate for the operating condition of stator flux linkage.

11.3. VOLTAGE-SOURCE INVERTER DRIVE

The motor models developed in the preceding section may be used to predict the steady-state performance of a wound-field synchronous motor driven from a voltage-source inverter. As explained in Section 9.2.1, if the motor is driven from an inverter with the type of pulse-width modulation illustrated in Fig. 9.3 the pulse rate can be made high enough to avoid any significant effect on motor performance of harmonics resulting from pulsing, and for all practical purposes the waveforms of line-to-line pd applied to the motor may be considered still to have the rectangular form shown in Fig. 9.2. As pulse width is decreased and frequency remains constant, the effective amplitude of the rectangular wave is reduced. Thus the line-to-neutral waveforms of motor terminal pd may be considered to be those in Fig. 9.5.

The waveform for v_a may be described by the Fourier series in Eq. 9.1 as

$$v_a = \frac{8}{3\pi} V_{LK} [0.7500 \sin \omega t + 0.1500 \sin 5\omega t + 0.1071 \sin 7\omega t + \cdots] \text{ V}$$

(11.11)

where V_{LK} is the direct pd at the inverter input terminals. From the waveform of v_a in Fig. 9.5 the rms value of v_a is expressed in Eq. 9.3 as

$$V_a = 0.4714 V_{LK} \text{ V}$$

(11.12)

The rms value of the fundamental component is given in Eq. 9.4 as

$$V_{a1} = 0.4502 V_{LK} \text{ V}$$

(11.13)

The harmonics in the waveform of v_a produce harmonics in the line current i_a. The rms magnitude of the current harmonics may be determined from any of the circuits in Fig. 11.3 in which the current or emf sources are set to zero. The current harmonic of order n is given by

$$\bar{I}_{an} = \frac{\bar{V}_{an}}{R_s + jn\omega_s L_s} \text{ A}$$

(11.14)

in which the value of V_{an} is obtained from Eq. 11.11.

Apart from causing some extra heating, which necessitates derating the motor, the effect of harmonics on the steady-state behavior of the motor is negligible, except at low speed, where the stepping effect of the rotating field, already mentioned in Section 9.2.1 in connection with the induction motor, would arise. This stepping effect will cause speed oscillations and vibration that may be unacceptable. Thus if the controlled-speed range is to extend down to zero, it may be necessary at some comparatively low speed to introduce the sinusoidal PWM described in Section 9.2.2. In the discussion to follow harmonics are ignored unless specifically noted.

11.3.1. Steady-State Operation

In view of the negligible effect of harmonics in the normal speed range, this discussion may be conducted in terms of the fundamental components of the variables. The effect of the stator resistance on the normal operation of a synchronous motor is small. Only when the motor is driven at very low speed with a corresponding low stator frequency does it become appreciable. Except in such discussion as that of efficiency, the stator resistance can often be ignored. However, as the speed is controlled down to zero, the terminal pd approaches the standstill value of $R_s I_a$.

From the equivalent circuit in Fig. 11.3c, the complex power that enters the machine after allowing for stator resistance loss is

$$\bar{S} = -3\bar{E}_a(\bar{I}_f')^* \text{ VA} \qquad (11.15)$$

where $(\bar{I}_f')^*$ is the conjugate of $\bar{I}_f'$. Because no power is transferred to the rotor winding by induction, all of the real component of $\bar{S}$ is converted to mechanical power.

$$P_{mech} = Re\bar{S} = 3P_{ma} = -3E_a n'' i_f \sin \beta_{oe} \text{ W} \qquad (11.16)$$

The air-gap torque is given by

$$T = \frac{P_{mech}}{\omega_m} = \frac{p}{2} \frac{3P_{ma}}{\omega_s} = \frac{-3p}{2\omega_s} E_a n'' i_f \sin \beta_{oe} \text{ N} \cdot \text{m} \qquad (11.17)$$

In the steady state, the load torque is the air-gap torque minus the friction and windage torque. The stator current and pd are given by

$$\bar{I}_a = \bar{I}_M - \bar{I}_f' \text{ A} \qquad (11.18)$$

and

$$\bar{V}_a = \bar{E}_a + R_s \bar{I}_a \text{ V} \qquad (11.19)$$

A phasor diagram for a synchronous machine operating as a motor with a lagging power factor is shown in Fig. 11.4a, where the power factor is

$$PF = \cos \varphi \qquad (11.20)$$

Figure 11.4b shows a phasor diagram for a machine in the regenerating mode. For this condition the converter combination suggested in Section 9.1.1 may be used.

It is usually advantageous to operate the synchronous machine near unity power factor, particularly at full load, because this will reduce the stator current to a minimum for a given power output and hence will reduce the inverter losses and its VA rating. Control of the power factor may be achieved by controlling the field current.

Example 11.1

A 500-hp (373-kw), 720 rpm, 2300-V, 60-Hz, three-phase synchronous motor has the following equivalent-circuit parameters:

$$R_s = 0.270 \ \Omega \qquad X_{ls} = 0.338 \ \Omega \qquad X_{ms} = 6.73 \ \Omega$$

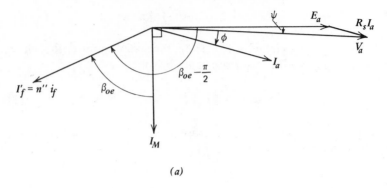

(a)

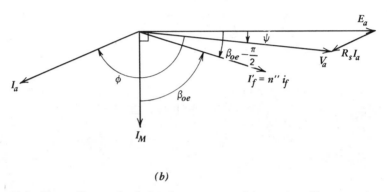

(b)

Fig. 11.4. Phasor diagrams for the synchronous motor: (a) motoring; (b) regenerating.

The ratio $N_{re}/N_{se} = 30.05$ and the motor is designed to operate under rated conditions at unity power factor. Rotational losses in the motor and power absorbed in the exciter may be neglected. The effect of harmonics may be ignored.

The motor is to be driven from a voltage-source inverter and coupled to a fan that presents a load torque described by

$$T_L = 0.75\omega_m^2 \text{ N} \cdot \text{m}$$

where ω_m is the angular speed of the motor. The speed range is $240 < n < 720$ rpm.

(a) Assuming that the motor is driven from a sinusoidal voltage source under rated conditions, determine line current I_a, ratio E_a/ω_s, magnetizing current I_M, and field current i_f.

(b) If the motor is supplied from the inverter, the ratio E_a/ω_s maintained at the value obtained in (a) and the field current i_f adjusted to give a power factor of unity at 720 rpm determine the line current I_a and the power factor at 240 rpm.

(c) If the field current is adjusted so that the motor is operating at unity power factor at 240 rpm determine the resultant line current I_a and power factor PF at 720 rpm.

Solution

(a) Under rated conditions

$$P_{\text{in}} = \sqrt{3} \times 2300 I_a = 3 \times 0.270 I_a^2 + 373 \times 10^3$$

$$I_a = 95.49 \text{ A}$$

Let

$$\bar{V}_a = \frac{2300}{\sqrt{3}} \underline{/0} = 1328 \underline{/0} \text{ V}$$

Then

$$\bar{I}_a = 95.49 \underline{/0} \text{ A}$$

$$\bar{E}_a = (1328 - 0.270 \times 95.49) \underline{/0} = 1302 \underline{/0} \text{ A}$$

$$\frac{E_a}{\omega_s} = \frac{1302}{120\pi} = 3.454$$

$$X_s = 0.338 + 6.73 = 7.07 \text{ } \Omega$$

$$\bar{I}_M = \frac{1302 \underline{/0}}{7.07 \underline{/90°}} = 184.2 \underline{/-90°} \text{ A}$$

$$\bar{I}_f' = \bar{I}_M - \bar{I}_a = -j184.2 - 95.49 = 207.5 \underline{/-117.40°} \text{ A}$$

$$n'' = \frac{6.73}{7.07} \times \frac{\sqrt{2}}{3} \times 30.05 = 13.48$$

$$i_f = \frac{207.5}{13.48} = 15.39 \text{ A}$$

(b) For any speed n rpm

$$\omega_s = \frac{p}{2} \frac{n\pi}{30} = \frac{n\pi}{6} \text{ rad/s}$$

$$\omega_m = \frac{\omega_s}{5} = \frac{n\pi}{30} \text{ rad/s}$$

At 720 rpm

$$\omega_s = 377.0 \text{ rad/s}$$

$$\omega_m = 75.40 \text{ rad/s}$$

$$T_L = 0.75 \times 75.40^2 = 4264 \text{ N} \cdot \text{m}$$

Let

$$\bar{E}_a = 3.454 \times 377.0 \underline{/0} = 1302 \underline{/0} \text{ V}$$

Output power of motor is

$$P_o = 0.75 \times 75.40^3 = 3 \times 1302 I_a$$

$$I_a = 82.31 \text{ A}$$

Because $\varphi = 0$, in Fig. 11.5 $\psi = 0$ and

$$\bar{I}_a = 82.31 \underline{/0} \text{ A}$$

Also from (a)

$$\bar{I}_M = 184.2 \underline{/-90°} \text{ A}$$

$$\bar{I}_f' = \bar{I}_M - \bar{I}_a = -j184.2 - 82.31 = 201.8 \underline{/-114.08°} \text{ A}$$

$$i_f = \frac{201.8}{13.48} = 14.97 \text{ A}$$

$$\beta_{oe} = -144.08 + 90° = -24.08°$$

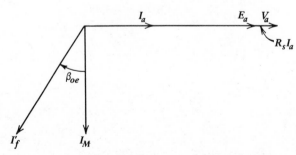

Fig. 11.5. Phasor diagram for unity power factor.

At 240 rpm

$$\omega_m = 25.13 \text{ rad/s}$$

$$\omega_s = 125.7 \text{ rad/s}$$

$$T_L = 0.75 \times 25.13^2 = 473.6 \text{ N} \cdot \text{m}$$

From Eq. 11.17

$$473.6 = -\frac{3 \times 10}{2} \times 3.454 \times 201.8 \sin \beta_{oe}$$

$$\beta_{oe} = -2.60°$$

$$\bar{I}_a = \bar{I}_M - \bar{I}_f' = 184.2\underline{/-90°} - 201.8\underline{/-92.60°}$$

$$= 9.154 + j17.4 = 19.66\underline{/62.25°} \text{ A}$$

$$\bar{E}_a = 3.454 \times 125.7\underline{/0} = 434.2\underline{/0} \text{ V}$$

$$\bar{V}_a = 434.2\underline{/0} + 0.270(9.154 + j17.4) = 436.7\underline{/0.62°} \text{ V}$$

$$\varphi = 62.25 - 0.62 = 61.63°$$

$$PF = 0.4752 \text{ leading}$$

(c) At 240 rpm

$$P_o = 0.75 \times 25.13^3 = 11900 \text{ W}$$

$$\bar{E}_a = 434.2\underline{/0} \text{ V}$$

Then for $PF = 1$

$$3 \times 434.2 I_a = 11900$$

$$\bar{I}_a = 9.136\underline{/0} \text{ A}$$

$$\bar{I}_M = 184.2\underline{/-90°}$$

$$\bar{I}_f' = \bar{I}_M - \bar{I}_a = -j184.2 - 9.136 = 184.4\underline{/-92.84°}$$

$$\beta_{oe} = -2.84°$$

$$i_f = \frac{184.4}{13.48} = 13.68 \text{ A}$$

At 720 rpm from (b)

$$T_L = 4264 \text{ N} \cdot \text{m}$$

From Eq. 11.17

$$4264 = \frac{-3 \times 10}{2} \times 3.454 \times 184.4 \sin \beta_{oe}$$

$$\beta_{oe} = -26.51°$$

$$\bar{I}_f' = 184.4 \underline{/-116.51°} \text{ A}$$

$$\bar{I}_a = \bar{I}_M - \bar{I}_f' = 184.2 \underline{/-90°} - 184.4 \underline{/-116.51°}$$

$$= 82.31 - j19.2 = 84.52 \underline{/-13.13°} \text{ A}$$

From (b)

$$\bar{E}_a = 1302 \underline{/0} \text{ V}$$

Thus

$$\bar{V}_a = 1302 + 0.270(82.31 - j19.2) = 1320 \underline{/0.22°} \text{ V}$$

$$\varphi = -13.13 - 0.22 = -13.35°$$

$$PF = 0.9730 \text{ lagging}$$

11.3.2. Methods of Control

At this stage is it possible to investigate the input quantities and system variables that need to be controlled for satisfactory operation. For this purpose three typical load characteristics are considered:

1. Constant load torque at all speeds. This approximates the characteristic of a hoist or mine winder.
2. Low torque at low speed and high torque at high speed. This is typical of a centrifugal pump and a fan.
3. Variable torque at all speeds. This is required, for example, in a transportation drive.

In most drives it is desirable to maintain the stator flux linkage (i.e., the ratio E_a/ω_s) constant at or near the rated value, thus avoiding magnetic saturation while making good use of the iron in the machine. It follows that the motor terminal pd V_a must be controlled. The field current i_f is also readily controlled. Stator current I_a and the angle β_{oe} may also be measured under any operating condition and used, if necessary, as feedback signals. The speed command determines the necessary value of frequency ω_s.

1. Constant load torque at all speeds. Figure 11.5 shows a phasor diagram for this drive with the field current adjusted to give a motor power factor of unity at maximum speed. This arrangement calls for the smallest possible VA rating of the inverter.

Consider what occurs if the field current i_f and the ratio E_a/ω_s are held constant, while the speed is varied by variation of the inverter frequency ω_s. The magnetizing current $\bar{I}_M$ in the equivalent circuit of Fig. 11.3c will also remain constant and will lag $\bar{E}_a$ by 90°. With constant torque T Eq. 11.17 shows that the angle β_{oe} is constant. Because current phasors $\bar{I}_M$ and $\bar{I}'_f$ are constant, stator current I_a is also constant. At all speeds the current phasor is as shown in Fig. 11.5. As speed falls V_a and E_a will be decreased until $\omega_s \rightarrow 0$, $E_a \rightarrow 0$, and $V_a \rightarrow R_s I_a$. The power factor remains at unity. If the load torque is changed to another value a change in the setting of i_f will be necessary and the angle β_{oe} will change. If the field current is adjusted for unity power factor the current I_a will be proportional to the torque.

Figure 11.6 shows a control system applicable for a drive for which the acceleration is slow and relatively little torque is required to overcome system inertia. An acceleration limiter is used to limit the rate of change of the inverter frequency ω_s. The stator emf E_a can be measured by sensor coils fitted in the bottom of the stator winding slots and can be compared with the value

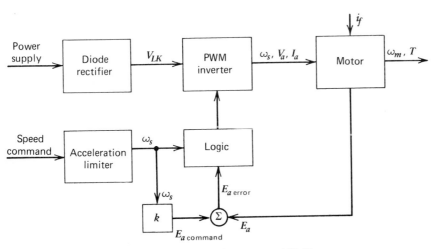

Fig. 11.6. Control of frequency and EMF.

required for the motor frequency to establish the inverter output pd V_a. If the motor is not fitted with sensor coils E_a may be simulated by measuring V_a and subtracting $R_s I_a$.

2. Torque increasing with speed. The control system in Fig. 11.6 can also be used for a drive when the torque increases with speed. Figure 11.7 shows a phasor diagram in which the field current i_f has been adjusted to give unity power factor at maximum torque. If the field current is maintained constant as torque is reduced, the phasor $\bar{I}_f'$ will follow a circular locus with reducing value of angle β_{oe}. The stator current $\bar{I}_a$ will also follow a circular locus as shown in Fig. 11.7. For most synchronous motors the rated value of I_a is less than the rated value of I_M. Accordingly, the magnitude of I_a will decrease as the torque is reduced, while the power factor will be leading. The stator current for low torque can be reduced somewhat by setting the field current at maximum torque so that the power factor is slightly lagging.

Although control with constant field current is applicable over the full torque range, control of the field current is required if optimum efficiency is desired at each setting of speed. This may be achieved by use of the control system shown in Fig. 11.8, in which the phase angle between stator pd and current is measured and used to control the rectifier supplying the field.

3. Variable torque at all speeds. In some drives the load torque is not directly dependent on speed but may vary widely in motoring and regenerating directions at any value of speed. An example is a traction drive that must be capable of driving, braking, hill climbing, acceleration, and deceleration.

If the rates of change of both load torque and speed are gradual, control systems, such as are shown in Figs. 11.6 and 11.8, may be used. Any sudden briefly applied load torque may, however, cause a speed oscillation to increase

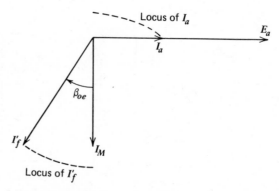

Fig. 11.7. Locus of stator-current phasor for variable torque and constant field current.

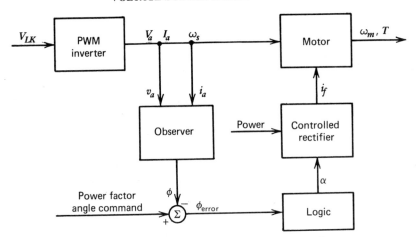

Fig. 11.8. Control of field current for constant power factor.

the angle β_{oe} to such a magnitude beyond 90°, where the maximum torque is developed, that the motor will be unable to recover the momentary loss of speed and consequently will fall out of synchronism. Also, a step increase in the speed command would have the same effect as a step increase in load torque were it not for the acceleration limiter in Fig. 11.6, which permits only a slow change in speed.

Synchronism can be maintained with rapid changes in command speed and in torque by a closed-loop control system that uses information on the instantaneous position of the motor shaft. A means of obtaining the required signal of rotor position is illustrated for a two-pole synchronous motor in Fig. 11.9. The three proximity detectors are spaced $\pi/3$ rad from one another. The three signals that indicate the presence or absence of the rotor-mounted shutter thus uniquely define six 60° intervals of the complete revolution of the two-pole motor. In a p-pole machine the detectors are spaced $\pi/3$ electrical

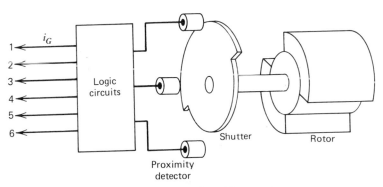

Fig. 11.9. Rotor shaft-position encoder.

rad from one another and the shutter has $p/2$ large diameter sectors. The shaft position sensor in Fig. 11.9 emits a signal six times per cycle to indicate the value at those instants of the angle β_{oe}. This information can be used in the logic circuits of the control system to produce the firing pulses for the inverter. Operation in both directions of rotation is possible because the sequence of signals from the shaft encoder reverses with reversal of the motor. Commercial shaft encoders may operate on optical or magnetic proximity signals.

It has been noted in relation to the phasor diagram in Fig. 11.5 that a given torque can be produced at any value of speed by fixing the values of the stator current I_a, the field current i_f (represented by the magnitude of I_f'), and the angle β_{oe}. The phasor $\bar{I}_f'$ is at angle β_{oe} to $\bar{I}_M$, which is 90° behind the emf $\bar{E}_a$ which has the same phase as $\bar{V}_a$ for unity power factor. Control of β_{oe} can therefore be obtained by using the shaft encoder signals and introducing a controllable phase delay of the firing signals for the inverter, as shown in the system in Fig. 11.10. With this approach synchronism is ensured at all values of torque and speed.

The ratio E_a/ω_s can be maintained constant at all values of speed by a control loop similar to that used in Fig. 11.6. The six pulses per electrical cycle produced by the shaft encoder can generate a signal proportional to frequency ω_s, which can be multiplied by the appropriate factor to determine the required value of E_a (Fig. 11.10).

Control of the torque of the system in Fig. 11.10 can be obtained by controlling the angle β_{oe}. As shown in Fig. 11.7, as the angle β_{oe} is reduced, with constant values of i_f and I_M, the stator current phasor $\bar{I}_a$ follows a

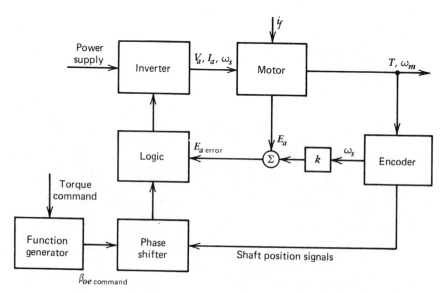

Fig. 11.10. Control system using shaft-position encoder and providing torque control.

circular locus with a reducing component in phase with $\overline{E}_a$ and thus with a reducing torque. An appropriate function generator will determine the required value of β_{oe} for any desired torque. Note that positive values of β_{oe} (i.e., I_f' leading $\overline{I}_M$) will produce negative torque for regeneration.

The system in Fig. 11.10 with constant i_f results in a leading power factor at low values of torque. If it is desired to regulate the power factor to near unity at all values of torque a field current control loop like that in Fig. 11.8 may be used.

Speed control may be achieved in the system in Fig. 11.10 by comparing the command speed with the inverter frequency and using the error to generate the torque command signal. The system may also be adapted to provide position control because the encoder signals can be counted to give the shaft position relative to a chosen reference point.

In some drives it is inconvenient or overly expensive to fit an encoder to the motor shaft and transmit its signals back to the inverter control. The encoder may be the least reliable component of the drive system, particularly in a hostile environment. In such a situation frequency and angle control can be achieved by using only pd and current signals measured at the inverter output to the motor (Fig. 11.11). With reference to the phasor diagram in Fig. 11.5, if V_a and I_a are known, the quantities E_a, I_f', i_f, and β_{oe} can be calculated for a given set of motor parameters. The speed or frequency can also be obtained from the measured quantities. Torque control in the system in Fig. 11.11 is provided by comparing the command torque with the torque computed from the values of stator current and phase and using the error to advance or retard the phase of the inverter firing signals relative to the phase of measured stator current. A considerable variety of control systems has been developed, most of

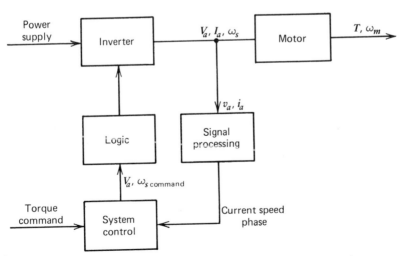

Fig. 11.11. Control system using inverter output measurements to generate inverter control signals.

which are capable of rapid response to load or command changes. Micro-processors are frequently used.

Example 11.2

The inverter and motor in Example 11.1 are to drive a mechanism over a speed range of $0 < n < 720$ rpm and to provide regenerative braking over a speed range of $720 > n > 50$ rpm, below which limit friction braking is applied. The mechanism may demand a driving torque of $0 < T_L < 4250$ N · m at any speed and a braking torque at any speed in the regenerative range of $-3750 < T_L < 0$ N · m. Below 50 rpm it may be assumed that sinusoidal PWM is introduced for driving. The system to be employed is that in Fig. 11.6, with the diode rectifier replaced by a direct voltage source capable of accepting regenerated energy. Under all conditions of speed and load the field current must be adjusted to cause the motor to operate at unity power factor.

Determine and tabulate n, T_L, V_a, and I_a and the required values of i_f and β_{oe} for the following conditions:

(a) Maximum speed driving on no load torque.
(b) Maximum speed driving on maximum load torque.
(c) Standstill (starting) on no load torque.
(d) Standstill on maximum load torque.
(e) Maximum speed braking at maximum braking torque.
(f) Minimum speed braking at maximum braking torque.

Draw a phasor diagram for condition (e).

Solution

When applicable, figures are taken from Example 11.1. Thus $E_a/\omega_s = 3.454$ and $n'' = 13.48$.

(a) At 720 rpm $T_L = 0$

$$\bar{E}_a = 1302\underline{/0} \text{ V}; \qquad \bar{I}_M = 184.2\underline{/-90°} \text{ A}$$

Because $T_L = 0$

$$I_a = 0, \qquad \beta_{oe} = 0$$

$$\bar{V}_a = \bar{E}_a = 1302\underline{/0} \text{ V}$$

$$\bar{I}_f' = \bar{I}_M = 184.2\underline{/-90°} \text{ A}$$

$$i_f = \frac{184.2}{13.48} = 13.66 \text{ A}$$

(b) At 720 rpm $T_L = 4250$ N $\cdot$ m,

$$\omega_m = 75.40 \text{ rad/s}$$

$$P_o = 75.40 \times 4250 = 320.5 \times 10^3 \text{ W}$$

$$I_a = \frac{320.5 \times 10^3}{3 \times 1302} = 82.04 \text{ A}$$

$$V_a = 1302 + 0.270 \times 82.04 = 1324 \text{ V}$$

$$\bar{I}_f' = \bar{I}_M - \bar{I}_a = -j184.2 - 82.04 = 201.6\underline{/-114.01°} \text{ A}$$

$$\beta_{oe} = -114.01 + 90 = -24.01°$$

$$i_f = \frac{201.6}{13.48} = 14.96 \text{ A}$$

(c) At standstill $T_L = 0$,

$$E_a = 0$$

$$I_a = 0$$

$$V_a = 0$$

$$\beta_{oe} = 0$$

$$I_f' = I_M = 184.2 \text{ A}$$

$$i_f = \frac{184.2}{13.48} = 13.66 \text{ A}$$

(d) At standstill $T_L = 4250$ N $\cdot$ m,

$$E_a = 0$$

From Eq. 11.17

$$4250 = \frac{-3 \times 10}{2} \times 3.454 I_f' \sin \beta_{oe}$$

$$I_f' \sin \beta_{oe} = -82.03$$

With unit power factor, from Fig. 11.5,

$$I_a = -I_f' \sin \beta_{oe} = 82.03 \text{ A}$$

$$V_a = 0.270 \times 82.03 = 22.15 \text{ V}$$

$$\bar{I}_f' = \bar{I}_M - \bar{I}_a = -j184.2 - 82.03 = 201.6 \underline{/-114.00°} \text{ A}$$

$$\beta_{oe} = -114.00 + 90 = -24.00°$$

$$i_f = \frac{201.6}{13.49} = 14.96 \text{ A}$$

(e) At 720 rpm, $T_L = -3750 \text{ N} \cdot \text{m}$

$$\omega_m = 75.40$$

$$P_o = -75.40 \times 3750 = -282.8 \times 10^3 \text{ W}$$

$$I_a = \frac{-282.8 \times 10^3}{3 \times 1302} = -72.39 \text{ A}$$

$$V_a = 1302 - 72.39 \times 0.270 = 1282 \text{ V}$$

$$\bar{I}_f' = \bar{I}_M - \bar{I}_a = -j184.2 + 72.35 = 197.8 \underline{/-68.55°} \text{ A}$$

$$\beta_{oe} = -68.55 + 90 = 21.45°$$

$$i_f = \frac{197.9}{13.48} = 14.68 \text{ A}$$

(f) At 50 rpm, $T_L = -3750 \text{ N} \cdot \text{m}$

$$\omega_m = 5.236 \text{ rad/s}$$

$$E_a = 3.454 \times 5.236 \times 5 = 90.43 \text{ V}$$

$$P_o = -5.236 \times 3750 = -19640 \text{ W}$$

$$I_a = \frac{-19640}{3 \times 90.43} = -72.39 \text{ A}$$

$$V_a = 90.43 - 72.39 \times 0.270 = 70.88 \text{ V}$$

I_f', β_{oe}, and i_f are as for (e). The results are

	n	T_L	V_a	I_a	i_f	β_{oe}
(a)	720	0	1302	0	13.66	0
(b)	720	4250	1324	82.04	14.96	−24.01
(c)	0	0	0	0	13.66	0
(d)	0	4250	22.15	82.03	14.96	−24.00
(e)	720	−3750	1282	−72.39	14.68	21.45
(f)	50	−3750	70.88	−72.39	14.68	21.45

The phasor diagram for condition (e) is show in Fig. 11.12.

The results of Example 11.2 reveal that a range of field current of $13.66 < i_f < 14.96$ A is sufficient to produce unity fundamental power factor over the whole operating area of the speed-torque diagram. Control of the power factor may be achieved by use of the field current control system shown in Fig. 11.9. Inverter frequency and motor emf may be controlled by the system in Fig. 11.6.

The feasibility of the drive in Example 11.2 operating satisfactorily with a fixed field current, as in the control system of Fig. 11.6, may be investigated by working Problem 11.2.

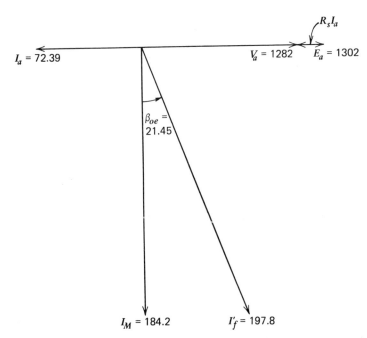

Fig. 11.12. Solution to Example 11.2.

11.3.3. Operation with Field Weakening

As in the case of the induction motor, it may be desirable to drive a synchronous motor at speeds in excess of that at which the stator emf can be made proportional to the speed because of a limit on the supply pd. At such speeds it may be assumed that the motor terminal pd V_a will be fixed while the inverter frequency ω_s is increased. In consequence the ratio E_a/ω_s will fall as speed increases, and field weakening takes place. In these circumstances the line current I_a must be maintained at or below the value permissible during operation at rated speed so that excessive heating due to resistive losses does not occur.

If the maximum torque per ampere of line current is to be obtained from the motor, the power factor PF must be held at or near unity. Thus the maximum permissible input power to the machine P_{in} will be constant over the field weakening range. Under these conditions resistive losses will be constant and, because other machine losses are being neglected, the output power P_o may be considered constant also. It therefore follows that permissible load torque T_L will be inversely proportional to speed; that is,

$$T_L = \frac{P_o}{\omega_m} \text{ N} \cdot \text{m} \tag{11.21}$$

Operation under the conditions described in the foregoing may be illustrated by a numerical example. It is assumed that the system of control is like that in Figs. 11.6 and 11.8, where the limit on V_a arises from the limited value of V_{LK}.

Example 11.3

The motor and inverter in Example 11.1 are to drive a mechanism that presents a load torque described by

$$T_L = 500 + 22.75\omega_m \text{ N} \cdot \text{m}$$

Above 720 r/min the terminal pd of the motor is to be held at the value of the rated pd and the line current may not exceed 85% of the rated line current. The system in Fig. 11.8 will maintain the power factor PF at unity. Determine the maximum speed at which the load may be driven and draw a phasor diagram for this condition of operation to show the magnitudes and angles of the phasors. Also determine the value of field current i_f.

Solution

At frequency $\omega_s = 120 \ \pi$, $V_a = 2300/\sqrt{3}$ V and

$$I_a = 0.85 \times 95.49 = 81.17 \text{ A}$$

$$P_o = \sqrt{3} \times 2300 \times 81.17 - 3 \times 0.270 \times 81.17^2 = 318.1 \times 10^3 \text{ W}$$

$$\omega_m = \frac{\omega_s}{5} = 24\pi \text{ rad/s}$$

For this current the permissible torque is

$$T = \frac{318.1 \times 10^3}{\omega_m} \ \text{N} \cdot \text{m}$$

For equilibrium with the load torque

$$\frac{318.1 \times 10^3}{\omega_m} = 500 + 22.75\omega_m \ \text{N} \cdot \text{m}$$

$$\omega_m = 107.8 \ \text{rad/s} = 1029 \ \text{rpm}$$

$$\omega_s = 538.8 \ \text{rad/s}$$

$$\overline{V}_a = 1328 \underline{/0} \ \text{V}$$

$$\overline{E}_a = (1328 - 0.270 \times 81.17) \underline{/0} = 1306 \underline{/0} \ \text{V}$$

$$L_s = \frac{0.338 + 6.73}{120\pi} = 0.01875 \ \text{H}$$

$$\overline{I}_M = \frac{1306 \underline{/-90^\circ}}{538.8 \times 0.01875} = 129.3 \underline{/-90^\circ} \ \text{A}$$

$$\overline{I}_f' = \overline{I}_M - \overline{I}_a = -j129.3 - 81.17 = 152.7 \underline{/-122.12^\circ} \ \text{A}$$

$$i_f = \frac{152.7}{13.48} = 11.33 \ \text{A}$$

$$\beta_{oe} = -32.12^\circ$$

Figure 11.13 is the phasor diagram.

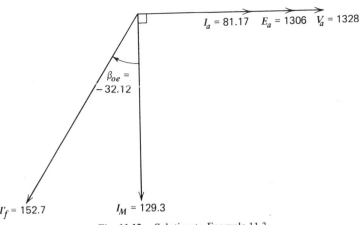

$I_a = 81.17 \qquad E_a = 1306 \qquad V_a = 1328$

$\beta_{oe} = -32.12$

$I_f' = 152.7 \qquad\qquad I_M = 129.3$

Fig. 11.13. Solution to Example 11.3.

11.4. PERMANENT-MAGNET SYNCHRONOUS MOTOR

A permanent-magnet (PM) synchronous motor may be envisaged as a normal synchronous motor that operates with fixed field current. The physical arrangement of the machine may be like a salient-pole synchronous motor without a field winding on the rotor and with a section of permanent magnet included in each pole. Other more advantageous configurations with rotors similar to those for fixed armature dc machines[1] have been developed.

Most modern PM synchronous motors use ferrite or rare-earth magnets that have linear magnetizing characteristics. As a result, the equivalent circuit for a PM synchronous motor may be taken to be that in Fig. 11.3c. The method of determining the circuit parameters is similar to that used for the wound-field machine. For convenience the symbols for the parameters and variables in the PM motor are made the same as those for the corresponding quantities in the wound-field motor. Stator winding resistance R_s can be measured directly. Short-circuit and open-circuit tests with the motor driven at rated speed yield the other two circuit parameters. Because $X_s \gg R_s$, it may be taken that the short-circuit test provides a direct measurement of I_f'. The terminal potential difference for the open-circuit test gives a measure of $\omega_s L_s I_f'$, and L_s may be determined to complete the equivalent circuit shown in Fig. 11.14.

One feature of the PM motor is that the synchronous reactance is usually low (about 0.5 per unit) because the material of the permanent magnets has a low permeability and the flux path has a correspondingly high reluctance. This value of synchronous reactance is somewhat lower than normally encountered in wound-field motors. A motor may be designed to be "over-excited" or "under-excited"; that is, to operate with a leading or lagging power factor under rated conditions.

Control of a PM motor is similar to the control of a wound-field synchronous motor except that the field current cannot be varied. If a slow response is

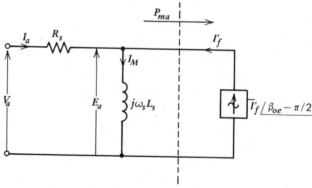

Fig. 11.14. Equivalent circuit for a permanent-magnet synchronous motor.

acceptable and the load is not subject to rapid changes the system in Fig. 11.6 can be used with the input i_f eliminated. If the motor is not fitted to measure stator flux linkage the emf E_a may be simulated from measurement of V_a and I_a. Because the magnetizing current I_M is considerably larger than the related value of stator current I_a, examination of the phasor diagram in Fig. 11.7 shows that the stator current will decrease in magnitude as torque is reduced toward zero.

If the load torque is subject to rapid variation or if rapid speed response is required a control system with a shaft position sensor (Fig. 11.10) may be used. With this means of control the motor may also be operated with field weakening over a limited speed range. For constant power the component of stator current I_a in phase with the stator pd is constant. Figure 11.15 shows a locus of stator current as the speed is increased from a base value ω_{mb} to $2\omega_{mb}$ at constant power while the angle β_{oe} is maintained constant. By appropriate choice of a lagging power factor at the base speed an equal value of leading power factor is achieved at twice the base speed.

Example 11.4

A 30-hp (22.4-kW), 1200-rpm, 460-V, 60-Hz, PM synchronous motor has the following equivalent-circuit parameters:

$$R_s = \text{negligible} \qquad X_s = 4.38 \ \Omega$$

The motor is designed to operate on full load at a lagging power factor of 0.9. It is to be driven from a voltage-source inverter over the speed range $0 < n < 2400$ rpm. Below rated speed the ratio E_a/ω_s is to be held at rated value.

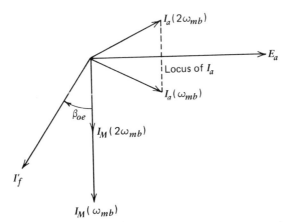

Fig. 11.15. Operation of a PM motor in the field-weakening region.

Above rated speed the line-to-line terminal pd is to be held at 460 V and the angle β_{oe} is maintained constant. The effects of harmonics and rotational losses are to be neglected.

Over the entire speed range draw curves of line-to-neutral terminal pd V_a, magnetizing current I_M, motor power factor PF, and torque T as functions of speed n.

Solution

Under rated operating conditions

$$P_{\text{in}} = \sqrt{3} \times 460 \times 0.9 I_a = 22400 \text{ W}$$

$$I_a = 31.24 \text{ A}$$

$$\cos^{-1}0.9 = -25.84$$

$$\bar{I}_a = 31.24\big/{-25.84°} \text{ A}$$

$$\bar{V}_a = \frac{460}{\sqrt{3}}\big/0 = 265.6\big/0 = \bar{E}_a \text{ V}$$

$$\frac{E_a}{\omega_s} = \frac{265.6}{120\pi} = 0.7045$$

$$\bar{I}_M = \frac{265.6\big/0}{j4.38} = 60.64\big/{-90°} \text{ A}$$

$$I'_f = \bar{I}_M - \bar{I}_a = 54.79\big/{-120.88°} \text{ A}$$

$$\beta_{oe} = -120.88 + 90 = -30.88°$$

$$L_s = \frac{X_s}{\omega_s} = 11.62 \text{ mH}$$

$$\omega_m = 1200 \times \frac{2\pi}{60} = 40\pi$$

$$T_L = \frac{22400}{40\pi} = 178.25 \text{ N} \cdot \text{m}$$

For $0 < n < 1200$ rpm

$$\omega_m = n \times \frac{\pi}{30} = \frac{n}{9.549} \text{ rad/s}$$

$$\omega_s = \omega_m \times 3 = \frac{n}{3.183} \text{ rad/s}$$

$$\bar{V}_a = \bar{E}_a = 0.7045\omega_s\big/0 = 0.221n\big/0 \text{ V}$$

$$\bar{I}_M = 60.64 \underline{/-90°} \ \text{A}$$

$$\bar{I}_f' = 54.79 \underline{/-120.88°} \ \text{A}$$

$$\beta_{oe} = -30.88°$$

$$T_L = 178.25 \ \text{N} \cdot \text{m}$$

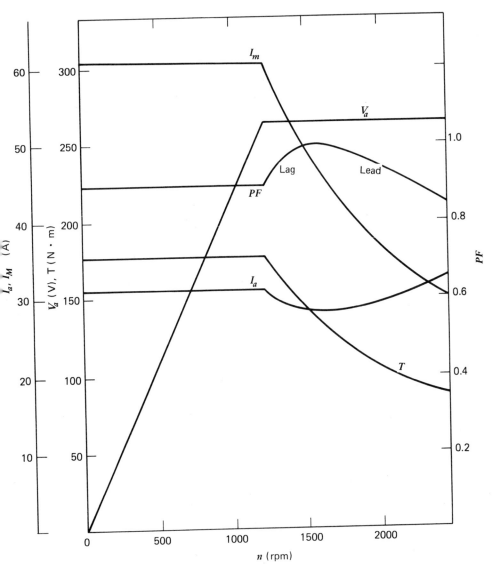

Fig. 11.16. Solution to Example 11.4.

For $1200 < n < 2400$ rpm

$$P_{mech} = 22400 \text{ W}$$

$$T_L = \frac{P_{mech}}{\omega_m} = \frac{213.9 \times 10^3}{n} \text{ N} \cdot \text{m}$$

$$\overline{V}_a = \overline{E}_a = 265.6 \underline{/0} \text{ V}$$

$$\frac{E_a}{\omega_s} = \frac{845.4}{n}$$

$$\overline{I}_M = \frac{\overline{E}_a}{j\omega_s L_s} = \frac{265.6}{0.01162} \times \frac{3.183}{n} = \frac{72.75 \times 10^3}{n} \underline{/-90°} \text{ A}$$

$$\overline{I}_f' = 54.79 \underline{/-120.88°} \text{ A}$$

$$\overline{I}_a = \overline{I}_M - \overline{I}_f' \text{ A}$$

At 2400 rpm

$$\overline{I}_M = \frac{72.75 \times 10^{-3}}{2400} \underline{/-90°} = 30.32 \underline{/-90°} \text{ A}$$

$$\overline{I}_a = -j30.32 - (-28.12 - j47.02) = 32.71 \underline{/30.71°}$$

$$PF = \cos 30.71 = 0.86 \text{ leading}$$

It is noted that as the speed approaches 2400 rpm the stator current slightly exceeds its rated value. This may be permissible in view of the improved cooling of the motor at this speed.

11.5. THREE-PHASE SYNCHRONOUS RELUCTANCE MOTOR

The diagram in Fig. 11.17 illustrates the structure of a two-pole, three-phase reluctance motor. Because this motor has no rotor mmf from field winding or permanent magnets it can operate only at a lagging power factor. Careful design of the rotor, however, can raise the full-load power factor to about 0.75. Like any other electromagnetic machine, the motor can also regenerate.

To develop a usable equivalent circuit of this motor[1] it is convenient to ignore the effects of harmonics and rotational losses and to neglect the stator winding resistance. This leaves the machine with only two parameters: the direct- and quadrature-axis inductances. Neglect of stator resistance means

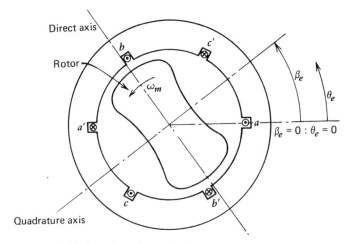

Fig. 11.17. Three-phase synchronous reluctance motor.

that the per-phase emf E_a induced in the stator winding is taken to be identical with V_a, the per-phase applied terminal pd. The equivalent circuit of the motor is shown in Fig. 11.18, in which the resistive element accounts for the per-phase energy converted to or from mechanical form.

The quantities L_d and L_q in the equivalent circuit are the direct- and quadrature-axis inductances of the motor, respectively. They can be measured by applying a small value of terminal pd at rated frequency to the motor and driving it at a little less than the synchronous speed. A trace on a recording oscilloscope may then be made of the line current, which will vary between a minimum and maximum amplitude. The minimum rms value of the observed current variation then gives $V_a/\omega_s L_d$, whereas the maximum rms value gives $V_a/\omega_s L_q$.

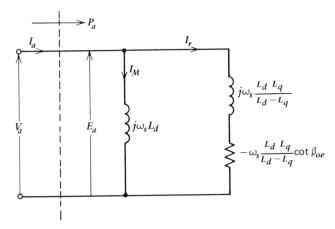

Fig. 11.18. Equivalent circuit of a reluctance motor.

As with any other synchronous machine, angle β_{oe} is that between the axis of the three-phase stator mmf and the direct axis of the rotor. When β_{oe} is zero the value of the resistive element in the equivalent circuit becomes infinite, no energy conversion takes place, and only magnetizing current flows into the machine. When β_{oe} becomes negative the resistive element becomes positive, that is, an energy sink, and the machine motors. When β_{oe} becomes positive the resistive element becomes negative, that is, an energy source, and the machine regenerates.

In the equivalent circuit let

$$\bar{V}_a = V_a \underline{/0} \text{ V} \tag{11.22}$$

The per-phase input power is

$$P_a = Re\left[\bar{V}_a \bar{I}_r^*\right] \text{ W} \tag{11.23}$$

where $\bar{I}_r^*$ is the conjugate of $\bar{I}_r$.

The impedance of the RL branch is

$$\bar{Z} = \left(-\frac{L_d L_q}{L_d - L_q}\cos\beta_{oe} + j\frac{L_d L_q}{L_d - L_q}\right)\omega_s \text{ } \Omega \tag{11.24}$$

From these three equations

$$P_a = -\frac{(L_d - L_q)}{2\omega_s L_d L_q}V_a^2 \sin 2\beta_{oe} \text{ W} \tag{11.25}$$

and this is also the air gap and output power of the machine. The developed torque for a p-pole machine is thus

$$T = T_L = \frac{3p}{2}\cdot\frac{P_a}{\omega_s} = -\frac{3p}{4\omega_s}\left(\frac{L_d - L_q}{L_d L_q}\right)V_a^2 \sin 2\beta_{oe} \text{ N} \cdot \text{m} \tag{11.26}$$

The pull-out torque of the machine is therefore

$$|T_{max}| = \frac{3p}{4\omega_s^2}\left(\frac{L_d - L_q}{L_d L_q}\right)V_a^2 \text{ N} \cdot \text{m} \tag{11.27}$$

It can be shown[1] that the relationship between $\bar{V}_a$ and $\bar{I}_a$ can be represented by the circle diagram in Fig. 11.19, in which

$$Oa = \frac{V_a}{2\omega_s}\times\frac{(L_d + L_q)}{L_d L_q} \text{ A} \tag{11.28}$$

$$ab = \frac{V_a}{2\omega_s}\times\frac{(L_d - L_q)}{L_d L_q} \text{ A} \tag{11.29}$$

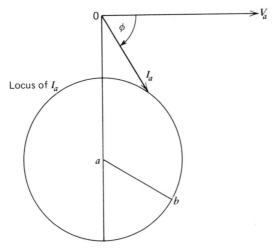

Fig. 11.19. Circle diagram for a reluctance machine.

The maximum power factor will occur when the phasor $\bar{I}_a$ is tangential to its locus, either in the third (regenerating) quadrant or fourth (motoring) quadrant of the circle diagram. For any value of I_a angle φ, and thence the power factor of operation, can be determined from the diagram. The power output is then given by

$$P_o = 3V_a I_a \cos \varphi \ \text{W} \qquad (11.30)$$

and the torque is

$$T = \frac{P_o}{\omega_m} = \frac{p}{2} \cdot \frac{P_o}{\omega_s} \ \text{N} \cdot \text{m} \qquad (11.31)$$

Angle β_{oe} may be determined from Eqs. 11.26 and 11.31.

Control of a reluctance motor is similar to the control of an induction motor. Frequency and emf may be controlled by a system of the type shown in Fig. 11.6.

11.6. CURRENT-SOURCE INVERTER DRIVE

The output-current waveform of a conventional current-source inverter approximates to the rectangular form shown in Fig. 10.3. At low speed and frequency other means are available to produce a nearly sinusoidal current waveform. The current-source inverter drive may produce higher losses in the motor than the voltage-source inverter due to current harmonics but will have the advantage of a less expensive combination of converters than required for a voltage-source inverter drive.

The motor equivalent circuits developed in Section 11.2.1 and the equations and phasor diagram of the voltage-source inverter drive in Section 11.3.1 may be applied equally well to a synchronous motor excited from a current-source inverter. So far as the motor is concerned there is no essential difference between driving it from a voltage-source inverter at a controlled line current and driving it from a current-source inverter that delivers the same current. The difference in the drive system lies in the possible combinations of converters and the method of control. Possible combinations of converters are similar to those shown in Fig. 10.1 for the induction motor, and Sections 10.1 and 10.2 apply equally to synchronous-motor drives. The advantages of using a synchronous motor are that the speed corresponds exactly to the inverter frequency and that the synchronous motor can be over-excited to draw a leading current and reduce the size of the commutating capacitors required in the inverter of Fig. 10.2.

The three wye-connected series RL circuit branches connected to terminals A, B and C in Fig. 10.2 represent the effect of an induction-motor load on the inverter. The effect of a load consisting of an overexcited synchronous motor may be represented by three wye-connected resistances R_{eq} in parallel with 3 delta-connected capacitors C_{eq}, as illustrated in the current-source inverter circuit of Fig. 11.20. The sequence of events corresponding to that in Fig. 10.4, when thyristor Q_3 is turned on, commutating thyristor Q_1, is illustrated in Fig. 11.21. The reactive components of the motor currents have the effect of additional commutating capacitances thus permitting reduction in the size of the actual commutating capacitors included in the inverter circuit. The extent to which this is the case, however, depends on the speed-torque characteristic of the motor load.

For any condition of operation at speed n and load torque T_L a fundamental phasor diagram similar to that shown in Fig. 11.4 may be drawn, but with a leading current. If, for this condition, the per-phase equivalent circuit of the motor is represented by a resistance and capacitance C_b connected in parallel the fundamental current in the capacitance element will be

$$I_c = I_a \sin\varphi \text{ A} \tag{11.32}$$

In Fig. 11.20

$$I_c = \omega_s C_b V_a \text{ A} \tag{11.33}$$

and

$$C_b = \frac{I_c}{\omega_s V_a} \text{ F} \tag{11.34}$$

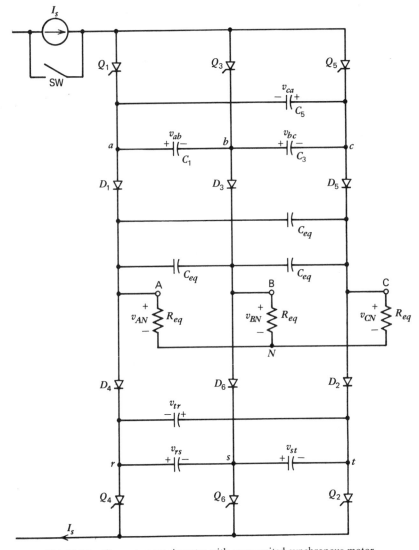

Fig. 11.20. Current-source inverter with over-excited synchronous motor.

Thus in Fig. 11.20

$$C_{eq} = \frac{C_b}{3} = \frac{I_a \sin \varphi}{3\omega_s V_a} \text{ F} \qquad (11.35)$$

As may be seen from Fig. 11.4, as speed approaches zero $V_a \to R_s I_a$ and $\varphi \to 0$, as does C_{eq} also. Thus the assistance in commutation offered by over-excitation will be zero at standstill, no matter what the starting torque

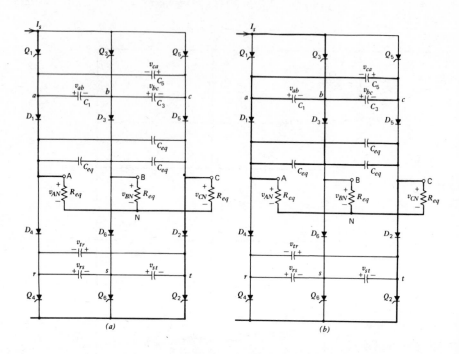

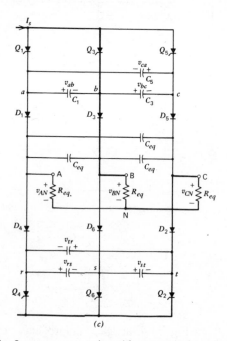

Fig. 11.21. Inverter commutation with over-excited synchronous motor.

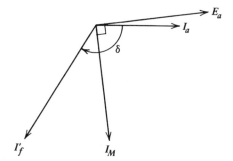

Fig. 11.22. Phase diagram for current-source drive.

may be. In determining the reduction, if any, that may be made in the size of the commutating capacitors the variation in C_{eq} over the entire operating area in the speed-torque diagram must be considered.

With a current source drive it is desirable to express the torque and other motor quantities in terms of the stator current. Using the equivalent circuit in Fig. 11.3c, consider the phasor diagram in Fig. 11.22 in which δ is the angle between I_a and I_f'. The stator emf is

$$\bar{E}_a = j\omega_s L_s \bar{I}_M = j\omega_s L_s \left(\bar{I}_a + \bar{I}_f' \right) \text{ V} \qquad (11.36)$$

The air-gap power power per phase is

$$P_{ma} = \text{Re}\left(\bar{I}_a \bar{E}_a^* \right) = -\omega_s L_s I_a I_f' \sin \delta \text{ W} \qquad (11.37)$$

The torque is then given by

$$T = \frac{3P_{ma}}{\omega_m} = \frac{-3p}{2} L_s I_a I_f' \sin \delta \text{ N} \cdot \text{m} \qquad (11.38)$$

Control of a synchronous motor with current-source inverter supply may be achieved by a system such as that shown in Fig. 11.23. A shaft position sensor provides signals that indicate the phase of I_f' and a phase shifter is then used with logic to fire the current source inverter at the appropriate angle δ. This system ensures synchronism at all values of torque and speed, in both directions of rotation. From Eq. 11.38, if field current and angle δ are held constant, the torque will be directly proportional to the stator current I_a at all values of speed. Thus a simple feedback loop to regulate the current input to the current source inverter (which is directly proportional to output current I_a) can provide torque control.

Operation with constant field current i_f and constant angle δ is possible if operating values are chosen to avoid excessive magnetizing current and therefore excessive stator emf. Figure 11.24 shows a locus for $\bar{E}_a$ as the torque varies

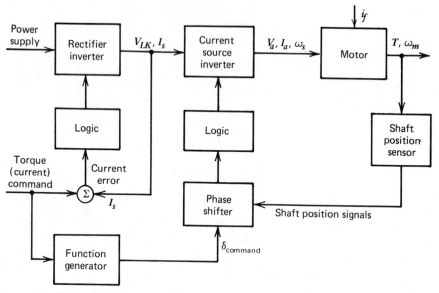

Fig. 11.23. Control system with current-source inverter and shaft-position sensor.

from zero to maximum. If the power factor is lagging at maximum stator current it can approach an equal leading value as stator current approaches zero. The result is equal values of emf E_a for both limiting conditions. This mode of control is particularly suitable for permanent magnet motors in which the field cannot be controlled.

If it is desired to maintain the power factor near unity or at some leading value the angle δ can be adjusted as the stator current varies using a function generator.

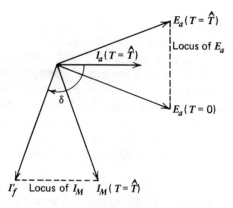

Fig. 11.24. Phasor diagram for control with constant field current and control angle δ.

Operation with field weakening is required for speeds above the value at which the pd limit of the rectifier in Fig. 11.23 is reached. Figure 11.25 shows how this can be accomplished over a limited speed range with constant field current by increasing the angle δ. At constant stator current the magnetizing current I_M reduces in magnitude as the angle δ is increased, thus causing a simultaneous decrease in torque. This approach is applicable for permanent magnet machines. For wound-field machines the field current can be controlled to control stator emf and power factor by using a system similar to that of Fig. 11.8.

Example 11.5

A 100-hp (74.6-kW), 1200-rpm, 460-V, 60-Hz, three-phase synchronous motor has the following equivalent-circuit parameters:

$$R_s = 0.0714 \ \Omega \qquad X_{ls} = 0.131 \ \Omega \qquad X_{ms} = 1.63 \ \Omega$$

The ratio $N_{re}/N_{se} = 25.1$ and the motor is designed to operate under rated conditions at a power factor of unity. Rotational losses in the motor, power absorbed in the exciter, and the effect of harmonics may be neglected. The motor is to be driven from a current-source inverter and coupled to a mechanical system that presents a load torque described by

$$T_L = 100 + \frac{n}{3} \ \text{N} \cdot \text{m}$$

where n is the speed of the motor in rpm.

(a) Assuming that the motor is driven from a sinusoidal voltage source under rated conditions, determine line current I_a, ratio E_a/ω_s, magnetizing current I_M, field current i_f, and angle δ.

(b) The motor is coupled to the load and supplied from a current source inverter. The value of δ is maintained at the value found in (a) and the

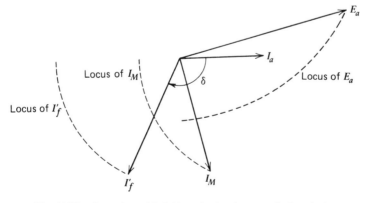

Fig. 11.25. Operation with field weakening by control of angle δ

field current is adjusted to keep E_a/ω_s constant. Determine T_L, ω_m, i_f, PF, and V_a when I_a is set at 75 A.

Solution

(a) Under rated conditions

$$P_{in} = \sqrt{3} \times 460 \times I_a = 3 \times 0.7141 I_a^2 + 74.6 \times 10^3 \text{ W}$$

$$I_a = 96.1 \text{ A}$$

$$\bar{V}_a = \frac{460}{\sqrt{3}} \underline{/0} = 265.6 \underline{/0} \text{ V}$$

$$\bar{I}_a = 96.1 \underline{/0} \ \because PF = 1.0$$

$$\bar{E}_a = 265.6 \underline{/0} - 0.0714 \times 96.1 \underline{/0} = 258.7 \underline{/0}$$

$$\frac{E_a}{\omega_s} = 0.686$$

$$X_s = 1.63 + 0.131 = 1.76 \ \Omega$$

$$L_s = \frac{X_s}{\omega_s} = 4.67 \text{ mH}$$

$$\bar{I}_M = \frac{258.7 \underline{/0}}{1.76 \underline{/90°}} = 147.0 \underline{/-90°}$$

$$\bar{I}_f' = \bar{I}_M - \bar{I}_a = 147 \underline{/-90°} - 96.1 \underline{/0} = 175.6 \underline{/-123.17°}$$

$$n'' = \frac{1.63}{1.76} \times \frac{\sqrt{2}}{3} \times 25.1 = 10.96$$

$$i_f = \frac{175.6}{10.96} = 16.02 \text{ A}$$

$$\delta = 123.17°$$

(b) Referring all phasors to the stator current as reference.

$$\bar{I}_a = 75.0 \underline{/0} \text{ A}$$

Because δ is maintained constant

$$\bar{I}_f' = I_f' \underline{/-123.17°} \text{ A}$$

To maintain constant E_a/ω_s the magnitude of the magnetizing current must be constant. Assigning $\bar{I}_M$ an angle α,

$$\bar{I}_M = 147.0 \big/\alpha$$

Solving the triangle formed by the phasor $\bar{I}_a$, $\bar{I}_f'$, and $\bar{I}_M$ gives

$$\alpha = -115.28°$$

and

$$I_f' = 174.17 \text{ A}$$

It is noted that this value is only slightly less than for rated stator current

$$T = \frac{-3 \times 6}{2} \times 4.67 \times 10^{-3} \times 75 \times 174.17 \sin(-123.17°)$$

$$= 459.56 \text{ N} \cdot \text{m}$$

$$n = (459.56 - 100)3 = 1078.7 \text{ rpm}$$

$$\omega_s = \frac{6}{2}\omega_m = \frac{6}{2} \times \frac{1078.7}{60} \times 2\pi = 338.88 \text{ rad/s}$$

$$\bar{E}_a = 0.686\omega_s \big/ -115.28° + 90° = 232.5 \big/ -25.28°$$

$$V_a = 232.5 \big/ -25.28° + 0.0714 \times 75 \big/ 0 = 237.33 \big/ -24.73°$$

$$PF = \cos 24.73° = 0.91 \text{ leading}$$

11.7. CYCLOCONVERTER DRIVE

The cycloconverter is a direct ac-to-ac converter in which no dc link exists. A useful circuit arrangement is shown in Fig. 11.26 but other circuits are possible.[7] That shown in Fig. 11.26 is made up of three dual converters, each supplying one phase of the load. By switching each of the dual converters cyclically thorough all four quadrants of operation a waveform of per-phase ac output terminal pd may be synthesized for each phase of the load. Each output waveform consists of segments of the waveforms of the input terminal pd's of one dual converter. The output frequency is lower than the input frequency and, because of the high harmonic content of both output pd's and input currents, the maximum output frequency must be limited to about 45% of the input frequency. The waveforms of the pd and smoothed current for one phase of the load are shown in Fig. 11.27.

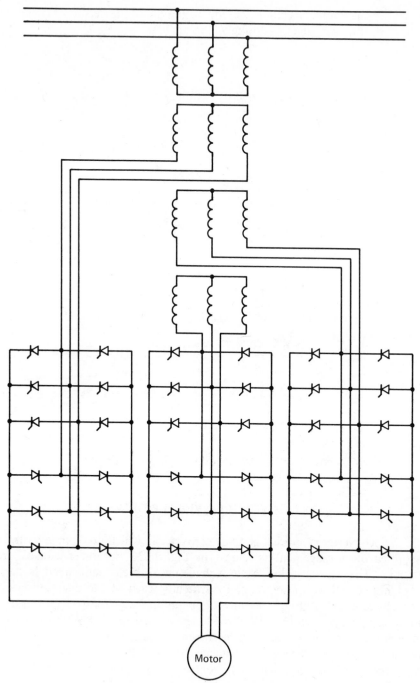

Fig. 11.26. Cycloconverter drive.

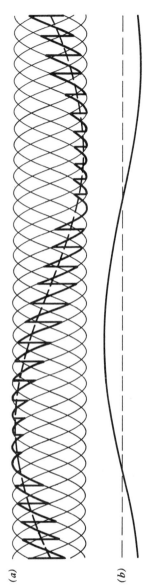

(a)

(b)

Fig. 11.27. Cycloconverter output waveforms: (a) unfiltered output pd– – –wanted component; (b) output current.

In the case illustrated in Fig. 11.27 the output pd is the maximum possible and the load current lags it by 60°. The converter can, however, operate in all four quadrants; therefore it is suitable for supplying multipole motors from which a very low speed is required without the use of gears. A typical example is the ball mill of a cement works in which the rotor of the motor is built directly onto the outer cylinder of the mill.

From the point of view of this text, in which the effect of harmonics is being neglected, the drive may be considered to be a voltage-source inverter drive and a suitable control scheme would be that in Fig. 11.6, with the rectifier and inverter combined as a single element.

PROBLEMS

11.1. A 100-hp (74.6-kW), 1200-rpm, 460-V, 60-Hz, three-phase synchronous motor has the following equivalent-circuit parameters:

$$R_s = 0.0893 \ \Omega \qquad X_{ls} = 0.163 \ \Omega \qquad X_{ms} = 2.04 \ \Omega$$

The ratio $N_{re}/N_{se} = 25.1$ and the motor is designed to operate under rated conditions at unity power factor. Rotational losses of the motor and power absorbed in the exciter may be neglected and the effects of harmonics ignored.

(a) Assuming that the motor is driven from a sinusoidal voltage source, determine for rated operation the line current I_a, ratio E_a/ω_s, field current i_f, and rotor angle β_{oe}.

(b) If the motor is driven from a voltage-source inverter, with E_a/ω_s and i_f maintained at the values obtained in (a), plot inverter input pd V_{LK}, motor efficiency η, and fundamental motor power factor PF as functions of speed n as the inverter frequency is varied from 60 Hz down to zero and the load torque is maintained at 85% of the rated value.

(c) Draw to scale a fundamental-component phasor diagram for speed $n = 200$ rpm.

11.2. Repeat Example 11.2 with a fixed field current $i_f = 14.30$ A, replacing i_f with PF in the tabulation of results, and omitting the phasor diagram.

11.3. The motor, inverter, and fan load in Example 11.1 are to be operated with the field current i_f controlled to cause the motor to operate at unity power factor at all speeds. Plot curves of line current I_a, required field current i_f, and rotor angle β_{oe} as functions of speed n over the specified speed range.

11.4. The motor, inverter, and fan load of Example 11.1 are to be operated with the field current i_f fixed at 15.0 A.

(a) Plot curves of line current I_a and power factor PF as functions of speed n over the specified speed range.

(b) For $n = 500$ rpm draw to scale a phasor diagram for the motor.

11.5. A 100-hp (74.6-kW), 1200-rpm, 460-V, 60-Hz, three-phase, synchronous motor has the following equivalent-circuit parameters:

$$R_s = 0.0893 \ \Omega \qquad X_{ls} = 0.163 \ \Omega \qquad X_{ms} = 2.04 \ \Omega$$

The ratio $N_{re}/N_{se} = 25.1$ and the motor is designed to operate at unity power factor under rated conditions. Rotational losses of the motor and power absorbed in the exciter may be neglected and the effects of harmonics, ignored. The motor is to be operated in the system formed by combining the diagrams in Figs. 11.6 and 11.8 with field weakening over the speed range $1200 < n < 2400$ rpm. The line current I_a is not to exceed 85% of rated line current at any speed and the field current i_f is to be controlled to cause the motor to operate at unity power factor PF over the entire speed range $0 < n < 2400$ rpm.

(a) Assuming that the motor is driven from a sinusoidal voltage source under rated conditions, determine I_a and ratio n''.

(b) With the motor driven from the inverter over the entire speed range plot a curve of speed n versus permissible load torque T_L.

(c) Plot curves of field current i_f, rotor angle β_{oe}, and magnetizing current I_M as functions of speed n.

11.6. A 2250-hp (186.5-kW), 1800 rpm, 600-V, 60-Hz, unity power factor, synchronous motor has the following equivalent-circuit parameters:

$$R_s = 0.0356 \ \Omega \qquad X_{ls} = 0.0455 \ \Omega \qquad X_{ms} = 0.888 \ \Omega$$

The ratio $N_{re}/N_{se} = 64.13$. Rotational losses in the motor and power absorbed in the exciter may be neglected. The motor is to be driven from a voltage-source inverter and coupled to a mechanism that presents a load torque described by

$$T_L = 250 + \frac{n}{7.2} \ \text{N} \cdot \text{m}$$

where n is the speed in rpm. The motor line current may not exceed 90% of rated current and the effect of higher harmonics may be ignored. If field weakening is used above 1800 rpm determine the speed at which the motor will drive the mechanism when it is operating at unity power factor and also calculate the required field current i_f.

11.7. A 25-hp (18.65-kW), 3600 rpm, 460 V, 60-Hz, unity-power-factor, PM synchronous motor has the following equivalent-circuit parameters:

$$R_s = 0.333 \ \Omega \qquad X_s = 4.82 \ \Omega \qquad I_M' = 55.1 \ \text{A}$$

The motor is to be driven from a voltage-source inverter and the line current is not to exceed 85% of the rated line current. The ratio of E_a/ω_s is to be held at the value for rated operation. The effects of harmonics and rotational losses may be neglected. For a speed of 3000 rpm plot curves of V_a, I_a, PF, and β_{oe} as functions of load torque T_L from zero up to the maximum permissible continuous value of T_L.

11.8. The motor of the system in Problem 11.7 is running at 3000 rpm when the speed command is reduced. Determine the regenerative braking torque that the motor can develop with the line current restricted, as in Problem 11.7. Sketch a phasor diagram for this condition of operation and show on it the symbols of the various phasors and phase angles. Determine also V_a and PF.

11.9. A 230-V, 1800-rpm, 60-Hz, three-phase reluctance motor has the following equivalent-circuit parameters:

$$X_d = 39.1\ \Omega \qquad X_q = 6.48\ \Omega$$

Six of these motors are to be driven in parallel from a voltage-source inverter and each one drives a constant load torque of 10.5 N · m. Using the approximations specified in Section 11.5, determine at 1800 rpm:

(a) The motor power factor;
(b) The VA rating of the inverter;
(c) Angle β_{oe} in each motor.

BIBLIOGRAPHY

1. G. R. Slemon and A. Straughen, *Electric Machines*, Addison-Wesley, Reading, Massachusetts, 1980.
2. A. Buxbaum and K. Schierau, *Berechnung von Regelkreisen der Antriebstechnik*, AEG-Telefunken, Berlin, 1978.
3. S. B. Dewan and W. G. Dunford, Improved Power Factor Operation of A Single-phase Controlled Rectifier Bridge through Modified Gating, IEEE, PES Conference, 1980, Conference Record, pp. 357–365.
4. S. B. Dewan and W. G. Dunford, Improved Power Factor Operation of a Three-phase Rectifier Bridge through Modified Gating, IEEE IAS Conference, 1980, Conference Record, pp. 830–837.
5. S. B. Dewan and A. Straughen, *Power Semiconductor Circuits*, Wiley, New York, 1975.
6. R. Bonert, Automatic Speed Control of One-Quadrant DC Drives, IAS 81:24A, IEEE-IAS Conference 1981, pp. 515–520.
7. B. R. Pelley, *Thyristor Phase-Controlled Converters and Cycloconverters*, Wiley, New York, 1971.

Appendix A

Fourier Analysis

The output terminal potential difference v_O of a power semiconductor converter operating in the steady state is a periodic function of time defined by

$$v_O(t) = v_o(t + T) \text{ V} \tag{A.1}$$

where T is the periodic time.

The fundamental angular frequency of this output pd is defined by

$$\omega_0 = \frac{2\pi}{T} \text{ rad/s} \tag{A.2}$$

and the frequency is

$$f_0 = \frac{1}{T} = \frac{\omega_0}{2\pi} \text{ Hz} \tag{A.3}$$

Eq. A.1, therefore, could also be written

$$v_O(\omega_0 t) = v_O(\omega_0 t + 2\pi) \text{ V} \tag{A.4}$$

Sometimes it is convenient to represent the waveforms of the variables in a converter system on a horizontal axis of t in seconds and sometimes on an axis of $\omega_0 t$ in radians.

The Fourier theorem states that subject to certain technical restrictions a periodic function $v_O(t)$ may be described by a constant term plus an infinite series of cosine and sine terms of frequency $n\omega_0$, where n is a positive integer. Thus

$$v_O(t) = \bar{v}_O + \sum_{n=1}^{\infty} \left[a_n \cos(n\omega_0 t) + b_n \sin(n\omega_0 t) \right] \text{ V} \tag{A.5}$$

The constants $\bar{v}_O$, a_n, and b_n may be determined by using expressions that are developed in standard texts on circuit analysis and, like the theorem itself, are stated here without proof. The constant $\bar{v}_O$ is simply the average value of v_O and

$$\bar{v}_O = \frac{1}{T}\int_0^T v_O(t)\,dt = \frac{1}{2\pi}\int_0^{2\pi} v_O(\omega_0 t)\,d(\omega_0 t) \text{ V} \qquad (A.6)$$

$$a_n = \frac{2}{T}\int_0^T v_O(t)\cos(n\omega_0 t)\,dt = \frac{1}{\pi}\int_0^{2\pi} v_O(\omega_0 t)\cos(n\omega_0 t)\,d(\omega_0 t) \text{ V} \quad (A.7)$$

$$b_n = \frac{2}{T}\int_0^T v_O(t)\sin(n\omega_0 t)\,dt = \frac{1}{\pi}\int_0^{2\pi} v_O(\omega_0 t)\sin(n\omega_0 t)\,d(\omega_0 t) \text{ V} \quad (A.8)$$

If $v_O(t)$ can be expressed as an analytical function these constants may be determined by a single integration. If, as is usually the case, $v_O(t)$ possesses a number of break points or discontinuities then an analytical expression for $v_O(t)$ between each pair of adjacent discontinuities is required and several integrations must be performed to determine $\bar{v}_O$, a_n, and b_n.

The series in Eq. A.7 may also be written as

$$v_O(t) = \bar{v}_O + \sum_{n=1}^{\infty} c_n\sin(n\omega_0 t + \vartheta_n) \text{ V} \qquad (A.9)$$

where

$$c_n = \left(a_n^2 + b_n^2\right)^{1/2} \text{ V} \qquad (A.10)$$

and

$$\vartheta_n = \tan^{-1}\frac{a_n}{b_n} \text{ rad} \qquad (A.11)$$

If a series that describes the terminal pd can be obtained, it is a simple matter to provide a corresponding series for the current through a linear circuit of known parameters to which the pd $v_O(t)$ is applied because each term in the series may be applied to the circuit impedance for that frequency and a term in the corresponding current series obtained. Thus in the prevailing case of an RL series load circuit, from Eq. A.9,

$$i_O(t) = \frac{\bar{v}_O}{R} + \sum_{n=1}^{\infty} \frac{c_n}{Z_n}\sin(n\omega_0 t + \vartheta_n - \varphi_n) \text{ A} \qquad (A.12)$$

where R is the circuit resistance and L, the circuit inductance:

$$Z_n = \left[R^2 + (n\omega_0 L)^2\right]^{1/2} \text{ } \Omega \qquad (A.13)$$

and

$$\varphi_n = \tan^{-1}\frac{n\omega_0 L}{R} \text{ rad} \tag{A.14}$$

In Fig. A.1a a hypothetical periodic waveform of $v_O(t)$ or $v_O(\omega_0 t)$ is shown because the horizontal axis is calibrated in seconds and radians. Provided that the equation to each section of this waveform is known, the constants $\bar{v}_O$, a_n, and b_n for any value of n may be determined from Eqs. A.6 to A.8. However, the determination of each constant by integrating from 0 to T would require no less than nine separate integrations and steps must be taken to reduce this mechanical labor. This may be done by applying the concept of symmetry.

As a first step, the average value $\bar{v}_O$ may be determined, probably by inspection, and a wave of $v_O - \bar{v}_O$, plotted, as shown in Fig. A.1b. This waveform possesses the property known as *alternating symmetry* defined by

$$v_O(t) = -v_O\left(t + \frac{T}{2}\right) \text{ V} \tag{A.15}$$

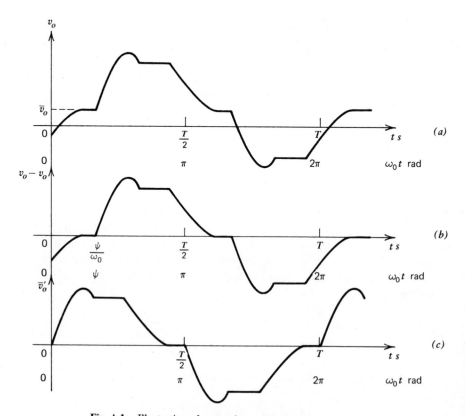

Fig. A.1. Illustration of a waveform with alternating symmetry.

or

$$v_O(\omega_0 t) = -v_O(\omega_0 t + \pi) \text{ V} \qquad \qquad \text{(A.16)}$$

In words, the negative half-wave is the mirror image of the positive half-wave, but shifted half a cycle ($T/2$ s or π rad) from it.

An important property of a waveform with alternating symmetry is that it possesses only odd harmonics; that is, $n = 1, 3, 5 \dots$. Equations A.6 and A.7 may now be replaced with

$$a_n = \frac{4}{T} \int_0^{T/2} [v_O(t) - \bar{v}_O] \cos(n\omega_0 t) \, dt$$

$$= \frac{2}{\pi} \int_0^{\pi} [v_O(\omega_0 t) - \bar{v}_O] \cos(n\omega_0 t) \, d(\omega_0 t) \text{ V} \qquad n = 1, 3, 5 \dots \quad \text{(A.17)}$$

$$b_n = \frac{4}{T} \int_0^{T/2} [v_O(t) - \bar{v}_O] \sin(n\omega_0 t) \, dt$$

$$= \frac{2}{\pi} \int_0^{\pi} [v_O(\omega_0 t) - \bar{v}_O] \sin(n\omega_0 t) \, d(\omega_0 t) \text{ V} \qquad n = 1, 3, 5 \dots \quad \text{(A.18)}$$

Because integration now takes place over only half a cycle, the number of integrations may be greatly reduced if the number of discontinuities is large. They may, however, in certain cases be reduced further.

In Fig. A.1c, the waveform of Fig. A.1b has been advanced along the horizontal axis by time interval ψ/ω_0 s or angular interval ψ rad. The resulting waveform may be signified by $v_O'(t)$ or $v_O'(\omega_0 t)$. This may be described by

$$v_O'(t) = \sum_{n=1}^{\infty} [a_n' \cos(n\omega_0 t) + b_n' \sin(n\omega_0 t)] \text{ V} \qquad \text{(A.19)}$$

where

$$a_n' = \frac{4}{T} \int_0^{T/2} v_O'(t) \cos(n\omega_0 t) \, dt$$

$$= \frac{2}{\pi} \int_0^{\pi} v_O'(\omega_0 t) \cos(n\omega_0 t) \, d(\omega_0 t) \text{ V} \qquad \text{(A.20)}$$

$$b_O' = \frac{4}{T} \int_0^{T/2} v_O'(t) \sin(n\omega_0 t) \, dt$$

$$= \frac{2}{\pi} \int_0^{\pi} v_O'(\omega_0 t) \sin(n\omega_0 t) \, d(\omega_0 t) \text{ V} \qquad \text{(A.21)}$$

Then, in Eqs. A.9 and A.12

$$c_n = \left[\left(a'_n\right)^2 + \left(b'_n\right)^2\right]^{1/2} \text{V} \qquad (\text{A.22})$$

and

$$\vartheta_n = \tan^{-1}\left(\frac{a'_n}{b'_n}\right) - n\psi \text{ rad} \qquad (\text{A.23})$$

The waveform has been advanced in phase for the determination of the constants and each term of the series retarded in phase; therefore it applies to the waveform in Fig. A.1b. The constants are now obtained by performing only three integrations.

In Fig. A.2a a hypothetical function $v_O(t)$ is shown which may have been obtained by subtracting the average value from a function that had a direct component. This waveform does not possess alternating symmetry, but if it is advanced by interval ψ/ω_0 s or ψ rad, as in Fig. A.2b, it is symmetrically disposed about the origin. This waveform is said to have *half-wave symmetry*, defined by

$$v'_O(t) = v'_O(-t) \text{ V} \qquad (\text{A.24})$$

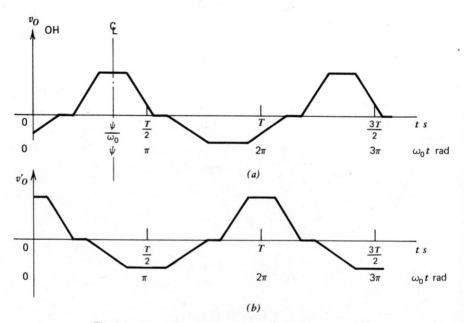

Fig. A.2. Illustration of a waveform with half-wave symmetry.

Equations A.20 to A.23 may be applied to this waveform to reduce the integrations required from the number that would be needed if Eqs. A.7 to A.11 were applied to the waveform in Fig. A.2a.

Another hypothetical function $v_0(t)$ which has no direct component and has alternating symmetry is shown in Fig. A.3a. It also possesses another form of symmetry that can be exploited to give further simplification to the calculation of the constants in the Fourier series. Because the negative half-wave is the mirror image of the positive half-wave, and each half-wave is symmetrical about its center line, it is said to have *quarter-wave symmetry*.

If now the waveform in Fig. A.3a is advanced along the horizontal axis by time interval η/ω_0 s or angular interval η rad the waveform shown in Fig. A.3b is obtained. This waveform is said to have *even symmetry*. From it

$$a_n'' = \frac{4}{T} \int_{-T/4}^{T/4} v_0''(t)\cos(n\omega_0 t)\, dt$$

$$= \frac{2}{\pi} \int_{-\pi/2}^{\pi/2} v_0''(\omega_0 t)\cos(n\omega_0 t)\, d(\omega_0 t) \text{ V} \qquad (A.25)$$

$$b_n'' = \frac{4}{T} \int_{-T/4}^{T/4} v''(t)\sin(n\omega_0 t)\, dt = 0 \text{ V} \qquad (A.26)$$

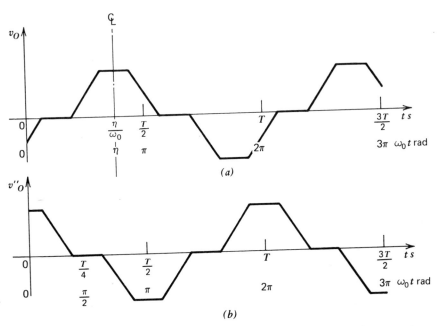

Fig. A.3. Illustration of a waveform with quarter-wave symmetry.

Thus

$$c_n = \left[(a_n'')^2 + (b_n'')^2 \right]^{1/2} = a_n'' \text{ V} \qquad \text{(A.27)}$$

and may be written as

$$c_n = \frac{8}{T} \int_0^{T/4} v_O''(t) \cos(n\omega_0 t) \, dt$$

$$= \frac{4}{\pi} \int_0^{\pi/2} v_O''(\omega_0 t) \cos(n\omega_0 t) \, d(\omega_0 t) \text{ V} \qquad \text{(A.28)}$$

Also

$$\vartheta_n = \tan^{-1}\left(\frac{a_n''}{b_n''} \right) - n\eta = \frac{\pi}{2} - n\eta \text{ rad} \qquad \text{(A.29)}$$

Although the upper limits of integration in Eq. A.28 are expressed as $T/4$ s or $\pi/2$ rad, in the waveform illustrated the upper limit of integration would be $T/6$ s or $\pi/3$ rad because $v_O''(t) = 0$ over the range $T/6 < t < T/4$ s.

Method of Discontinuities

The waveform illustrated in Fig. A.4a consists entirely of rectangular sections. The output waveforms of some converters approximate to waveforms of this type, and the Fourier series that describes them may be rapidly determined by a simple method.

As a first step, the average value $\bar{v}_O$ may be determined, probably by inspection. If this average value is removed from the waveform and the resulting waveform is given a phase advance of η rad the waveform in Fig. A.4b is obtained. In this modified waveform

$$f(\vartheta) = -f(\vartheta + \pi) \text{ V} \qquad \text{(A.30)}$$

Thus the waveform has alternating symmetry, so that only odd harmonics are present. Also

$$f(\vartheta) = -f(-\vartheta) \text{ V} \qquad \text{(A.31)}$$

Thus all terms in the series that describes the waveform in Fig. A.4b must be sine functions. It can be shown that for this waveform

$$c_n = \frac{v_m}{n\pi} \sum_{\vartheta_k=0}^{2\pi} \delta_k \cos(n\vartheta_k) \text{ V} \qquad n = 1, 3, 5 \ldots \qquad \text{(A.32)}$$

where δ_k is the jump of the function at angle ϑ_k expressed as a fraction of v_m.

Because the waveform in Fig. A.4*b* has quarter-wave symmetry, it follows that

$$c_n = \frac{4v_m}{n\pi} \sum_{\vartheta_k=0}^{\pi/2} \delta_k \cos(n\vartheta_k) \text{ V} \qquad n = 1,3,5\ldots \qquad (A.33)$$

Thus

$$c_1 = \frac{4}{\pi}\left[v_1\cos\vartheta_1 + (v_2 - v_1)\cos\vartheta_2 + (v_m - v_2)\cos\vartheta_3 \right] \text{ V} \qquad (A.34)$$

$$c_3 = \frac{4}{3\pi}\left[v_1\cos 3\vartheta_1 + (v_2 - v_1)\cos 3\vartheta_2 + (v_m - v_2)\cos 3\vartheta_3 \right] \text{ V} \quad (A.35)$$

and so on. For the waveform in Fig. A.4*b*

$$v_O'' = \sum_{n=1,3,5} c_n \sin(n\omega_0 t) \text{ V} \qquad (A.36)$$

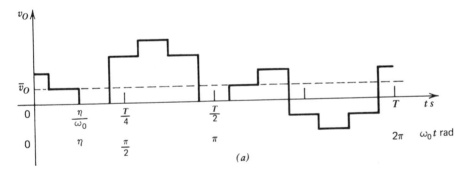

(a)

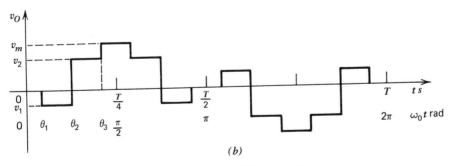

(b)

Fig. A.4. Method of discontinuities.

For the waveform in Fig. A.4*a*

$$v_O = \bar{v}_O + \sum_{n=1,3,5} c_n \sin(n\omega_0 t - n\eta) \text{ V} \qquad (A.37)$$

Care must be taken when applying Eq. A.32 or A.33 to a waveform that includes a jump from negative to positive at $\omega t = 0$ (and $\omega t = 2\pi$). This jump should be considered as two separate jumps to and from zero, one occurring at $\omega t = 0^-$, the other at $\omega t = 0^+$. The converse would apply to a jump from positive to negative.

Appendix B

Typical Nameplate Data and Parameters of 230-V DC Motors

Frame	n	hp	P	I_{rated}	R_a	L_a
283	3500	15	12.2	54	0.153	1.30
	2500	10/7.5	7.46/5.60	37/27	0.301	2.30
$W_f = 150$	1750	5	3.73	19	0.615	4.50
	1150	3	2.24	11	1.43	10.4
$J_m = 0.068$	850	2	1.49	7.8	2.61	19.2
	500	1	0.75	4.1	7.56	55.0
284	3500	20	14.9	73	0.142	1.10
	2500	15	12.2	56	0.279	2.10
$W_f = 160$	1750	10/7.5	7.44/5.60	39/28	0.570	4.30
	1150	5	3.73	20	1.36	10.0
$J_m = 0.088$	850	3	2.24	12	2.42	18.5
	500	2	1.49	10.0	6.71	53.2
	300	1	0.75	4.8	12.3	147
286	3500	25	18.6	89	0.070	0.70
	2500	20	14.9	72	0.137	1.40
$W_f = 180$	1750	15	12.2	56	0.280	2.81
	1150	10/7.5	7.46/5.60	39/29	0.657	6.50
$J_m = 0.087$	850	5	3.73	20	1.19	12.0
	500	3	2.24	12	2.32	34.4
	300	2	1.49	11	7.50	95.0
288	3500	40	29.8	141	0.045	0.73
	2500	30/25	27.4/18.6	108/89	0.089	1.44
$W_f = 200$	1750	20	14.9	74	0.180	2.93
	850	10/7.5	7.46/5.60	40/29	0.762	12.5
$J_m = 0.156$	500	5	3.73	22	1.33	36.0

PARAMETERS OF 230-V DC MOTORS

Frame	n	hp	P	I_{rated}	R_a	L_a
365	1750	25	18.6	89	0.086	2.20
$W_f = 210$	1150	15	11.2	55	0.199	5.10
$J_m = 0.296$						
366	2500	50/40	37.3/29.8	176/140	0.033	0.50
	1750	40/30	29.8/22.4	143/107	0.067	1.00
$W_f = 220$	1150	25/20	18.6/14.9	92/73	0.155	2.40
	850	15	12.2	56	0.284	4.40
$J_m = 0.397$	500	7.5	5.60	29	0.772	13.0
	300	3	2.24	12	2.27	35.0
367	2500	60	44.8	209	0.0203	0.52
	1750	50	37.3	177	0.0415	1.10
$W_f = 230$	1150	30	22.4	108	0.0963	2.50
	850	20	14.9	73	0.176	4.60
$J_m = 0.462$	500	10	7.46	40	0.478	13.0
	300	5	3.73	20	1.41	36.0
368	1750	60	44.8	213	0.0363	0.85
	1150	40	29.8	146	0.0964	2.00
$W_f = 242$	850	30/25	23.4/18.6	112/92	0.153	3.60
	500	15	12.2	58	0.417	11.0
$J_m = 0.560$	300	7.5	5.60	32	1.24	29.0
503	1750	100/75	74.6/56.0	349/261	0.0144	1.10
	1150	60/50	44.8/37.3	211/176	0.084	2.50
$W_f = 325$	850	40	29.8	143	0.066	4.50
	500	20	14.9	73	0.168	13.0
$J_m = 1.82$	300	10	7.46	38	0.500	36.0
504	1750	125	93.3	434	0.0150	0.85
	1150	75	56.0	264	0.0237	2.00
$W_f = 410$	850	50	37.3	177	0.0420	3.60
	500	25	18.6	90	0.115	11.0
$J_m = 1.94$	300	15	12.2	57	0.342	29.0
505	1750	150	112	523	0.0099	0.73
	1150	100	74.6	353	0.0206	1.70

	n	hp	P	I_{rated}	R_a	L_a
$W_f = 430$	850	75/60	56.0/44.8	268/213	0.0380	3.10
	500	30	22.4	109	0.109	9.00
$J_m = 2.20$	300	20	14.9	79	0.350	25.0
506	1150	125	93.3	436	0.0125	1.20
$W_f = 500$	500	40	29.8	143	0.0660	6.50
$J_m = 2.83$						

n = rated speed in rpm

hp   = horsepower rating, 1 hp = 746 W.

P = full-load output power in kW.

I_{rated} = rated armature current in A.

R_a = armature-circuit resistance in Ω.

L_a = armature-circuit inductance in mH.

W_f = field power in W.

J_m = rotational inertia in kg·m^2.

Appendix C

Test Data for Standard 460-V, Three-Phase, 60-Hz Squirrel-Cage Induction Motors

(In calculating equivalent circuit parameters it may be assumed that $X_{ls} = 0.4X_L$ and $X_{lr}' = 0.6X_L$.)

hp	n	P_{FL}	I_{rated}	I_{NL}	P_{FW}	R_s	J_m
2	860	1987	4.1	3.05	10	5.34	0.0195
3	1150	2798	5.0	33.5	15	3.53	0.0195
3	865	2868	6.0	4.45	10	3.065	0.0272
5	1145	4538	7.6	4.25	15	2.08	0.0272
5	875	4635	7.9	4.5	20	2.03	0.0983
7.5	1745	6868	11.2	6.5	30	1.44	0.0230
7.5	1170	6789	10.7	5.8	30	1.29	0.0983
7.5	875	6744	12.0	6.85	20	1.13	0.124
10	3475	8897	12.8	4.45	70	1.02	0.0110
10	1740	8807	13.5	6.1	30	1.01	0.0312
10	1165	9003	13.3	5.7	30	1.09	0.124
10	875	8751	15.5	9.1	50	0.911	0.223
15	3490	13040	18.3	5.5	70	0.542	0.0165
15	1750	13150	20.0	8.0	60	0.660	0.0588
15	1165	13120	20.1	8.5	60	0.714	0.223
15	880	13180	22.5	11.6	50	0.518	0.339
20	3510	17570	24.8	7.6	170	0.4025	0.0276
20	1760	17310	26.6	12.1	60	0.420	0.0753

20	1165	17540	25.9	9.6	60	0.492	0.293
20	885	17330	27.0	11.8	44	0.543	0.469
25	3515	21640	30.0	8.5	170	0.299	0.0340
25	1765	21070	32.4	13.0	100	0.320	0.124
25	1179	21480	31.0	10.8	84	0.455	0.423
25	884	21060	34.0	14.6	54	0.365	0.597
30	3540	24840	37.5	12.1	250	0.238	0.0753
30	1765	25030	37.3	12.9	100	0.245	0.150
30	1180	25040	38.0	14.1	77	0.317	0.469
30	885	25360	40.0	17.1	74	0.328	0.542
40	3537	32940	47.8	13.1	250	0.1675	0.0923
40	1768	32690	49.0	17.9	193	0.185	0.234
40	882	32990	52.0	20.3	80	0.189	0.790
50	3524	41350	59.0	16.1	504	0.123	0.142
50	1770	40850	60.0	19.1	199	0.130	0.326
50	1181	41260	59.0	15.7	148	0.191	0.694
50	882	41260	65.0	29.7	133	0.157	1.30
60	3528	49760	71.0	20.2	593	0.08945	0.165
60	1775	48990	72.0	24.1	232	0.119	0.464
60	1178	49410	70.0	21.3	260	0.142	1.14
75	3559	60450	85.0	23.3	823	0.0650	0.239
75	1776	61610	88.0	23.6	231	0.0862	0.593
75	1174	62540	88.0	22.8	275	0.106	1.46
75	885	61950	98.0	39.7	300	0.0836	2.00
100	3550	81650	112	24.6	901	0.0498	0.308
100	1776	81570	117	30.2	414	0.0600	0.859
100	1179	81820	119	34.1	203	0.0591	1.80
100	886	81260	127	51.2	575	0.0531	2.92
125	3549	102400	142	31.6	825	0.0410	0.574
125	1776	100700	141	36.5	308	0.0409	0.965
125	1181	100600	147	43.5	271	0.0406	2.29
150	3554	122300	167	32.8	1131	0.0406	0.749
150	1771	121400	167	40.8	532	0.0314	1.45

200	3553	162700	227	50.0	1000	0.0240	1.12
200	1779	159200	220	57.0	504	0.0188	1.91
250	3549	204100	282	46.4	1100	0.0203	1.45

n = rated speed, rpm.

hp   = rated horsepower, 1 hp = 746 W.

P_{FL} = full-load input power, W.

I_{rated} = rated line current, A.

I_{NL} = no-load line current, A.

P_{FW} = friction and windage loss, W.

R_s = per-phase stator resistance, Ω.

J_m = rotational inertia, kg·m^2.

Numerical Answers to Problems

Chapter 1. Variable-Speed Drive Systems

1.1. $2.13 \text{ kg} \cdot \text{m}^2$

1.2. 1910 rpm, 6.92 kW. Say 2000 rpm, 7.5 kW

1.3. $28.5 \times 10^3 \text{ N}$

1.4. 780 m, 11.1 m/s

1.5. Up run; $0.152 \text{ J/kg} \cdot \text{m}$, 27.7 m/s. Down run; $-0.0916 \text{ J/kg} \cdot \text{m}$, 39.7 m/s

1.6. 292 kW, 491 kW, 300 kW

1.7. 0.5 kW, 1720 rpm, $-0.850 \text{ N} \cdot \text{m}$

1.8. (a) Yes. (b) $18.2 \text{ N} \cdot \text{m}$, 909 rpm; $29.1 \text{ N} \cdot \text{m}$, 1455 rpm

Chapter 2. Separately Excited Dc Motors

2.1. 803 rpm, $3.23 \ \Omega$; 1016 rpm, $22.4 \ \Omega$

2.2. Motoring: 2200 rpm, 127 V, $30 \ \Omega$; 106 rpm, 11.7 V, 0. Generating: 1980 rpm, 103 V, $30 \ \Omega$; 106 rpm, 0, $19.2 \ \Omega$

2.3. (a) 1800 rpm, (b) 93.0 V

2.4. (a) 1743 rpm, (b) 1516 rpm

2.6. 75 hp, 1150 rpm

2.7. (a) $\dfrac{\Omega(s)}{V_t(s)} = \dfrac{0.842}{(0.126s + 1)(0.125s + 1)}$

$\dfrac{\Omega(s)}{-T_W(s)} = \dfrac{0.128(0.0163s + 1)}{(0.126s + 1)(0.125s + 1)}$

(b) 1610 rpm

2.8. $k_2 = 0.191$, $k_1 = 29.2$

Chapter 3. Single-Phase Rectifiers with Motor Load

3.1. $49.7° < \alpha < 123.7°$, $-61.4 \text{ rad/s} < \Omega_m < 28.9 \text{ rad/s}$

3.2. 70°, 1.15 s, 6.16°

3.3. (a) Yes, 157.7° > α > 70.0°; (b) 0.880 s; (c) 4.32°; (d) 18.6 s

3.4. (a) Yes, 145.7°; (b) Yes, 12.8°

3.5. α = 90.1°, β = 185.9°

3.6. (a) 64.9 N · m, 883 rpm, 31.7°; (b) 86.9 N · m, 942 rpm, 328.3°

3.7. (b) 0.670

3.8. (b) 0.746, (c) 0.680, (d) Yes

Chapter 4. Three-Phase Rectifiers with Motor Load

4.1. (a) 1500 rpm, (b) −1710

4.4. (a) Yes; (b) 3.41 s; (c) $\alpha = \cos^{-1}\left[\dfrac{1.84\Omega_m + 8.62}{281}\right]$; (d) 45.5°

4.6. (a) 10.72; (b) −4.48 V

4.7. (a) 200 rpm, (b) 27.7 rpm

4.8. (a) 0.814; (b) (i) 31.2 A, (ii) 0.793, (iii) 24.9 A, (iv) 0.801, (v) 0.765

Chapter 5. Chopper Drives

5.1. (a) 61.9 N · m, (b) 924 rpm.

5.2. (a) 0 < n < 910 rpm; (b) 0 < b < 1040 rpm

5.4. (a) 2.30 ms, 56.0 A, 63.8 A, 50.3 A; (b) 2.01 ms, −48.4 A, −31.4 A, −66.5 A

5.6. (a) 1.08 s, 0.216, 0.5, 0.382; (b) 0.752 s; (c) 3.96 A, 2.74 A

5.8. 0.0912

Chapter 6. Three-Phase Induction Motors

6.1. 28.1 A, 47.1 A, 99.9 N · m, too high

6.2. 394 N · m, 1240 rpm

6.3. (b) 0.908, 0.949; (c) 2680 W

6.4. 1770 rpm

6.5. 1320 rpm, 0.900

Chapter 7. Speed Control by Ac Power Controller

7.1. (a) 1560 rpm, (b) 94.6 A, 78°

7.2. (a) 1560 rpm, (b) 96.5 A, 86°

7.3. 756 < n < 1620 rpm, 98° > α > 33°

7.4. 1020 < n < 1690 rpm

7.5. Motor C

Chapter 8.   Speed Control by Slip-Energy Recovery

8.2. (a) 0.194, (b) 7580 VA, (c) 25.5%
8.3. 0.746, 0.787; 0.487, 0.744
8.4. 30.8 A, 0.767, 0.742
8.5. 91.0 A, 69.4 A, 0.573, 0.807
8.6. 41.6%

Chapter 9.   Induction Motors with Voltage-Source Inverters

9.2. (a) 244 V, 370 rad/s, 216 A; (b) 109 V, 161 rad/s, 238 A
9.3. (a) 406 V; (b) 0.475
9.6. (a) 0.839, 216 A; (b) 0.797, −103 A
9.7. 489 N · m, 636 rad/s, 264 A
9.8. (a) 72.1 A, 51.7 A; (b) 0.955

Chapter 10.   Induction Motors with Current-Source Inverters

10.1. (a) 81.4%; (b) 273 rad/s, 30.5 A, −256 V; (c) 115.6°
10.4. 1790 rpm, 60.4 Hz, 108 A, 397 V
10.8. (a) 5500 rpm; (b) 0.712

Chapter 11.   Synchronous Motor Drives

11.1. (a) 0.682 V/rad/s, 13.8 A, −39.6°
11.2.

	n	T_L	V_{a1}	I_{a1}	PF_1	β_{oe}°
(a)	720	0	1302	8.60	0.00174 leading	0
(b)	720	4250	1324	82.6	0.993 lagging	−25.18
(c)	0	0	2.32	8.60	1.0	0
(d)	0	4250	22.3	82.6	1.0	−25.18
(e)	450	−3750	1282	72.6	0.997 leading	22.05
(f)	50	−3750	70.9	72.6	0.995 leading	22.05

11.5. (a) 96.8, 11.0
11.6. 2620 rpm, 10.4 A
11.7. 4.17 N · m, 0.0768
11.9. −41.8 N · m, 208 V, −0.994
11.10. (a) 0.593; (b) 20.0 kVA; (c) −17.8°

Index